THE NEW NATURALIST
A SURVEY OF BRITISH NATURAL HISTORY

WILD ORCHIDS OF BRITAIN

The aim of this series is to interest the general reader in the wild life of Britain by recapturing the inquiring spirit of the old naturalists. The Editors believe that the natural pride of the British public in the native fauna and flora, to which must be added concern for their conservation, is best fostered by maintaining a high standard of accuracy combined with clarity of exposition in presenting the results of modern scientific research. The plants and animals are described in relation to their homes and habitats and are portrayed in the full beauty of their natural colours, by the latest methods of colour photography and reproduction

THE NEW NATURALIST

WILD ORCHIDS OF BRITAIN

with a key to the species

by

V. S. SUMMERHAYES

WITH 61 PHOTOGRAPHS IN COLOUR
BY ROBERT ATKINSON AND OTHERS
39 PHOTOGRAPHS IN BLACK AND WHITE
19 TEXT FIGURES AND 43 DISTRIBUTION MAPS

COLLINS
14 ST JAMES'S PLACE LONDON
1951

TO THE MEMORY
OF
JOHN LINDLEY
THE FATHER
OF ORCHIDOLOGY

First published in 1951 by
Collins 14 St. James's Place London
Produced in conjunction with Adprint
and printed in Great Britain by
Collins Clear-Type Press
London and Glasgow

CONTENTS

		PAGE
	Editors' Preface	xiii
	Author's Preface	xv
CHAPTER		
1	The Life History of the Orchid Plant	1
2	The Orchid Flower	26
3	Pollination and Fertilisation	40
4	Distribution, Geographical and Ecological	60
5	Classification	102
6	The Lady's Slipper	118
7	The Helleborines	123
8	Twayblades	167
9	The Ladies' Tresses	175
10	Saprophytic Orchids	192
11	The Habenaria Group	206
12	Orchis Relatives	229
13	Orchis Proper	244
14	The Spotted Orchids	265
15	The Marsh Orchids	278
16	The Bee Orchid and its Allies	298
17	Bog Orchids	312
18	What of the Future?	319

v

CONTENTS

	PAGE
APPENDIX: KEY FOR DETERMINATION OF SPECIES	323
GLOSSARY	336
BIBLIOGRAPHY	342
DISTRIBUTION MAPS	345
INDEX	357

COLOUR PLATES

		FACING PAGE
1	Colony of Creeping Ladies' Tresses	46
2	Early Spider Orchids in Dorset	47
3	Fragrant and Spotted Orchids and hybrid between them	62
4	Lady's Slipper	63
5a	Large White Helleborine	110
5b	Red Helleborine	110
6	Sword-leaved Helleborine	111
7	Flower spike of Red Helleborine	126
8	Marsh Helleborine	127
9	Broad-leaved Helleborine	130
10	Dune Helleborine	131
11	Dark Red Helleborine	138
12	Violet Helleborine	139
13a	Green-leaved Helleborines	142
13b	Pendulous-flowered Helleborine	142
14	Isle of Wight Helleborine	143
15	Common Twayblade	158
16a	Lesser Twayblades	159
16b	Autumn Ladies' Tresses	159
17	Summer Ladies' Tresses	174
18	Irish Ladies' Tresses	175
19a	Creeping Ladies' Tresses	190
19b	Common Coral Root	190
20	Bird's Nest Orchid	191

FACING PAGE

21	Spurred Coral Root	194
22	Musk Orchids	195
23a	Frog Orchids	202
23b	Small White Orchids	202
24	Greater Butterfly Orchid	203
25a	Beechwood form of Lesser Butterfly Orchid	210
25b	Moorland form of Lesser Butterfly Orchid	210
26	Fragrant Orchid	211
27	Marsh Fragrant Orchid	218
28	Dense-flowered Orchids	219
29	Group of Pyramidal Orchids	226
30	Lizard Orchid	227
31	Man Orchids	234
32	Monkey Orchids	235
33a	Soldier or Military Orchid	242
33b	Spike of Soldier Orchid	242
34	Lady Orchids	243
35a	Dwarf or Burnt Orchid	250
35b	Hebridean Orchid	250
36	Group of Green-veined Orchids	251
37	Early Purple Orchids	258
38a	Common Spotted Orchid	259
38b	Wicklow Marsh Orchid	259
39	Hebridean Orchids	266
40	Irish sub-species of Common Spotted Orchid	267
41	Heath Spotted Orchids	274
42	Early Marsh Orchid	275
43a	Sand-dune form of Early Marsh Orchid	282
43b	Dwarf Purple Orchid	282
44a	Common Marsh Orchid	283

		FACING PAGE
44b	Leopard Marsh Orchid	283
45a	Fly Orchid	286
45b	Bee Orchid	286
46	Early Spider Orchid	287
47	Late Spider Orchids	302
48a	Fen Orchid	303
48b	Bog Orchid	303

It should be noted that throughout this book Plate numbers in arabic figures refer to Colour Plates, while roman numerals are used for Black-and-White Plates

CORRIGENDUM

Caption to plate 38b: for Orchis strauntinerioides read Orchis traunsteinerioides

PLATES IN BLACK AND WHITE

		FACING PAGE
I	Flowers of Common Spotted Orchid	18
IIa	Doubled flower of Helleborine	19
IIb	Roots of Common Spotted Orchid	19
IIIa	Abnormal form of Bee Orchid	26
IIIb	Abnormal spike of Pyramidal Orchid	26
IV	Variation in Early Spider Orchid	27
Va	Variation in Broad-leaved Helleborine	78
Vb	Hybrid between Frog and Fragrant Orchids	78
VI	Bee and Late Spider Orchids and hybrids	79
VII	Red Helleborine	94
VIIIa	Columns of Broad-leaved and Violet Helleborines	95
VIIIb	Column of Green-leaved Helleborine	95
IX	Clump of Violet Helleborine	162
X	Flower spikes of two forms of Violet Helleborine	163
XIa	Flower spike of Summer Ladies' Tresses	170
XIb	Flower spike of Irish Ladies' Tresses	170
XIIa	Flower spike of Creeping Ladies' Tresses	171
XIIb	Bird's Nest Orchids	171
XIIIa	Flowers of Greater and Lesser Butterfly Orchids	222
XIIIb	Flower spikes of Greater and Lesser Butterfly Orchids	222
XIVa	Dense-flowered Orchids	223
XIVb	Colour variants of Pyramidal Orchid	223
XVa	Flower spikes of Man Orchid	238
XVb	Flower spike of Monkey Orchid	238

FACING PAGE

XVIa	Flower spikes of Lady Orchid	239
XVIb	Dwarf or Burnt Orchids	239
XVII	Flowers of Heath Spotted Orchid	254
XVIIIa	Flower spike of Early Marsh Orchid	255
XVIIIb	Flower spike of Small White Orchid	255
XIX	Flower spikes of Common Marsh Orchid	270
XX	Irish Marsh Orchid	271
XXIa	Leopard Marsh Orchids	306
XXIb	Flower spike of Wicklow Marsh Orchid	306
XXIIa	Late Spider Orchids	307
XXIIb	Flower of Bee Orchid showing self-pollination	307
XXIII	Wasp Orchid	314
XXIVa	Broad-leaved Fen Orchid	315
XXIVb	Bog Orchids	315

EDITORS' PREFACE

IF COMPETITIONS were to be held for the most beautiful and for the most biologically interesting of our native wild flowers, the orchids would stand a good chance of first place in both contests. What other group can combine the almost legendary loveliness and rarity of the lady's slipper orchid, the grotesque fascination of the pseudo-copulatory pollination-mechanism of the fly orchid and its allies, and the baffling complexity of variation and distribution of the palmate orchids? It is not surprising, therefore, that the orchids have always been a favourite family for collection and study by British botanists. A number of earlier books have been written about them, culminating in Colonel Godfery's lavish monograph published in 1933; but so much intensive work has been carried out during the last twenty years, especially on the spotted and marsh orchids and on the helleborines, that a new treatment is badly wanted. Apart, however, from incorporating these recent researches, the present volume approaches our orchids from a wider and less parochial view-point than did the earlier books. The author, Mr. V. S. Summerhayes, is in charge of the unrivalled orchid collections at the Kew Herbarium and he is able, therefore, to look at our fifty odd species in relation to his knowledge of this vast family as it occurs throughout the world. He has attempted, successfully we think, to cover not only the general biology and natural history of the family in Britain, but also a detailed account of our species, varieties and hybrids, including a key for their identification and maps of their distribution. Not every orchid specialist—and there are quite a number in Britain at the moment—will agree with Mr. Summerhayes on all the various controversial points of classification with which he has to deal, but his book will, undoubtedly, remain a standard work for many years to come, serving as an introduction and guide to a group of plants which will never lose its unique appeal to students of the British Flora.

A word must be added about the colour photographs, representing every British species except *Orchis cruenta*, discovered in Ireland too late for inclusion, and *Orchis occidentalis*. The great majority have been taken in their natural British habitats by Mr. Robert Atkinson, and they not only form a series of outstanding beauty but will be of great help in identification by supplementing Mr. Summerhayes' descriptions and key.

THE EDITORS

AUTHOR'S PREFACE

IN SPITE of the evident popularity of our British orchids among wide sections of the community, few comprehensive accounts of this interesting group of plants have been written. The most notable is Colonel M. J. Godfery's monumental work *Monograph and Iconograph of native British Orchidaceae* published in 1933. Unfortunately only a limited edition was produced, while the high price put the book beyond the reach of most people. The present book is an effort to produce in a more convenient form an account of our orchids, especially as regards their general manner of life and their place in the flora and vegetation of these islands.

It was with some misgivings that I undertook this task, as I was not certain whether the subject-matter would be adequate to fill a volume of the size envisaged. In the event, however, the difficulty has been to keep the account within the required limits. In some parts of the subject, for example mycorhiza, there is such a tremendous literature, expressing such varied points of view, that it is quite impossible in the space available to discuss, even superficially, the merits and demerits of the different view-points. It has, therefore, been necessary to present as a definite explanation what is felt to be the most satisfactory interpretation of the facts. But science is never static, and the discovery of fresh data may at any time necessitate a profound modification of the views set forward here.

The book falls naturally into two more or less complementary sections. The introductory chapters, which form the first part, deal with the group as a whole, while in the later chapters accounts are given of groups of allied species and of each individual species. It is thought that most readers will like these accounts to be as complete in themselves as possible, thus making them more useful for reference. This necessitates some repetition of information, but such repetition is reduced to a minimum.

The scientific reader will notice that there is no mention in the text of chromosomes, the minute bodies in plants which carry the hereditary qualities (genes) of each individual. So little of significance is known about the chromosomes in our native orchids that the inclusion of the available information would serve no useful purpose to either the scientific or general reader.

Notwithstanding the wide interest in orchids, they are not very convenient subjects for research ; consequently they have been left aside while other more easily cultivated plants have been studied. The reader will notice in many places the comparatively simple observations which yet remain to be made, most of them requiring patience and care rather than any great amount of skill or special scientific training. If this book persuades any of my readers to carry out some of these observations I shall feel that my labours have been well rewarded.

One of the pleasures of writing a book like this is that one makes many new friends. The kindness and help which I have received from nature lovers and scientists alike testify to the bond of friendship which is built up by the common study of nature. To all these I tender my sincere thanks for their aid and encouragement. In particular I should like to express my indebtedness to my colleagues at the Royal Botanic Gardens, Kew. Some have accompanied me on field excursions, others have made observations in, or have sent me living specimens from, regions which I have not been able to visit personally, while all have given me the benefit of their great botanical experience. Their critical comments have contributed much to the shaping of the decisions and ideas set forth in the following pages.

During the preparation of the accounts of the very difficult group of the helleborines (*Epipactis*) I have had the advantage of constant contact with Mr. Charles Thomas and Dr. D. P. Young, both of whom have made a special study of these plants. I am also much indebted to Dr. J. Heslop Harrison and to the late Mr. H. W. Pugsley for valuable information about some of the palmate orchids. Mr. N. Y. Sandwith kindly looked over the chapter on the marsh orchids, while other friends have criticised various other parts of the manuscript. To all these I wish to convey my best thanks for their help.

Most of the coloured plates are from photographs by Mr. Robert Atkinson, and I think they speak for themselves. As regards the monochrome plates I am much indebted to Messrs. R. Atkinson, E. J.

Bedford and C. Thomas, and to the late Mr. A. J. Wilmott for permission to use Plate XX. I should also like to thank Messrs. B. J. Hammond, G. Atkinson and D. Paton for the plates bearing their names. I must also acknowledge my indebtedness to my colleague, Mr. F. Ballard, for his expert advice on all matters relating to photography.

The preparation of the distribution maps has not only involved the laborious examination and analysis of numerous records, but could not have been completed without the co-operation of others. To all who have helped I express my sincere gratitude. The text figures were prepared by Mr. Charles Green, mostly from sketches made by myself. The great majority are original, but a few have been derived from other sources; all such are acknowledged in the appropriate places.

Finally I should like to thank my wife for doing nearly all the typing, and for her constant encouragement and help at all stages.

V. S. S.

KEW
August 1950

CHAPTER I

THE LIFE HISTORY OF THE ORCHID PLANT

INTRODUCTION

WHY HAVE our wild orchids such an attraction for nature-lovers? Although there are only about 50 different kinds of orchids native to these Islands, it would not be unfair to state, I think, that they have almost as many devotees as all our other wild flowers put together. The causes of this are many and varied, depending much on the individual. For many, no doubt, accounts of exciting adventures in search of tropical members of the family, or highly imaginative stories of the discovery of weird and sinister varieties, have invested the name orchid with a glamour equalled by no other plants. This is enhanced by the exotic beauty of many of these tropical orchids, and their almost inevitable association with wealth and splendour.

But surely our orchids themselves contribute in no small degree to their popularity. Many of them are extremely rare, and nearly all are local in occurrence and capricious in their appearance from year to year. This feature gives an added zest to any excursion through districts in which orchids are suspected to occur. What orchid enthusiast in Britain has not experienced the thrilling hope of re-discovering the rare lady's slipper, soldier orchid or red helleborine in its erstwhile haunts—or even of finding it in a yet unrecorded locality? Furthermore, examination of most of our wild orchids shows that, in miniature, they possess all the attractive qualities of their tropical relatives, such as delicacy of colouring, fantastic resemblances to other living beings, and variety of fragrance.

Whatever may be the reasons, there is little doubt about the general appeal of British orchids, both to amateur botanists, of which there are a considerable number especially interested in orchids, and to the great bulk of nature-lovers. To both of these groups our native orchids can yield an ever-increasing interest if they are prepared to search for and to study them.

Beauty of form and colour, marvellous adaptations to the external world at almost all stages of their life history, striking problems in distribution and variation ; all these provide the student, whatever his knowledge and primary interest may be, with a continuous revelation of new delights.

The British have sometimes been described as a nation of gardeners ; at all events the number of people in this country who grow plants of some kind or another must be immense. Most of my readers will therefore be more or less well acquainted with the way in which " ordinary " plants grow. A study of orchids, however, shows so many remarkable features in their life history, that it is well worth while considering this in some detail, so as to form a background for the later chapters dealing with more special aspects of our orchids.

GERMINATION

In most plants the early stages in the development of a new individual can be easily followed from the seed. Even if the seed, and the seedling arising therefrom, are not large, as they are in such plants as the broad bean, garden pea, runner bean, etc., germination, once it has started, is a comparatively quick process. Gardeners have little difficulty in deciding whether their seeds have grown or not, the first-formed leaves or seed-leaves (cotyledons) normally being easily recognisable.

Such is not the case in orchids. Here the seeds are so small that there is very little room in which to store the food reserves on which the young seedlings of other plants depend for their rapid growth. Consequently at the beginning growth is very slow, and nothing resembling a normal-looking seedling is visible for months or in some species even several years. Leaves may not be produced until the second, third or subsequent years, and even after their appearance development is slow, and several years elapse before flowers are formed. Some of the various spotted and marsh orchids, and also the green-veined orchid, have been brought to flower in four or five years after the seeds have germinated. Many other species, for example,

the bee orchid and its allies and the two butterfly orchids, do not
flower until from five to eight years after germination, while the bird's
nest orchid (*Neottia*) and the large white helleborine (*Cephalanthera
damasonium*) are nine to eleven years of age when they first flower.
Yet others, for example, the common twayblade (*Listera ovata*), autumn
ladies' tresses (*Spiranthes spiralis*) and burnt orchid (*Orchis ustulata*)

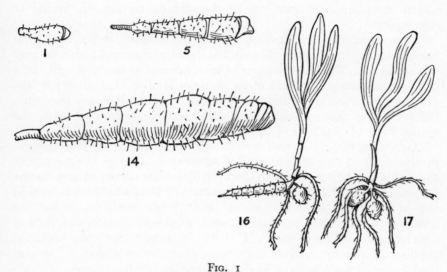

FIG. I

Development of *Orchis ustulata* from seed

The numbers show the age in years of each stage. Nos. 1, 5 & 14 show
different stages in the development of the underground mycorhizome;
nos. 16 & 17 are the early years after the appearance of the aerial shoot. In
17 note that the mycorhizome has disappeared and is replaced by a tuber.
(1, 5 & 14 much enlarged; 16 & 17 natural size) (After Ziegenspeck)

(Fig. 1, p. 3) require thirteen to fifteen years' development before
flowering. An extreme example is furnished by the lady's slipper
(*Cypripedium*) which is thought to grow in a purely vegetative state for
sixteen or more years before being sufficiently developed to produce
flowers. Owing to the great difficulty in raising orchids from seed
there are few accurate data available; the above figures have mostly
been obtained by the careful examination and comparison of seedlings

discovered in nature. The few examples in which plants have been raised from seed indicate, however, that perhaps the estimated periods of development suggested by some authorities are somewhat excessive. Even allowing for this it is clear that the growth after germination is relatively slow. Naturally there are differences in the period required for the development of flowers in different individuals of the same species, these differences depending on the nature of the habitats in which the plants are growing, or the climate during the period of development.

Apart from the slow development of the seedlings it has long been known among cultivators that orchid seeds are very difficult to germinate at all. The most successful method was to sow the seeds in a pot in which an adult plant of the same or similar kind of orchid was growing, but even then there were many failures. It was a long time before it was realised that these failures were connected with the special type of nutrition of the orchid seedling.

Green plants, as is well known, manufacture their own energy-producing food (sugars and similar substances) through the agency of the green colouring matter (chlorophyll) which occurs mostly in the leaves. As the seed of a plant germinates the food stored up is used in the initial stages of development, so it becomes necessary for the seedling to make its own food as soon as possible, otherwise further development will be checked. It is for this reason that most seedlings produce at a comparatively early stage green leaves, either the special seed-leaves already present in the seed, or fresh foliage leaves.

How then does the orchid seedling, which may not produce leaves until from six months to ten years after germination, manage to keep alive, let alone continue its development, in view of the very small amount of food stored up in the minute seed? It is on consideration of this problem that we realise the importance of one of the strangest features in the life of an orchid, namely, the constant presence of a fungus growing within the seedling.

MYCORHIZA

The association of these fungi with ordinary plants, a phenomenon usually termed mycorhiza, is widespread in nature. It has been recorded for the great majority of our forest trees (beech, oak, birch, pine, etc.,) and also for many of the herbaceous plants which grow in or near woods. Mycorhiza is also known in plants growing on heaths and moorlands, such as the common ling or heather (*Calluna vulgaris*). In most plants the fungus is associated only with the roots of the plant, as in the trees and woodland plants mentioned, and this gave it its name mycorhiza, literally rendered, fungus-root.

Further study has shown that there are many types of occurrence of mycorhiza, but it is convenient to divide these into two main groups, one in which the fungus forms a kind of superficial covering or mantle to the root, termed ectotrophic mycorhiza, and secondly, a group in which the fungus penetrates deeply into the tissues of the root or other part of the plant, the so-called endotrophic mycorhiza. As we shall see later there is really no hard and fast line between these two groups, but they do indicate the two main lines along which mycorhiza has developed in plants. In orchids the mycorhiza is essentially of the internal or endotrophic type, but there is always active communication between the fungus and the surrounding soil, and, in some species, the external or ectotrophic type occurs as well.

Now what is the significance of this association between the plant and fungus, particularly as regards orchids? We may revert, for the moment, to the suggestion that the mycorhiza is connected with the nutrition of the orchid seedling. The fungi form a large and very varied group of plants, including such diverse types as the moulds which appear on food, the mildews which attack cultivated crops and other plants, and the numerous kinds of toadstools, among which is the edible mushroom. These all differ from green plants in not possessing chlorophyll, and are therefore unable to make their own sugar and similar food. They are instead dependent upon their ability to obtain this food from other sources, either directly from green plants, or from the dead remains of plants and animals. Those which adopt the former method are parasites, those adopting the latter method are termed saprophytes. The mycorhizal fungi obtain their food in the second way, from the abundant fragments of dead plants occurring in the soil—the humus. From these, by means of ferments (enzymes) which they secrete, they obtain energy-producing food, not necessarily sugars, but substances which can be used for the same purposes. This food, obtained by that part of the fungus which lives in the soil outside the orchid's roots or underground stem, is passed on to the fungus growing within the plant. From the internal mycorhiza the food is, in due course, transferred to the orchid itself, and serves to nourish it.

It is in this way that the young orchid seedling is able to obtain food although it has no green leaves.

But the reader may well ask " Why should the fungus go to all this trouble to obtain food merely to feed the orchid ?" Formerly the association was looked upon as a sort of mutual aid, the orchid, according to this view, receiving the food and the fungus some other advantage, such as protection from insect enemies or unfavourable climatic conditions. Indeed it seems probable that the fungus does obtain certain food substances from the orchid, which it could not obtain from other sources. Careful investigation has, however, indicated that fundamentally the explanation is quite different. There seems little doubt that the association started as a form of parasitic attack on the orchid by the fungus, of the type we find in well-known plant diseases such as rusts, smuts, damping-off, potato blight, grape mildew and the like. In the orchids (and other plants with mycorhiza), after an initial success on the part of the invading fungus, the plant launches a partially successful counter-attack which, though insufficient to eject the fungus completely, suffices to pin the enemy to a circumscribed territory within the plant. There then ensues a more or less continuous struggle during the course of which the fungus, by means of food obtained from the soil as described above, makes temporary advances within its host. The orchid then counter-attacks in turn, and large parts of the invading fungus are digested and the food obtained used for nourishing the seedling. In the course of time the balance established between the two opposing powers has become delicately adjusted so that any external conditions which favour one or other of the protagonists lead to a corresponding advantage in the struggle. Thus in our native orchids the fungus is usually in the ascendant during autumn and winter, whereas the orchid itself has the better of things during the spring and summer. There is, however, a certain amount of variation in this respect as between one orchid species and another.

Culture and inoculation experiments show that there are a number of distinct species or forms, whatever they may be, of mycorhizal fungi, closely similar to one another, and mostly referable to the genus *Rhizoctonia*. The only known exceptions are in a number of saprophytic orchids, including the Japanese species *Gastrodia elata* and *G. septentrionalis*, in which the associated fungus is the common parasitic honey fungus (*Armillaria mellea*) or allied types. It has been shown, however, that the mycorhizal fungi in the lady's slipper and early purple orchid are also members of this latter group.

In all orchids which have been examined infection of the germinating seed takes place at a very early stage ; indeed this is clearly necessary in natural conditions. The seeds of some species will not even germinate except in the presence of the proper fungus, but extensive experiments have shown that the fungus can be dispensed with so long as the food required by the seedling is provided from some other source. This possibility of managing without the fungus has been used extensively by orchid growers in raising many of the magnificent hybrids of tropical orchids which may be seen at the Chelsea Flower Show or elsewhere. By germinating the seeds under sterilised conditions into which no unwanted fungi or bacteria can penetrate, and by supplying the growing seedlings with sugar and the usual mineral food (nitrates, phosphates, etc.), plants have been brought to the flowering stage without fungal infection. Better results are obtained, however, if some vegetable extract is also present. There are advantages in this " aseptic " method of cultivation, since the grower can control accurately the conditions in which the seedlings are growing. The method is also cleaner, and avoids the danger of a too vigorous attack by the fungus, which might result in the death of the seedlings. In the normal procedure sterile conditions are maintained only during early stages of development, since many adult orchids, including many British species, can get along quite well without external supplies of sugar or help from the fungus. It has been shown that several sorts of sugar, for instance, grape sugar (glucose) and cane sugar (sucrose), and even other substances, can be used as energy-providing food, and this may well be true in natural conditions. The breaking-up by the fungus of the complex material forming the humus probably yields a great variety of food substances, some of which may be used directly by the plant, even if most of such food is obtained by digestion of the fungus at a later stage. Other substances formed may be of the nature of accessory food substances, comparable with vitamins in animal nutrition.

DEVELOPMENT OF SEEDLING

As already mentioned, the seed on germination gives rise to a special structure which has few of the features of an ordinary seedling. This is known as the protocorm or, better, the mycorhizome, and is always heavily infected by the fungus. It varies in appearance, usually being at first rather like a small peg-top with a minute bud-like projection at the broader end. Subsequent growth varies considerably in different species, depending, among other things, on the type of growth adopted finally by the adult. In such plants as the lady's slipper and marsh helleborine, which have a long creeping underground stem (rhizome), or other helleborines (*Epipactis* and *Cephalanthera* spp.), in which this stem is a shorter more or less upright rootstock, the mycorhizome produces one or more large fleshy roots in the first two or three years, and then gives rise to the first aerial stem bearing leaves. The roots produced at this stage, and subsequently, are infected, but the rhizome as it develops becomes free from fungal infection. After forming non-flowering aerial shoots of increasing vigour over a number of years flowers are eventually produced, the growth in the creeping forms being as in solomon's seal or lily of the valley, and in the erect types by a series of aerial stems arising each year from much the same point on the short root-stock. A similar method of development to that in the lady's slipper occurs in the common twayblade (*Listera ovata*), where the first leaf is formed in the fourth year, but flowers do not appear until the seedling is about fifteen years of age. The two English species of ladies' tresses (*Spiranthes spiralis* and *S. aestivalis*) provide an interesting contrast in development. The adult plant in each case possesses several fleshy root-tubers, comparable to those in dahlias, but of course much smaller. In the summer ladies' tresses (*S. aestivalis*) the first leaf and first proper tuber are formed in the second year following germination, and the mycorhizome withers away. In the autumn ladies' tresses, on the other hand, the mycorhizome develops very slowly for about eight years ; the first tuber does not appear until the end of this period, followed by the production of the first leaf in the eleventh year. These differences are thought to be related to the different habitats of the two species, the former growing in swamps and the latter in dry grassy places.

Similar differences may be noted among the various members of the large genus *Orchis*, which includes many of our commonest species. In the marsh and spotted orchids, many of which normally grow in damp places, the mycorhizome produces a foliage leaf in the second year, while the first root-tuber is formed soon after, the mycorhizome then dying away. In the early purple orchid (*Orchis mascula*), as well as in the monkey orchid and its allies, all of which grow in comparatively dry habitats, early development is slower, the first leaf not appearing until four years after germination, though a tuber may be formed in the second year. Curiously enough the green-veined orchid (*O. morio*), which also generally occurs in rather dry places, produces a leaf at the end of the first year's growth and a tuber in the second year, the underground stage of development in this species being extremely short.

The burnt orchid (*O. ustulata*, Fig. 1, p. 3) provides, however, the most remarkable example of delayed development among all our leafy orchid species, indicating a marked dependence on the associated fungus during the early part of the plant's life. In this species the fleshy cylindrical mycorhizome produced during the first year continues to grow horizontally for ten or more years, adding a new section each year. Each section is slightly swollen in the centre and constricted at each end so that a kind of caterpillar effect is produced. No roots are formed during this period, the seedling obtaining all its food by the activities of the fungus with which it is heavily infected. At the end of ten to fifteen years' growth in this manner several normal slender roots are produced, and the growing bud turns above ground to form the first aerial stem bearing three large foliage leaves. Flowers are normally first produced when the plant is thirteen to fourteen years old, but sometimes may not be formed until even later. Following the leafy shoot the first tuber is formed, the caterpillar-like mycorhizome dies away, and the normal sequence of one new tuber a year is established.

It will be seen from the above that there are great differences between British orchid species as regards their dependence on the mycorhizal fungus in the early stages. In some species the plant soon starts to manufacture some, at least, of the food it requires, whereas in others many years pass before any contribution is made by the orchid plant itself. As will be seen later, these differences extend into the adult life of the plant, some species being virtually independent of the fungus as adults, whereas others always obtain a substantial proportion of their food from their fungal associate. The slow development of most orchid species is clearly disadvantageous, as during this preparatory period various destructive agencies may reduce the population, without there being any possibility of compensating for the loss by the production of more seeds. No doubt this is one of the reasons lying behind the immense seed production of orchids.

DURATION AND PERENNATION

As is well known, plants may be classified into several groups according to the duration of their life. In the first place are the plants we term annuals, including such common weeds as the groundsel and shepherd's purse, and many of the most ornamental of our garden " flowers ", for example, lobelia, " nasturtium " (*Tropaeolum*), candy-tuft, larkspur and many others. These go right through their life-cycle in a single year, the seeds germinating in the spring, and the plant dying in the summer or autumn after producing flowers and fruit. Then there are the so-called biennials, such as wallflowers, foxgloves and canterbury bells among garden flowers, and carrots, parsnips and onions among vegetables, in which the first growing period after germination is spent in building up a store of food, which is expended entirely in the production of flowers and fruit in the following season. Finally there are the perennials exemplified by michaelmas daisies, phloxes, delphiniums and rhubarb among herbs, and the immense variety of trees and shrubs, in which growth is carried on for many years, reaching to several hundreds in our longest lived trees.

In view of the long period before maturity is reached, all our orchids are of necessity perennial plants in the sense that the same individual lives through several growing seasons, and, what is more significant, through several winters. The problem of protecting the plant during the severe weather of winter is solved by different species in different ways, some of which need not be considered here. Most of the British orchids adopt the method, found in many other her-baceous perennials, of dying down to the surface of the ground each year, so that the remaining living part of the plant is well underground and protected by the surrounding soil. In a few species, however, such as the autumn ladies' tresses and the bee orchid and its allies, the leaves, which are developed in the autumn, remain green throughout the winter. The food which has been manufactured during the growing season is stored in the underground parts until wanted again for the resumption of growth in the next spring or, in the " wintergreen " species just mentioned, for the production of the flower spikes.

Some of our orchids, including the lady's slipper, helleborines, creeping ladies' tresses, twayblades, etc., store the food in horizontal or vertical underground stems (rhizomes or rootstocks, Fig. 12, p. 137, and Fig. 13, p. 153), and also partly in the rather fleshy, but otherwise ordinary, roots (Fig. 13, p. 153). These stems continue to grow each year, forming, as well as the aerial stems, fresh food-storage space in front, and dying away behind. The horizontal stems on the whole grow much more extensively than the vertical ones. The latter are prevented from growing right above the ground by the action of some of the roots which, by contracting in length, forcibly draw the root-stock down into the ground and, by repetitions of this process, keep it at approximately the same level in the soil.

A more common method of storing food is in very fleshy swollen roots or root-tubers, comparable to those found in the dahlia (Fig. 2, p. 12). Sometimes these roots, like those in the dahlia, terminate in a narrow part and help also to absorb water, as in the summer ladies' tresses (*Spiranthes aestivalis*) and, to a less extent, in the marsh and spotted orchids (Fig. 2, A and B, p. 12), fragrant orchid, etc., but in many species of *Orchis* and *Ophrys* (Fig. 2C) the tubers are more or less spherical and serve merely for food storage. In all these tuber-bearing orchids the food in the old tuber or tubers is used to produce the leaves and flowering stem in the current year. Excess food manufactured by the plant later on in the season is stored in a newly formed tuber or tubers, which eventually take the place of the old ones. In the middle of the growing season, when the plant is flowering, for instance, two tubers can be found, the old one which is not yet exhausted, and the new one which will serve for next year's growth. In the ladies' tresses several new tubers are formed each year (Fig. 2D), so that four or six tubers may be found, half of them old and half new.

Although the ordinary roots of most orchids are almost invariably heavily infected with the mycorhizal fungus, particularly in the autumn when the fungus is at its maximum activity, this is not always true for the root-tubers. In the ladies' tresses the tubers remain free from infection for some time after their formation, but become infected later, whereas the spherical tubers of *Orchis* and *Ophrys* are never infected. As regards the underground stems (rhizomes) there is a good deal of difference from one species to another, but in most orchids the rhizome eventually becomes free from infection, though this may not happen until seven or eight years after germination of the seed.

Two of our native orchids, the bog orchid (*Hammarbya paludosa*, Pl. XXIVb, p. 315) and the fen orchid (*Liparis loeselii*), adopt a different method of food storage, one which is found in many tropical orchids, especially those inhabiting trees (epiphytes). In these species

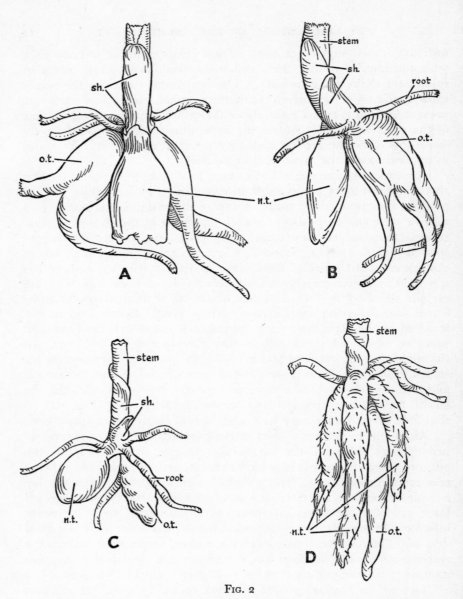

Fig. 2

A, B. Root system of spotted orchid, *Orchis fuchsii*, from front and side respectively, to show old and newly forming tubers. C. Root system of fly orchid, *Ophrys muscifera*. D. Root system of Irish ladies' tresses, *Spiranthes romanzoffiana*. n.t. new tuber; o.t. old tuber; sh. leaf sheath. (All × 1⅓)

the stem just above the ground swells to form a green bulb-like structure, which is termed a " pseudobulb " since, unlike a true bulb (e.g.
onion, daffodil, lily, etc.), its leaves are not swollen, but form thin
covering tunics as in a corm (e.g. crocus, gladiolus, etc.). These
pseudobulbs serve the same purpose as the root-tubers already described, a new one being formed each year, and the food stored in it
being used up in the succeeding year in the formation of the new leaves
and flower spike. In many tropical orchids the pseudobulbs may be
comparatively large (up to a foot long and two or three inches in diameter), but in the two British species they are quite small. It should be
noted that the pseudobulbs in many tropical orchids are not used
primarily for storing food, but act rather as water reservoirs, since
drought is a more serious danger for tree-inhabiting plants than shortage of food. In these regions the dry season is the period unfavourable
for growth, the " winter " not usually being cold enough to necessitate
any special protective measures.

In many orchids, for example spotted orchids, marsh orchids and
man orchid, flowering is continued over a period of years, the plants
behaving in this respect much as do delphiniums, michaelmas daisies,
daffodils, etc. Evidently the production of flowers and fruit does not
entirely exhaust the food available each year, the surplus being stored
up in the tuber, where it can be drawn upon in the following year.
We do not know exactly how long a single orchid plant can maintain
itself in this manner, but there is reason for thinking that wild specimens will flower for a number of years, since one not infrequently sees
the old dried-up flower stalks of the two previous years side by side
with the current year's flowering stem. Ziegenspeck records rhizomes
of the common twayblade bearing the remains of as many as twenty-
four old flowering stems. Since one flower spike is produced each year,
and a twayblade plant does not usually flower until it is fifteen years
old, such individuals must be at least forty years of age. Cultivated
clumps of spotted orchids have been observed to flower for five years
or longer, while many of our orchids will flower for several years in
succession in cultivation. Many tropical orchids can be cultivated for
long periods, some of the plants in the orchid houses at Kew having
been there since about 1880. These are, however, mostly tree-inhabiting orchids, and there is some evidence that they are, on the whole,
more long-lived than the terrestrial kinds.

It is fairly clear that some of our British orchids do not behave in the manner described above. In these species, of which the bee orchid and fragrant orchid are widespread examples, the food stores built up during the development of the seedling to maturity are in most cases all expended in the first production of flowers and fruit, after which the plant dies, relying on the large seed-production to carry on the race. Some plants, however, may flower a second time, or very exceptional individuals three times. Plants which flower only once and die after producing their seeds are said to be monocarpic. These include, of course, the great majority of annual plants, as well as many biennials, and the perennials here spoken of. The so-called century plant (*Agave americana*) of Mexico and the talipot palm (*Corypha umbraculifera*) of Ceylon are extreme examples of this type of development, the pre-flowering period in these cases being as much as 50 to 100 years. This method of flowering does to a certain extent explain the considerable fluctuations in the numbers of monocarpic orchids in any given locality which have been so often described. The immense populations sometimes recorded represent the offspring from a single favourable year for seed-production or for the establishment of young plants, whereas the few found in subsequent years are the result of plants starting in less favourable seasons. This fluctuation is particularly noticeable in those orchids which grow in grassy places, the narrow juvenile leaves closely simulating those of the surrounding grasses. On flowering, especially if a large batch of seedlings come to maturity at once, numerous plants seem to appear as if by magic in a spot where none had been noticed for several years previously.

In the kinds of orchids which are more truly perennial the populations tend to remain more constant ; any differences in the apparent numbers present are more likely to be due to good or bad flowering seasons, many of the individuals missing flowering when the conditions have not been favourable, and producing leaves only. For instance, it is usually not difficult to find numerous non-flowering specimens of helleborines and marsh orchids whenever one examines a locality where these species occur.

It has already been shown that during the first years of its life, the period varying from one species to another, the orchid plant is entirely dependent on its mycorhizal fungus for organic (energy-producing and body-building) foods. Some species, however, always remain to some extent dependent on the fungus, which is in these species much more active than in most orchids, but this apparently undesirable feature may even be of advantage to the plant, especially as regards woodland species. Two of our orchids, the red helleborine (*Cephalanthera rubra*) and creeping ladies' tresses (*Goodyera repens*), both of which are inhabitants of woods or forests, are excellent illustrations of this apparent paradox.

In the red helleborine most of the roots are long, comparatively slender and grow horizontally, favouring especially the upper layers of the soil where there is the greatest amount of humus. These roots are usually heavily infected with the mycorhizal fungus, from which they are able to obtain ample food, which is stored in the roots and not in the rootstock. So long as there is plenty of light reaching the plant, the leaves can manufacture food which is used to produce flower-spikes and the new aerial shoots each year. If, however, the vegetation grows up so that the plant is heavily shaded, it can no longer obtain food by the activities of its leaves ; the onus of doing this is then thrown on the fungus growing in the roots. The food thus obtainable is sufficient to maintain only a more or less stunted plant, while if the tree cover becomes very thick the roots may continue to grow underground, supported on the food supplied by the fungus, without any aerial parts appearing at all ! Plants have been known to persist in thick forest for over twenty years by means of this special type of nutrition. On partial clearing of the trees, coppicing of the undergrowth, or any other not too violent change which allows more light to reach the ground, the helleborine plant develops a normal aerial shoot and flowering is resumed.

The creeping ladies' tresses is also normally a woodland orchid, occurring in pinewoods in Scotland. It has a slender creeping stem which in the lower part is more or less enveloped in the mosses and half-decayed pine-needles covering the ground. The stem bears a few rather short roots at intervals, while horizontal growth is continued by long thin branches (runners) (Fig. 14, p. 189). These runners, and also the roots, are heavily infected by the associated fungus, which no doubt contributes towards the nutrition of the plant even in lighter spots. As the wood becomes thicker and shadier, however, the orchid becomes more dependent upon the fungus, and, like the red helleborine, may persist without flowering for a long time until conditions favourable to flowering are restored.

Even the lady's slipper, which is very little infected in the adult stage, and is therefore under normal conditions independent of help from the fungus, may, in unfavourable circumstances, revert to its youthful state of dependence. Re-infection of the roots takes place from the soil outside, and the plant behaves subsequently like the two species just described, producing no leaves and living an entirely underground existence until the amelioration of the conditions permits a return to normal life.

It is clear from these and other examples that the occurrence of the associated mycorhizal fungus is an important factor in the continued existence (perennation) of orchids. There is, however, considerable diversity among our British orchids, for whereas some species, like the common twayblade and lady's slipper, after an initial dependence on the fungus while the seedling is becoming established, are almost entirely self-supporting after reaching maturity, others remain dependent to varying extents, the most extreme cases among green plants being the two examples described above. A noticeable feature of many orchids is the small size of the leaves in comparison with the large and imposing flower-spike, this evidently being related to the help obtained from the fungus.

SAPROPHYTIC ORCHIDS

The dependence of orchids on the mycorhizal fungus, however, is carried much farther in the bird's nest orchid (*Neottia nidus-avis*, Pl. 20, p. 191), common coral-root (*Corallorhiza trifida*, Pl. 19b, p. 190) and spurred coral-root (*Epipogium aphyllum*, Pl. 21, p. 194). These orchids, which are without leaves, are almost devoid of the green colouring matter chlorophyll by means of which ordinary plants manufacture their food, and are therefore entirely dependent on food from other sources. The extensive underground stems or roots are heavily infected with the mycorhiza, which occurs both in the external (ectotrophic) and internal (endotrophic) forms, the first named forming quite a felt-like covering to the roots in the bird's nest orchid. This species and the spurred coral-root almost invariably occur in woods where there is a thick layer of dead and decaying leaves, by which the underground parts of the plant are completely surrounded. The fungus threads penetrate this humus layer, extracting food by means of ferments, and passing it to the internal parts of the fungus, which are, in due course, digested by the orchid. The common coral-root also usually grows in soil rich in humus, but this species can also thrive in more mineral soils. Examples of saprophytic orchids may be found in most other parts of the world, where they usually inhabit much the same sort of localities as do our native species. The underground parts of such plants are very remarkable, differing from one species to another very considerably. In the bird's nest orchid (Fig. 15, p. 194, Pl. XIIb, p. 171) there is a rather woody rootstock, somewhat like that in the helleborines, which produces a dense tuft of short but thick and fleshy roots, the whole being thought to resemble a bird's nest. In the two coral-roots there are no roots at all, the underground stem or rhizome containing the fungus and replacing the roots. A complicated branched rhizome is formed in the common coral-root, each branch bearing a number of undeveloped secondary branches in the form of knobs, the whole strongly reminiscent of certain sorts of corals. In the spurred coral-root (Fig. 16, p. 199), on the other hand, the rhizome is somewhat flattened with many large rounded lobes, forming a much more solid structure than in the other species. Food is stored up in the roots, or rhizomes as the case may be, until enough has been accumulated to produce a flower-spike. This, which is the only part of the plant to appear above the ground, is pale brown or pinkish in *Neottia* and *Epipogium*, but contains an appreciable amount of chlorophyll in the case of *Corallorhiza*. This latter species is therefore capable of manufacturing some food for itself, this being probably used up in the formation of fruits and seeds. Flower-spikes are produced at fairly regular intervals in the bird's nest orchid and common coral-root, though probably not every year. No doubt sometimes the food available is only just sufficient for the production of the seeds, and in that case the plant dies, but observations make it clear that many individuals are not monocarpic.

The spurred coral-root, in sharp contrast to the other two species, only flowers very rarely at long intervals. There are no actual records of the length of these intervals, but they are probably of the order of ten or twenty years. It is because of this that the records of its occurrence in this country are so few—less than a dozen all told. Since the species grows in deep shade under beech and other trees it could very easily be overlooked even when in flower. The plant lives entirely underground all this time, fed through the agency of the mycorhizal fungus, until suitable conditions enable a flower-spike to be produced. Indeed so degraded has the spurred coral-root become in its entire dependence on the mycorhiza, that it has no means of rapidly absorbing and conveying to the growing flower-spike enough water to provide for its necessarily rapid growth. The rudiments of the flower-spikes can be seen on most rhizomes in the autumn, but it is probable that continuously damp weather in the spring and summer is needed in order that the required amount of water may be stored right at the base of the spike.

Even the spurred coral-root is not by any means the most remark-able of saprophytic orchids. There are, for instance, two orchids, natives of Australia, in which not only is the vegetative part of the life-cycle passed underground, but the flower-spikes also are either buried in the soil or only just reach the surface. Indeed one at least of these species was only discovered when the plants were turned up in the course of ploughing virgin soil. There may yet be more of these remarkable plants awaiting discovery ! It is presumed that these orchids are either fertilised by small animals living in the soil, or that they are self-pollinated without the flowers opening at all. This latter alternative is not an infrequent occurrence even in ordinary green plants growing above ground, violets and pansies being good examples, as well as the Isle of Wight helleborine (*Epipactis vectensis*). Underground flower-spikes have also been recorded in the bird's nest orchid, some of which had formed fruits and seeds, but nothing is known of the mechanism of fertilisation. The production of these spikes is thought to be due to obstructions in the soil preventing normal development. Underground inflorescences have also been observed rarely in the spurred coral-root, but there is no evidence that they ever develop completely or produce seeds in such a position.

The Japanese leafless orchid *Gastrodia elata*, already referred to, appears, from observations made in the field, to be a sort of secondary parasite. The associated mycorhizal fungus here is the very wide-spread parasitic honey fungus (*Armillaria mellea*) common in this country. This fungus produces long thick branching threads which penetrate the soil and sometimes attack the underground tubers of the *Gastrodia*. This attack is usually kept within bounds by the orchid, and the fungus is able to penetrate only a short distance into the tuber. Food is absorbed from the trees (oaks, etc.) on which the honey fungus is truly parasitic, or also from dead stumps, and is passed on to the orchid, which as a result is able to accumulate enough food to produce a flower-spike.

PLATE I

B. J. Hammond

Flower spike of Common Spotted Orchid, *Orchis fuchsii*, to show structure of typical orchid flower. The large marked petal is the lip ($\times 5\frac{1}{2}$)

PLATE II

C. Thomas

a. Incompletely separate flowers of Pendulous-flowered Helleborine, *Epipactis pendula*, showing two distinct lips and columns, but adjacent perianth members not properly formed (×3)

C. Thomas

b. Clump of plants of Common Spotted Orchid, *Orchis fuchsii*, to show roots; the right-hand stem is forming an additional new tuber above the normal one (×¾)

VEGETATIVE MULTIPLICATION

It is a commonplace among those who cultivate or study plants that many species multiply more readily by vegetative means than by seeds. Indeed, not a few species, particularly those which are natives of woods or other shady places, on the one hand, or those which grow at high altitudes or latitudes, on the other, rarely produce any seeds at all, relying almost entirely on vegetative growth for their maintenance. This is generally accepted as being a response to low temperatures, shortness of the growing season, or reduced light available, all of which hinder the production of flowers, and especially the ripening of fruits and seeds. At the same time, the conditions associated with such habitats mentioned above tend to enable active growth to continue throughout what favourable season there is, drought being conspicuous by its absence. The food manufactured is therefore expended in the formation of additional growths, which in one way or another become separate from the parent and lead an individual existence. For instance, the well-known lesser celandine (*Ranunculus ficaria*), a common woodland plant, though flowering freely, seldom produces seed. The plants survive the winter, however, in the form of numerous tiny potato-like tubers produced on the aerial stems, which otherwise die right away. Each tuber grows out in the spring to form a new individual, so it is clear that a rapid increase in the population is possible under suitable conditions. No doubt in most places so many of the tubers are destroyed by insects, slugs and other agencies that the population is merely maintained at a more or less constant level.

Among plants at large we may find all gradations between those in which multiplication is merely the natural result of the method of growth, and others in which parts of the plant are specially modified to serve for the rapid and efficient production of offspring by vegetative means. Examples of the first class which easily come to mind are the natural increase in daffodils or crocuses, while the runners of the garden strawberry provide an excellent illustration of the second group. This great variety of method is also to be found among orchids.

Let us deal first with what we may term the ordinary or automatic methods of vegetative increase in orchids. It will be remembered that some of our native species, for example lady's slipper, common twayblade and marsh helleborine, have creeping under-ground stems or rhizomes. These grow forward continually in front, while the rear parts gradually die away and decay on passing their maturity. Should the rhizome branch—a not uncommon occurrence in the marsh helleborine—a time will come, sooner or later, when the progressive death of the rear part reaches the fork, and the two branches become separate individuals. This is, of course, a common phenomenon among other plants, such as lily of the valley (*Convallaria majalis*) and garden mint (*Mentha spicata*).

In those orchids which have relatively short tuberous roots, such as the various species of *Orchis* and *Ophrys*, the butterfly orchids, fragrant orchid, etc., the course of events leading to multiplication is rather different. In these plants the new tuber is produced in associa-tion with a lateral bud at the base of the current season's stem. Some-times, and in some species not infrequently, more than one lateral bud develops, and consequently more than one new tuber is produced during the year (Pl. IIb, p. 19), particularly if plenty of spare food is available for storage. During the next year two aerial stems may be produced, each of which forms its own tuber ; eventually with the death of the old parts two distinct plants are formed. This is, of course, similar to the type of multiplication occurring in tulips, crocuses or dahlias. In nature, where there is no artificial separation and spacing-out of the new individuals, they remain together to form a clump, all the individuals of which produce flowers identical in colour, etc. Such clumps may frequently be seen in populations of spotted or marsh orchids (Pl. IIb, p. 19), and also less frequently in the man orchid and other species. If the additional tubers are small it may be some years before the new plant is large enough to flower, the stages of development being very similar to those following germination of the seed. Some years ago one of my colleagues at Kew, Mr. C. E. Hubbard, brought me a sod of turf containing a clump of five flowering spikes of heath spotted orchid, which he had dug up near Aberystwyth, and which he thought would provide excellent specimens for preserva-tion. The flowers in all the spikes were identical in colour and lip markings, indicating that the plants had arisen vegetatively from one original plant. In order to obtain the plants undamaged I washed away the soil very carefully under a tap. Judge of my amazement when I found that instead of about ten plants, five flowering and five sterile, there were no fewer than 130 individual plants in the clump !

These ranged from tiny plants with a single extremely narrow grass-like leaf and a minute unbranched tuber, up to the full-sized flowering specimens. In 1947 I saw a clump of the same species in Staffordshire containing no fewer than 20 flowering spikes, all exactly alike in colour and markings, while many groups nearby had from 5 to 10 flower-spikes. In all these clumps the individuals were close to one another, but with the death of some of the older centrally placed plants a looser arrangement would in time be developed. The complete separation of the individuals is no doubt a slow process, but after a period of years the divisions of one original plant might well be scattered over a quite appreciable area.

In the musk orchid (*Herminium monorchis*) we find a modification of the above method, which ensures that the additional plants are spaced out at some distance from the parent. In this species two or more tubers are produced each year, but instead of being crowded together they are borne at the ends of slender roots or "stolons" of varying length. The longer of these may be as much as four or even eight inches in length, depending on the vigour of the parent plant. Each tuber, with its associated bud, gives rise in the following year to a new leafy or flowering shoot, the food available usually only permitting one of the new plants to flower. An extra robust plant may, however, be replaced by two or more flowering offspring.

In two of our orchids, namely the creeping ladies' tresses (*Goodyera*) and the spurred coral-root (*Epipogium*), the main stem or underground rhizome, as the case may be, produces special branches, the whole or parts of which soon become detached and develop into independent individuals. In the former species these special stems (Fig. 14, p. 189) grow among the moss, etc., covering the surface of the ground, whereas in *Epipogium* the "runners" or "stolons" are entirely underground (Fig. 16, p. 199), like the rest of the vegetative body. In *Goodyera* the lateral stem itself becomes detached, either early in its development or at a later stage, depending no doubt on the food available and possibly on other factors. In *Epipogium*, however, the runners produce small lateral buds which swell up and form new rhizomes either while still attached or after becoming separate. The young plants in both species owe their rapid development to infection by the mycorhizal fungus, which provides them with the food necessary for growth. Seed production in both species is extremely poor, so they depend almost entirely upon vegetative multiplication for occupying new areas.

This is naturally a very slow process, and is limited by the extent of country over which favourable conditions for vegetative growth exist.

Vegetative multiplication is carried out in another group of species by means of buds which arise from the ordinary roots of the plant. In some cases, as in the bird's nest orchid (*Neottia*), the roots are short, so that the new individuals are not far distant from the parent. There is reason to think that in this species, however, the production of these buds is usually the result of injury to the root or their separation from the rhizome. This latter alternative probably takes place when a plant dies after flowering, for as the roots are nourished by the fungus they are more or less independent of the rest of the plant. Some, if not all, may survive the death of the rhizome, and each will then give rise to a new individual. Buds arise either from the tip of the root or just below it ; they soon produce roots of their own, and in a comparatively short time cannot be distinguished from five-year-old seedlings. The time gained by vegetative multiplication as compared with development from the seed is well shown in this example.

Other orchids have much longer roots than those in *Neottia*, the new plants consequently arising some distance from the parent. The dark red helleborine (*Epipactis atrorubens*) is an example of a species in which root-buds are a comparatively rare occurrence. The roots in this species are very long and branched, penetrating into the cracks in the rocks among which the plants usually grow. Occasionally the root tip produces a bud which grows up to form a new plant ; this may then be as much as a foot or more from the aerial stem of the parent. Root-buds arise rather more frequently in the large white helleborine (*Cephalanthera damasonium*), producing new aerial shoots which become independent of the parent plant. This is no doubt an important means of multiplication in conditions, such as deep shade, where flower and seed production is at a minimum. As the mature roots in this species are almost or quite free from fungus, the new shoot must obtain its food in the early stages from the main shoot, in which respect the large white helleborine contrasts markedly with its relative the red helleborine (*C. rubra*).

Rather a different state of affairs is found in the common and lesser twayblades (*Listera ovata* and *L. cordata*, Fig. 3A, p. 23) and in the red helleborine. Here the roots almost invariably give rise to buds which develop rapidly into new plants. In the common twayblade the roots continue to grow for ten years, extending farther and farther into the soil. Anybody walking through a wood in which *L. ovata* is common will frequently observe numerous small plants close together, or sometimes even arranged in lines or more or less regular designs. These plants have nearly all arisen from the special buds developed on the ordinary long roots of the mature plant. Food is stored up in slightly swollen parts of the roots ; this is used to form buds either just

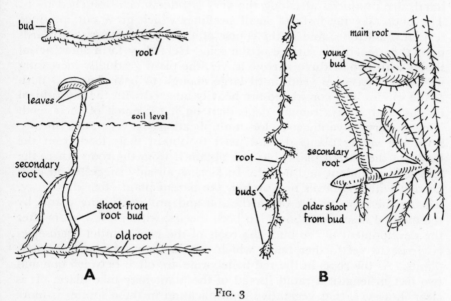

Fig. 3

Roots of A, lesser twayblade, *Listera cordata*, and B, red helleborine, *Cephalanthera rubra*, to show development of buds, which ultimately form aerial shoots. (A ×¾; B, on left ×¾, on right much magnified) (After Ziegenspeck)

behind or less frequently at the tip of the root. Such buds grow to the surface of the soil to form a small aerial shoot, which gradually develops to full size and produces eventually a flowering spike. Flowers may be produced in the third or subsequent years, a marked speed-up compared with the fifteen years which elapse between germination of the seed and flowering. Multiplication can also take place actively where the shade is so dense that flowers are not produced, or if they are, pollination by insects is very doubtful and incomplete. Should a clearance of the wood take place, however, the numerous sterile plants can rapidly develop flowers in the normal manner.

A similar state of affairs exists in the lesser twayblade and red helleborine, the root-buds developing in the former (Fig. 3A, p. 23) in much the same manner as in *Listera ovata*, and producing flowers by the third year. The buds in the red helleborine (Fig. 3B), on the other hand, are produced all along the very slender much-branched roots. The buds take the form of small swellings which grow out, produce several small roots, and in the course of a few years elongate upwards until they reach the surface of the soil. Here they form short aerial shoots with two or three narrow leaves, the plant gradually increasing in size in successive years until large enough to bear flowers. Both of the species here considered are heavily infected with the mycorhizal fungus, and always remain dependent on it for much of their food. This is very advantageous for multiplication by vegetative means, since the young plants do not need to obtain their food from the leaves of the parent plant, but can obtain it from the roots where the fungus is abundant and active. In fact, as already suggested in connection with the bird's nest orchid, the parent plant often dies away, leaving the roots to live on in the soil and produce young plants by the method described above. In both species, within a few years after the development of the bud, the roots of the new plantlet themselves give rise to yet further buds, which can in their turn produce new plants. As the roots in the red helleborine are often between one and two feet in length, a rapid spread of the plant may take place. It is clear, however, that vegetative multiplication in these species is more a means of tiding over unfavourable conditions, for example, excessive shade, than a means of migration into new areas. For this purpose the seeds are the only really effective agents.

Probably the most remarkable method of vegetative reproduction among British orchids is that found in the bog orchid (*Hammarbya paludosa*). Here the young plants arise on neither the stems nor the roots, but on the edges of the leaves in the form of small fleshy knobs, usually about six in number. *Hammarbya* normally grows in wet bogs, the plants being small and almost buried in tussocks of bog-moss in which they are rooted. Consequently the leaves are continually damp, and the small buds on becoming detached can continue growth without any delay. These plantlets are soon infected by the mycorhizal fungus, and are no doubt entirely nourished by it in the early stages.

The very first leaves formed on the young plants develop buds at their tips, so that under favourable conditions multiplication is very rapid. The adult stage is reached in quite a short time, much more quickly than from germination of the seed. In this example the habitat being continuously favourable for vegetative growth is the important factor, not the necessity for making up for the absense of flowers, as in the species previously mentioned.

CHAPTER 2

THE ORCHID FLOWER

A DIFFICULTY which will probably occur to the reader may be expressed in the question "How can I tell whether any plant which I find is an orchid or not?" To answer this is not quite so easy as may appear to those who are well acquainted with our British orchids. In some respects orchids resemble other plants; for instance, the leaves may be very similar to those of a bluebell, on the one hand, or of a plantain on the other. The flower-spikes, or flowers of some orchids, may bear a strong resemblance to those of plants belonging to quite different families, for example, broomrapes or butterworts. The orchid family belongs, together with grasses, rushes, lilies, daffodils, irises and many other well-known plants, to the large group of plants known as Monocotyledons. These are characterised by the embryo plant in the seed possessing only one leaf (Cotyledon), instead of the two which occur in the seeds of the other great group of flowering plants (Dicotyledons). Familiar examples of the latter are the French bean and the common mustard, both well-known garden vegetables, in which the two seed-leaves come above the ground and are very evident when the seeds grow. Monocotyledons almost invariably have leaves in which the veins or prominent ribs run the whole length of the leaf in a more or less parallel manner, usually joining at the tip where the leaf narrows and ends (Fig. 4, p. 28). When the leaves are very broad, as in the common twayblade, or the lower leaves of the common spotted orchid, convergence of the veins at the tip of the leaf can be very clearly seen.

Owing to the close resemblances of the stems and leaves of plants of different families, it is necessary to examine the flowers in greater

PLATE III

C. Thomas

b. A spike of Pyramidal Orchid, *Anacamptis pyramidalis*, with the flowers not inverted as on the normal plant ($\times 2\frac{1}{2}$)

E. J. Bedford

a. Spikes of Bee Orchid, *Ophrys apifera*, with abnormal flowers in which the lip resembles the sepals ($\times \frac{3}{4}$)

PLATE IV

E. J. Bedford

Flowers of Early Spider Orchid, *Ophrys sphegodes*, showing variation in lip shape and markings ($\times 2\frac{1}{2}$)

detail in order to see how orchids differ from the other kinds of mono-cotyledons mentioned above.

There can be no doubt that orchids are comparatively closely related to the members of the lily family, such as the lily itself, the tulip and the hyacinth or bluebell. In all these flowers there are brightly coloured outer portions forming the so-called perianth, which is the obvious part of the flower (Fig. 5A, p. 30). The perianth serves the double purpose of protecting the delicate reproductive organs during the early stages of development of the flower, and of attracting insects to the flower after it has opened. Inside this are the male and female reproductive organs which eventually give rise to the fruit and its contained seeds. Now in a tulip, for instance, all the parts of the perianth, or " petals " as they are sometimes not quite accurately termed, are much the same size and shape, thus giving the flower a regular and tidy appearance. A similar state of affairs is found in the lily and hyacinth, for although the " petals " curl back they all do so in the same manner.

Such is not the case in an orchid flower (Fig. 5B, p. 30 ; Pl. I, p. 18). Here the parts of the perianth differ considerably from one another, one of them especially often being most complicated in structure. This petal is termed the *lip* or *labellum*, and the presence of this curious petal is a characteristic feature of the flowers of all orchids. The lip differs from the other petals not only in coloration, but frequently in being variously lobed or with a number of finger-like outgrowths (Fig. 6, p. 31). In the man orchid (Pl. XVa, p. 238), for instance, there are two arm-like portions and two leg-like portions, the whole lip bearing a distinct resemblance to the trunk of a man, while the " head " is formed by the rest of the flower. Often the base of the lip is drawn out into a tube-like portion which may be short and broad, very much resembling the finger of a glove, as in the marsh orchids, or, on the other hand, may be quite long and slender like a pipe, as in the fragrant orchid. This is known as the *spur* and often contains the nectar or other liquid for which insects visit the flowers. Not infrequently the colour scheme of the lip is quite elaborate, consisting of a series of lines, loops or other marks on a sharply contrasting ground colour which itself may be different in different parts of the lip. The result of these inequalities in the perianth is an irregular flower in which the front and back (top and bottom, if you prefer it that way) are quite dissimilar although the sides are identical ; such

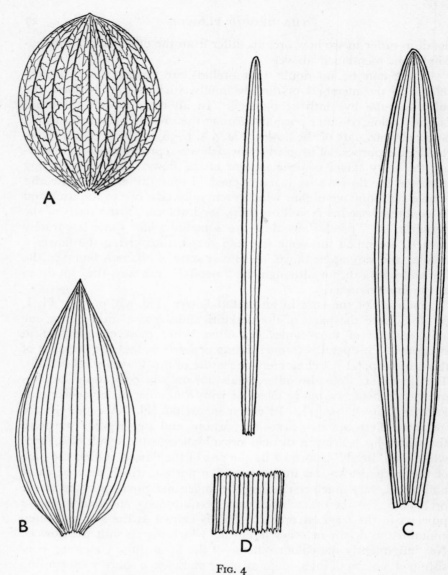

FIG. 4

Leaves of various orchids to show venation

A. Twayblade, *Listera ovata*. B. Broad-leaved helleborine, *Epipactis helléborine*. C. Common marsh orchid, *Orchis praetermissa*. D. Fragrant orchid, *Gymnadenia conopsea*. The lower drawing in D is enlarged to show the actual number of veins. (All but lower D × ¾, lower D × 3)

a general arrangement, in fact, as we find in the sweet pea, delphinium or violet. Such flowers are said to be zygomorphic.

If we examine the interior of the orchid flower we shall find that instead of the male organs (*stamens*) being quite separate from the female (*pistil*) as in the tulip, they are joined together to form a special structure named the *column* (Fig. 7, p. 33), which is the second characteristic feature of the orchid family. This structure in some orchids may actually be pillar-like and resemble what we generally understand by a column. In other kinds, on the other hand, it may be very diversified in shape, with all manner of humps and other projections.

In most orchids, as in the lily family, the perianth is composed of six parts, three of which are outside the others, and are termed sepals, while the three inner ones, including the lip, are the petals properly so-called. Usually the lip is at the apparent front or bottom of the flower, but in some cases, such as the British bog orchid (*Hammarbya*) and the spurred coral-root (*Epipogium aphyllum*) (Pl. 21, p. 194), it is at the top or back. The sepals may all be almost alike, or the single one opposite the lip may be different in shape or colour from the other two, which are alike and termed the lateral sepals. Two of the petals, one on each side, are also alike and often show a marked resemblance in colour, if not in shape, to the lip or third petal.

In the lily family and, indeed, in most other common plants, the male reproductive bodies, the pollen grains, are borne in the upper part of the stamens. Thousands of these minute dust-like grains are exposed to the air by the opening of the stamens, and in many cases being slightly sticky, adhere to the bodies of bees and other insects which visit the flowers for the nectar there. In other plants, for example grasses and many of our large native trees (oak, beech, elm, etc.), the pollen is dry and powdery and is blown about freely by the wind.

In the orchids, however, with the exception of the lady's slipper, the pollen grains, instead of being separate and capable of being carried or blown away singly, are joined together in various ways to form more or less solid masses termed *pollinia* (Fig. 5 C, p. 30). Each of these pollinia or pollen masses contains thousands, or perhaps even millions, of individual pollen grains. There may be from two to eight pollinia in each orchid flower, the number being always the same in any given species, but in no British species are there more than four. Part of the pollinium itself may be sticky or it may be furnished with a special adhesive attachment (*viscidium*). In either case the whole or part of the mass of pollen adheres to any insect with which it comes into contact and is carried away by the insect to another flower. The pollen masses are contained in the single stamen, which is usually placed near the top or towards the back of the column. The stamen, when ripe, consists of two bag-like containers placed side by side, or

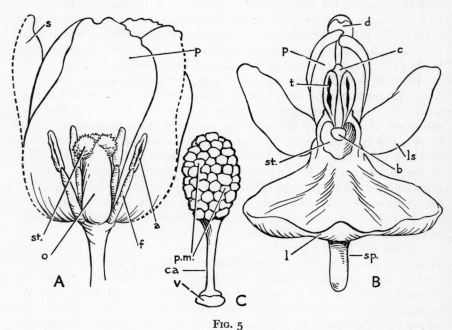

FIG. 5

A. Flower of tulip cut through to show inner parts. B. Flower of spotted orchid, *Orchis fuchsii*, from front. C. Pollinium of heath spotted orchid, *O. ericetorum*. — a, anther ; b, bursicle ; c, anther connective ; ca, caudicle ; d, dorsal sepal ; f, filament ; l, lip ; l.s, lateral sepal ; o, ovary ; p, petal ; p.m, pollen masses ; s, sepal ; sp, spur ; st, stigma ; t, theca ; v, viscidium.

(A natural size ; B ×4½ ; C ×20)   (B after Le Maout & Decaisne)

more rarely diverging from one another, each containing one or two (in some exotic orchids three or four) pollinia.

In the lady's slipper, however, there are two stamens, placed one on each side of the column (Fig. 7A, p. 33). These look more or less like the stamens of other flowers, except that they have no stalk. The pollen here is also more like that of many other plant families,

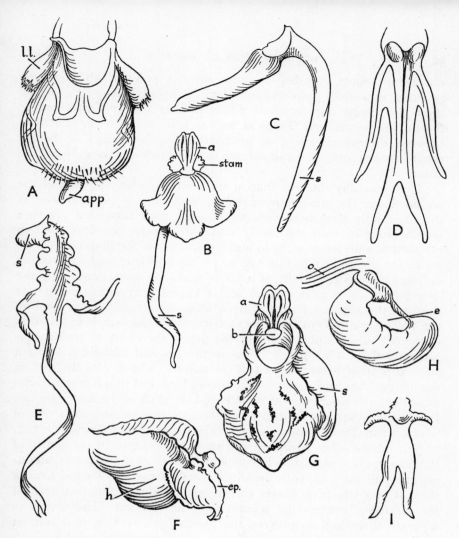

FIG. 6

The lip in nine orchid genera to show the great differences in
shape and size

A. Bee orchid, *Ophrys apifera*. B. Fragrant orchid, *Gymnadenia conopsea*.
C. Lesser butterfly orchid, *Platanthera bifolia*. D. Man orchid, *Aceras anthropophorum*. E. Lizard orchid, *Himantoglossum hircinum*. F. Broad-leaved helleborine, *Epipactis helleborine*. G. Dwarf purple orchid, *Orchis purpurella*. H.
Lady's slipper, *Cypripedium calceolus*. I. Lesser twayblade, *Listera cordata*.—a.
anther ; app. appendix ; b. bursicle ; e. entrance ; ep. epichile ; h. hypochile ; l.l. lateral lobe ; o. ovary ; s. spur ; stam. staminode. (A–D ×4 ;
E ×2 ; F ×5 ; G ×4 ; H natural size ; I ×10)

not being joined together to form distinct pollinia, although the grains lie in a sticky paste-like substance. The lady's slippers, of which there are about one hundred different sorts widely distributed in North Temperate and Tropical regions, are therefore intermediate between the remainder of the orchids and such families as the lily family, possessing the lip and column of the former and the pollen of the latter.

It is generally thought that in the course of the evolution of the orchid flower the other four or five stamens present in the flowers of the lily family have been suppressed, since their continued presence would interfere with the nicely adjusted mechanisms developed in connection with insect visits to and fertilisation of the flowers.

In the lily and tulip (Fig. 5A, p. 30) the female reproductive organ or pistil consists essentially of a lower part, the *ovary*, containing the as yet unfertilised seeds (*ovules*) and a knob-like receptive portion at the top, the *stigma*. This, having a rough surface, detaches some of the pollen grains from the insect's back, following which fertilisation of the ovules takes place. In the lily family the ovary or seed case is surrounded by the " petals ", but in the iris and daffodil it forms a swollen portion below the rest of the flower. This is also the case in the orchids, but as the ovary is often very long and thin it is sometimes difficult to tell where the ovary ends and the stalk of the flower begins. Inside the ovary are immense numbers of tiny ovules, each one of which is capable of forming a seed. The two receptive stigmas (Fig. 7, p. 33), on the other hand, are borne on the column in the centre of the flower, often immediately below or in front of the stamen containing the pollinia. There is usually a special structure, formed from a third stigma which no longer carries out its original function, termed the *rostellum*, between the stamen and the stigmas. This serves to separate them and to prevent the pollen from coming into contact with the stigmas of the same flower. The rostellum exhibits great diversity in different orchids, varying from a minute ball or tooth in some species to a quite large and complicated structure in others. It frequently plays an important part in the elaborate mechanisms designed to facilitate pollination, which are described more fully in the next chapter.

It will be seen from the preceding account that any orchid flower possesses a number of characteristic or diagnostic features, such as the number and arrangement of the perianth parts (petals and sepals), the

remarkable special petal or lip, and the central column, which enable
the student to recognise it as being an orchid. These various parts of
the flower show great diversity in themselves from one orchid species
or group of orchid species to another, but in any one kind of orchid,
such as the bee orchid (Pl. 45b, p. 286) or the well-known early purple
orchid (Pl. 37, p. 258), the general pattern produced is relatively

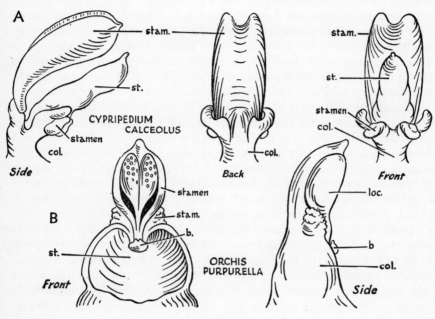

FIG. 7

Various views of the column of A, lady's slipper, *Cypripedium calceolus*, and
B, dwarf purple orchid, *Orchis purpurella*.—b. bursicle ; col. column ; loc.
anther loculus ; st. stigma ; stam. staminode. (A ×3 ; B ×10)

uniform, giving a readily recognised and distinct appearance to the
flower.

VARIATION

In spite of what has just been stated, it must not be imagined that
every individual bee orchid or early purple orchid plant is an exact

replica of every other one, as though they had been mass-produced from a factory. This is no more the case in orchids than in other sorts of plants or in animals, most individuals differing from others with respect to many parts of the plant. Indeed in the orchid family the curious shapes and often complicated colouring of the various parts of the flower permit—perhaps even give exceptional scope for—considerable variations from one individual to the next (Pl. Va, p. 78). Most orchid enthusiasts have frequently noticed, among the many early purple orchid plants bearing spotted leaves, scattered individuals in which the leaves are quite devoid of the usual purplish spots, or on other occasions have noticed specimens of the green-veined orchid with pale mauve or pink coloured flowers (Pl. 36, p. 251) among the overwhelming majority of individuals bearing deep mauve flowers.

Careful examination of the orchids in any locality will, however, reveal the presence of some variability, although the differences between the individuals may not be of such a nature as to be evident at a cursory glance. In fact our British orchids exhibit considerable differences from one another in this respect, some, such as the two butterfly orchids, showing relatively little variability in colour or size, whereas in others, for example the heath spotted orchid or the early marsh orchid, almost any large group of individuals will show a great range of colour forms, the variants sometimes being so strikingly different from one another that the inexperienced person does not recognise them as belonging to the same species. Even in an orchid which is frequently very variable it is, however, possible to find localities where only one of the colour forms is present, and that in considerable numbers. Sometimes uniform and diverse populations may occur in adjacent fields in which the external conditions appear to be identical, but at present we have no satisfactory explanation of these differences.

The most distinct, and by many people thought to be the most beautiful, of these colour forms are undoubtedly those with white flowers. These are known as albinos, and, of course, are found in many other kinds of plants, for example bluebells and heather, as well as in many animals. The absence of colour is usually hereditary, the plants breeding true if inbred. Pure white forms are found in most of our native orchids with red, pink or purple flowers ; examples may frequently be found in the green-veined orchid and the common spotted orchid, and occasionally in the early purple orchid and the pyramidal orchid (Pl. XIVb, p. 223). Albinos are very rarely found in species with greenish or yellowish flowers, this being true also of other families of plants. Where, however, the normal colour of the flowers is caused by a mixture of red or purple and yellowish pigments, individuals may be found in which the former colours are absent, but the latter remain. Such partial albino forms have been recorded in the bee orchid, the early spider orchid and the man orchid, as well as in numerous tropical species. Many of the colour forms mentioned above have been given special Latin names, but there seems no reason for considering them as of any more importance than any other colour variants. The fact that these albinos and partial albinos may occur should, however, always be borne in mind by the nature-lover when faced by what is apparently an unknown orchid. May I also urge that when found, these interesting plants should not be picked, but should be left to multiply. Natural crossing with normally coloured individuals will in any case keep down the number of albinos, since the offspring of such crosses will in the vast majority of cases have coloured flowers, so there is no necessity for man to help in the process of elimination.

Apart from differences in the ground colour of the flowers, which in some species, for instance the green-veined orchid (*Orchis morio*, Pl. 36, p. 251), may vary from white or pale pink through pale mauve to bright mauve, there is often quite great variation in the darker markings or spottings of the lip (Pl. IV, p. 27). These markings may be more or less evident or differently coloured or, within definite limits, may show variations in the actual patterns, a good example being the heath spotted orchid (*Orchis ericetorum*). Where both ground colour and markings vary independently, as is often the case, the total possible range of variation is obviously very great and a really striking diversity may indeed be found in an area no larger than a tennis court.

Another common type of variation, besides the colour or markings of the flowers, is the presence or absence of reddish coloration (anthocyanin) in the leaves or stems. This is, of course, not confined to orchids, being found in many other plants such as dandelions, docks, and deadnettles. Among orchids the helleborines perhaps provide the best examples of this type of variability, particularly the broad-leaved helleborine. Where the flowers are greenish in ground colour they may, or may not, be tinged reddish, in conformity with the colour of the leaves, but there is no necessary agreement between flowers and vegetative parts in this respect. Examples of variation in flower colour due to presence in varying amounts or absence of anthocyanin pigments are found in the frog orchid (*Coeloglossum viride*), man orchid (*Aceras anthropophorum*) and common twayblade (*Listera ovata*).

Spotting of the leaves, which is limited to a comparatively small number (about seven species) of British orchids, also shows considerable variability from plant to plant of the same species. In the early purple orchid (*Orchis mascula*, Pl. 37, p. 258) and the dwarf purple orchid (*O. purpurella*) there is nearly always a substantial proportion of plants with unspotted leaves, though such may be commoner in some localities than in others. The spots themselves may be darker or paler—they may even be so faint as only to be noticeable on careful examination—or they may occur in greater or smaller numbers on each leaf. This type of variation, that is, in the intensity and number of the spots, is frequently to be seen in populations of the two common spotted orchids, and will often be found to bear a relation to the variation in the colour and markings of the flowers in the plants concerned. On the other hand, the type of spotting, such as small and neat, large and irregular, or in the form of rings, is often characteristic of a certain kind of orchid. For instance, the common spotted orchid (Pl. 38a, p. 259) and the early purple orchid have rather large often irregular solid (that is, not ringed) spots, the dwarf purple orchid (Pl. 43b, p. 282) very small regular ones, while in the leopard marsh orchid (*Orchis pardalina*, Pl. 44b, p. 283) the spots are irregularly ring-like, recalling the markings on a leopard. Nevertheless a few kinds of British orchids are known, as for example, the Irish marsh orchid (*Orchis occidentalis*, Pl. XX, p. 271), in which different individuals bear spots of quite different kinds, the species in this respect combining the features of several allied species.

Most of the individual differences mentioned above are due to the inherited qualities of the plants themselves and are not affected to any marked degree by the soil or other external conditions. Of course, these do have their effect on each plant, but their results are usually reflected in differences of size of the entire plant or in the production of more or fewer flowers. The fact that individual plants differing very strikingly may frequently be found within a few inches of one another is strong evidence against the idea that the external conditions are responsible for these differences. If such plants are transplanted to a rock or marsh garden (often not an easy thing to do successfully) the differences are maintained under cultivation. On the other hand, plants with red coloration in the leaves and stems are usually more common in open sunny places, whereas those growing in comparatively deep shade are more frequently green or at least have the red colour poorly developed. This is because these anthocyanin pigments can be developed to their maximum extent only when the light available is of sufficient strength.

Abnormalities

All the differences so far dealt with, between individuals of the same kind of orchid, are examples of normal variability, each specimen being perfectly formed and able to reproduce its kind given suitable conditions. On the other hand, one may sometimes come across individual plants, or even small groups of plants, in which some, or perhaps all, of the flowers are in some way abnormal, that is to say, not properly constructed. The flowers of these sports or freaks, which actually are more common than is generally realised, may differ from those of an ordinary individual in one or more respects, depending upon what parts of the flower are affected. Sometimes there are more or fewer perianth parts than in the normal flower, or again the numbers may be the same but the shape or structure of one or more parts is unusual. Perhaps the most easily recognised type is that in which a single flower appears to have tried to turn into two, with varying success in different cases. In the most complete examples the two flowers are easily distinguishable, but are joined together in the lower parts (Pl. IIa, p. 19) ; in the least developed ones only the presence of two lips side by side suggests the division of the flower, while practically all intermediate stages have been recorded. Among our native orchids the bee orchid, with its large singly placed flowers, provides the best examples of this type of freak, which has been found also in many tropical orchids. It is no doubt due to the equal splitting of the growing point of the very short branch which forms the flower.

" Doubling " of flowers, that is, the addition of extra parts, is not uncommon, but, owing to the zygomorphic or " back and front " structure, the effect produced by doubling is usually rather untidy. The results are therefore seldom attractive and cannot compare in this respect with similar freaks in other plants with regular, more or less circular flowers. The type of abnormality which is of greatest interest is that in which the three petals are more or less identical, instead of the lip differing markedly from the other two as in the normal flower. This may take place in two ways, of which much the commoner is when the lip has lost its own peculiarities and looks just like a third ordinary petal. Specimens of many different orchids have been discovered showing this sort of freak, although in some examples the transformation has not been complete, the lip still retaining some of its special features (Pl. IIIa, p. 26). A much more striking freak is produced when the two ordinary petals become two additional lips with all the curious structure of the third or ordinary lip. This has been recorded in the fly orchid, where there are consequently three " bodies " to the fly, but no " antennae ", as these are the ordinary petals, and also in the two butterfly orchids, the flowers of which as a result then bear three long spurs, one on each lip. These transformations provide definite evidence that the two petals and the lip are essentially comparable structures, the general theory being that the lip is merely a petal which has been much changed in the course of time so that it now plays its proper part in the pollination and fertilisation of the flower by visiting insects. On the whole, the lip shows a greater tendency to become abnormal than any other part of the flower, usual variants being simplification in shape, the reduction in size or even the disappearance of the spur, and the loss of special coloration or markings (see Pl. XXIII, p. 314).

Another interesting class of abnormalities is that in which additional stamens or portions of stamens are produced, either separately or attached to other parts of the flower. It will be remembered that whereas there are six stamens in a tulip flower, there is only one in most sorts of orchids, the others presumably having become superfluous and lost in the course of the evolution of the relatively complicated orchid flower. The commonest position for these additional or " resurrected " stamens to occur is either on or in the immediate vicinity of the two ordinary petals towards the " back " of the flower. It is generally considered that stamens in these positions really correspond to the two properly developed stamens in the lady's slipper orchid, which two stamens are lacking in many orchids. Although this may well be the true explanation in some cases, it is not always so. In some of our orchids, for example the fragrant orchid (*Gymnadenia conopsea*) and frog orchid (*Coeloglossum viride*), these two back stamens are normally present in the form of a small sterile knob (*staminode*) on each side of the column (Fig. 7 B, p. 33). The occurrence of additional stamens on or near the petals in such plants therefore requires a different explanation from that suggested above. A possible explanation is to be sought in the fundamental similarity between petals and stamens, which is made evident by the occurrence of structures intermediate in character between petals and stamens in water-lilies or in double or partially double flowers, such as roses, delphiniums and the like. The extra stamens in some orchids may therefore correspond to petals or portions of petals and not to any of the five " lost " stamens of the lily-like ancestor.

CHAPTER 3

POLLINATION AND FERTILISATION

IT HAS long been known that the result of fertilising the flowers of one plant with pollen from a different plant of the same kind, or even from other flowers on the same plant (cross-fertilisation), is frequently the production of more robust or free-growing offspring than if the pollen came from the same flower. Indeed in some kinds of plants, as in some grasses, pollen from a separate individual is needed to produce any fertile seeds at all. The advantages of cross-pollination and cross-fertilisation are no doubt due to the continual redistribution of the various genes present in the whole population. If self-pollination takes place generally, on the other hand, the usual effects of inbreeding may become evident, with the multiplication of useless or even deleterious characters among the population.

Consequently we find in the flowers of many plants devices for ensuring that the pollen which is deposited on the stigma (the female receptive organ) shall in the great majority of cases come from another flower, and in a substantial number of cases, from another plant. This is particularly so with respect to the numerous plants which are pollinated by insects, and among these the orchids take a high position on account of the ingenuity and great variety of the devices which occur. The wide range and complexity of these devices, taken in conjunction with the occurrence of the pollen in the form of curiously shaped masses (the *pollinia*), bring into play a great variety of pollination mechanisms, that is, special ways in which the pollen is detached from one flower and deposited on the receptive stigma of a different flower. We must remember that orchids are predominantly inhabitants of the tropics, where insect life reaches its greatest development and variety of form, and it is consequently in this region that the most remarkable adaptations to pollination by insects may be found. Nevertheless the representatives of the family in more temperate regions also provide a number of outstanding examples of pollination mechanisms, some of which may be seen in our own British species.

Insects exhibit an immense variety in size and complexity of structure, as well as in the degree to which their instincts have been developed, varying from tiny creeping or flying insects to large and beautiful butterflies and moths and the highly developed bees with their more elaborate instincts and behaviour. Correlated with these differences in the insects we find corresponding differences in the mechanisms by which the orchids which they visit are pollinated, simpler mechanisms, on the whole, being associated with the visits of the less highly developed insects, and more elaborate mechanisms with those of the more highly developed ones. In many orchids the structure of the flowers and of the visiting insect are very delicately adjusted to one another so that maximum efficiency in the pollination process may be achieved. The insects, of course, do not visit the flower in order to carry out its pollination, but rather to obtain nectar or pollen on which they feed themselves or their young. An essential part of the mechanism is therefore the provision of nectar, or its equivalent, in such a position that in obtaining the nectar the pollination of the flower is effected. This nectar or other liquid is frequently, though not always, in some part of the lip, and particularly in the hollow spur which is often an obvious feature of the flower.

Apart from the differences in the mechanisms associated with the different insects, there are also differences resulting from the inherent qualities of the orchids themselves. The more highly evolved types are characterised by greater complexity of the floral structure, developed in conjunction with the more elaborate pollination mechanisms. The less evolved types, on the other hand, make do with fewer resources and the mechanisms frequently are simpler and often more " straight-forward " in operation.

Pollination Mechanisms

Following what has just been said, it will be useful to consider the mechanisms in several British orchids, beginning with the less specialised and going on to the more specialised and elaborate. We will start, therefore, with the lady's slipper (*Cypripedium*), since this resembles the lily family in possessing the pollen-grains separate and not joined together in the pollen-masses or pollinia which occur in all other orchids and play such an important part in the other mechanisms to be described. In this orchid it will be remembered that the pollen-grains are not, however, dry and dusty, but embedded in a sticky paste-like substance.

The flowers are quite large (larger than in any other British orchid), being about two inches across. The lip is in the form of a slipper (Fig. 8, p. 43 ; Pl. 4, p. 63), the entrance being immediately in front of the column which is stemlike in the lower part, but divides into two farther up. The upper part of this is a flat heart-shaped plate (*staminode*) which is so shaped as to leave a larger opening in front, while on each side of the column there is a much smaller opening. Beneath the staminode, and inside the slipper, is the large fleshy stigma, which is covered with numerous very short stiff projections providing a rough surface. The two stamens are placed, one on each side of the column, at the mouths of the smaller openings.

The flowers are visited by various kinds of small bees which are attracted by the nectar inside the lip. The bees land on the crimson spotted staminode and enter the slipper by the only feasible route, that is, the large entrance. After remaining there for some time they try to escape, but cannot crawl out by the way they came in as the sides of the lip are very smooth and slippery and the edges are curled inwards. They therefore crawl up towards the column in order to escape through one of the two small side openings, in which endeavour they are helped by numerous stiff hairs which afford a foothold. Each exit is, however, a very tight fit, and considerable pressure is required to enable the bee to squeeze through, in the course of which it rubs against the stamen, carrying away some of the sticky pollen in the process. The bee then visits another flower where it again eventually makes for the side exits. On the way to these its back rubs against the rough stigma projecting downwards into the body of the lip, some of the pollen previously gathered being rubbed off and retained by the stigma. As there is usually only one flower on a stem cross-pollination is the normal result. It is an essential part of the mechanism that in trying to escape the bee comes *first* in contact with the stigma, on which it often leaves pollen from another flower, and *afterwards* collects more pollen at the moment of escape. The size of the exits ensures that the pollen can be carried away only by insects of exactly the right size to make contact with the stigma in the next flower visited. Smaller ones get out without touching the stamen, but such small insects would not rub against the stigma in the next flower and they would therefore be of no use as pollinating agents. No pollen is therefore wasted during the visits of these insects. Larger insects sometimes enter the lip, but they cannot get through the smaller openings and usually die miserably after vainly attempting to escape.

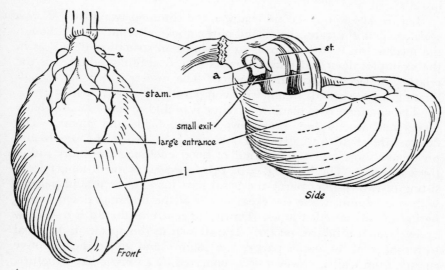

FIG. 8

Two views of the lip and column of lady's slipper, *Cypripedium calceolus*, to illustrate pollination.—a. anther ; l. lip ; o. ovary ; st. stigma ; stam. staminode. (×2)

The transference of pollen in this plant is carried out much in the same way as in many other families of plants, except that the pollen here is, in effect, sticky and is rubbed off the insect by a rough dry surface, whereas in most other families the pollen is drier and is removed by a sticky stigma. The interesting feature is that the remarkable shape of the lip determines the route followed by the insect, thus ensuring cross-pollination ; in this respect the lady's slipper resembles the other plants dealt with in the following pages.

As mentioned previously, the pollen grains in most orchids are joined together to form large masses of thousands of grains, termed pollinia. It is clear that these, owing to their relatively great weight, cannot be carried away by an insect unless they can be securely attached to some part of its body. In all the pollination mechanisms described, therefore, some means of attachment is provided, this being either in the form of a special sticky disc (*viscidium*) attached to the pollinium, or in other cases being created anew at the time of the insect's visit.

Let us take as our second example the common twayblade (*Listera ovata*), which illustrates the second of the above alternatives. Although the mechanism is by no means so elaborate in structural details as in the examples described later, it shows how beautifully adjusted is the relation between insects and flowers. The insects which act as pollinating agents are all small, with comparatively short tongues.

The common twayblade is a frequent orchid in more or less shady places and woods, but also grows in open fields and moors. The flowers are small and green (Pl. 15, p. 158), while the sepals and petals are short and form a kind of hood enclosing the short rather thick column. The lip (Fig. 9, p. 45), however, is much longer, consisting of two distinct parts, the basal part being close to and parallel with the column, while the greater part of the lip hangs down, terminating in two rounded lobes. Down the centre of the lip is a shallow groove which produces nectar. The stamen in this species is attached to the back of the upper part of the column and above the receptive stigma, from which, however, it is separated by a tongue-like structure, termed the *rostellum* (or little beak). The stamen contains two club-shaped pollinia, each of which is entirely or nearly divided into two. The pollinia are rather loose in texture, consisting of masses of pollen-grains joined together by very delicate threads, the whole very easily crumbling into pieces. When the pollinia are mature the stamen opens and deposits them on the slightly hollowed rostellum immediately below, where they rest with their thin ends on the front edge, the stamen afterwards shrinking away upwards.

The flowers are visited by small flies, ichneumon flies, beetles and other similar insects, which on approaching are attracted by the nectar in the groove on the lip. Alighting on the latter they climb up, following the groove until they reach the spot where the lip bends abruptly under the column, the nearest portion of which is the projecting rostellum. Immediately the insect touches the rostellum, be the touch ever so gentle, a kind of internal explosion takes place. A small drop of a sticky liquid is forced out of the tip of the rostellum, and this drop, coming rapidly into contact with both the ends of the pollinia and the insect causing the reaction, fixes the pollinia firmly to

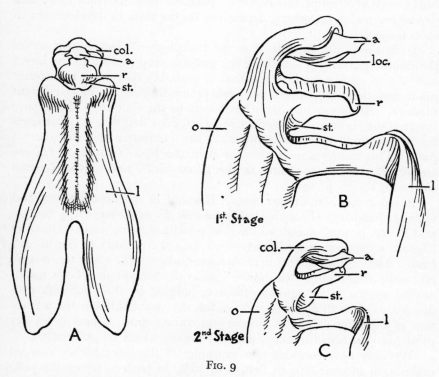

FIG. 9

Lip and column of twayblade, *Listera ovata*, to illustrate pollination. A, front view, B and C, side views at different stages in development of flower. a. anther; col. column; l. lip; loc. anther loculus; o. ovary; r. rostellum; st. stigma. (A and C × 7½, B × 15)

the insect's head or back and sets hard in a matter of two or three seconds. The startled insect flies off carrying the pollinia, and alights on another flower, probably on another plant. Here it follows the nectar trail again and may, of course, collect another pair of pollinia, but if the flower is more mature than in the previous case the rostellum will have withdrawn upwards, leaving the stigma as the first object to be touched (Fig. 9C, p. 45). The smaller masses of pollen, into which the pollinia are divided, are only weakly attached to the central stalk and are readily detached on contact with the sticky stigma. The insect may visit numerous flowers, collecting pollinia from some and depositing pollen on others, depending on the state of development of each flower.

It is interesting to note that the " explosive " mechanism serves the double purpose of attaching the pollinia very rapidly to the insect and of frightening the latter so that it probably flies away to another plant and therefore carries out cross-pollination in the most efficient manner. Attention may also be drawn to the fact that almost any insect of the right size is an effective agent, provided that it is attracted by nectar and therefore approaches the column along the correct path. This mechanism is also found in the lesser twayblade (*Listera cordata*, Pl. 16a, p. 159) and in the allied bird's nest orchid (*Neottia nidus-avis*, Pl. 20, p. 191).

A somewhat similar mechanism is found in the broad-leaved and violet helleborines (*Epipactis helleborine* and *E. purpurata*, Pl. 9, p. 130, and Pl. 12, p. 139), the small bag-like rostellum being easily broken to liberate a drop of sticky liquid which fixes the pollinia to the insect's head. The visiting insects here, however, are wasps, while there is no especially frightening " explosion " as in the twayblade. Both mechanisms appear to be equally effective, judging by the abundant production of seeds in all three species, but the twayblade has the advantage of a greater variety of visitors and consequently a shortage of any particular species of insect would not greatly affect its pollination.

We may now consider two examples of the most highly evolved pollination mechanisms in British orchids, in both of which the pollinia are provided with their own adhesive portions. The visiting insects belong to highly evolved groups with well-developed instincts, and the whole mechanism is more complicated and delicately adjusted than in the last examples.

Let us examine in the first place a flower of the common early purple orchid (*Orchis mascula*), one of our commonest and most widely spread orchids. In this plant we find the back sepal and the two side petals forming together a kind of hood at the top of the flower, with the two side sepals, one on each side, folded back out of the way. The shortly three-lobed lip forms a sloping convex platform in front

PLATE I

Creeping Ladies' Tresses (*Goodyera repens*). Strath Spey; August

PLATE 2

Robert Atkinson

Early Spider Orchids (*Ophrys sphegodes*). Dorset; May

with, near its point of attachment, a rather long tubular spur running out at the back either almost horizontally or in a nearly upright position (Fig. 10A, p. 48). In the centre of the flower, within the hood and immediately above the mouth of the spur, is the column, which here is very short and thick. As the column is joined to the sides of the lip, a kind of broad tube or antechamber is formed leading to the spur proper. The central part of the column is surmounted by the single stamen with its two bag-like pollen containers (*anther loculi* or *thecae*) placed almost erect side by side. The pollinia are two in number, one lying loosely in each half of the stamen. They consist in the upper part of a number of smaller masses of pollen attached lightly by threads to a central spindle or axle, which is drawn out in the lower (front) part to form a long stalk (*caudicle*), the whole being club-shaped. At the extreme front or bottom this stalk is furnished with a small round sticky disc (*viscidium*) which, however, is kept hidden in a sort of flap or purse-like container (*bursicle*) and is not visible at first sight (Fig. 10B). The bursicle, which is placed on a special part of the column (*rostellum*) projecting downwards into the mouth of the spur, contains a sticky liquid which prevents the disc from drying up until the whole pollinium is removed by an insect visiting the flower. The viscidia, one to each pollinium, can be removed separately, the flap, which is elastic, returning to its original position in order to keep the remaining disc still moist. Underneath the stamen is a shallow cave-like hollow which is lined by the very sticky receptive stigmas.

The stage is now set for the pollination mechanism to be carried into operation. An insect, usually a bee or a humble-bee, alights on the lip, and, probably guided by the group of small darker spots in front of the mouth of the spur, thrusts its tongue into the spur in order to obtain the liquid within its fleshy walls. In doing so its head pushes down the elastic flap on the column and exposes the viscidia, which adhere singly or both to the upper part of the head. As the insect retires it pulls the whole pollinium from its bag-like container and flies away bearing the entire structure attached in an erect position to its head. Within a very short time (a few seconds, to be exact) the adhesive liquid hardens to form a cement-like mass which fixes the apparatus firmly to the insect. It has frequently been observed that the insect attempts to scrape off the pollinium with its legs ; before it is firmly attached these efforts may sometimes be successful. Once the cement has set, however, the removal of the pollen apparatus is extremely difficult. As the insect flies away a remarkable change now takes place, the whole pollinium pivoting forwards from the attached base until it takes up an almost horizontal position. It is quite easy to extract the pollinia by inserting the point of a sharp pencil or similar object into the mouth of the spur. On withdrawing the pencil the two

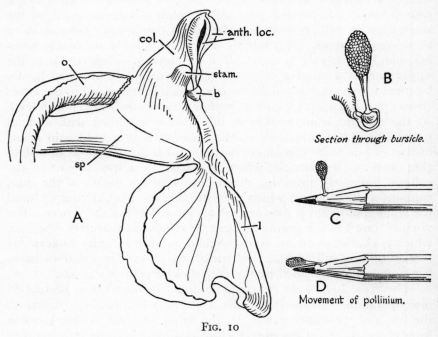

FIG. 10

Early purple orchid, *Orchis mascula*

A. Lip and column in side view. B. Single pollinium in position with its viscidium in the protective bursicle. C & D. Two stages showing forward movement of pollinium after removal from flower. anth. loc. anther loculus ; b. bursicle ; col. column ; l. lip ; o. ovary ; sp. spur ; stam. staminode. (A ×7½ ; B ×12 ; C & D ×5) (B, C & D after Darwin)

pollinia will be seen attached in an erect position to its upper side, and the forward pivoting movement of the pollinia which follows can readily be observed (Fig. 10C and D, p. 48). Meanwhile the bee has been visiting the other flowers on the plant where it may collect yet further pollinia in the same way, until perhaps as many as fifteen are adhering to it. Until the downward movement of the pollinia has been completed they do not come into contact with the receptive stigma, but simply brush against the upright stamen and therefore pollination does not take place.

As soon, however, as the pollinia have taken up a horizontal position, which is probably not until the insect has reached an adjacent plant, pollination can be effected. As the bee now enters a flower, the club-shaped end of the pollinium, with its loosely attached masses of pollen, comes into contact with the sticky stigmas in the cavity below the stamen. The tenacious surface holds some of the small lumps of pollen and these, which are only attached to the central stalk by very slender threads, are left behind as the insect backs from the flower still carrying the remainder of the pollinium. This process is continued at every subsequent flower visited until all the pollen has been removed, and the pollination of many flowers has been achieved.

Special points to be noted in the above beautiful and elaborate process are the peculiar modification of the rostellum to form the flap- or pouch-like bursicle in which the sticky discs are kept ready for use, and the movement of the pollinium from its original upright position into one in which it can make contact with the stigma of another flower. Pollination is always carried out by bees or humble-bees, that is, by insects with a proboscis of moderate length. This is evidently correlated with the length of the spur, from which the visiting insects obtain the liquid which lies within its fleshy walls. There is no nectar, the actual cavity of the spur being dry.

There are some kinds of British orchids with longer spurs than those described above, and we find that in such instances the pollinating insect is a moth or butterfly, which has a much longer proboscis than those of bees. We may take as our next example the pyramidal orchid (*Anacamptis pyramidalis*, Pl. 29, p. 226, and XIVb, p. 223), which provides a good example of the type of pollination mechanism operated by such insects.

The arrangement of the sepals and petals in this species is much the same as in the early purple orchid, but the lip (Fig. 11A and B, p. 50), which is generally rather more deeply, but more or less equally, three-lobed, has on each side of the mouth of the spur a short upright wall-like structure. These " walls " are placed in such a manner that they are widest apart on the outside or front and converge inwards so as to leave only a narrow space between them at the back where

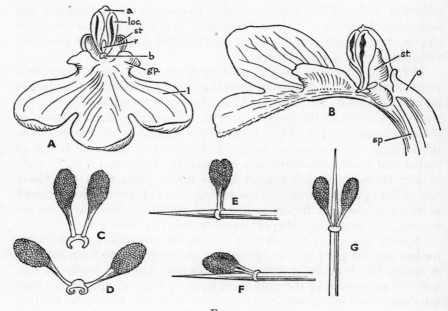

FIG. 11

Pyramidal orchid, *Anacamptis pyramidalis*

A. Lip and column in front view. B. The same in side view, with near half of
lip cut away. C & D. Pollinia removed without support, showing outward
movement. E, F & G. Pollinia removed on needle, showing forward
and lateral movements. a. anther ; b. bursicle ; g.p. guide plate ; l. lip ;
loc. anther loculus ; o. ovary ; r. rostellum ; sp. spur ; st. stigma. (A $\times 7\frac{1}{2}$;
B $\times 9$; C–G much magnified) (C–G after Darwin)

the spur mouth is. The spur is very slender and thread-like, reaching
a length of half an inch. The short centrally placed column bears an
erect stamen, which agrees in most features with that in the species
of *Orchis*, but with the important difference that the two pollinia,
instead of each having its own viscidium, are joined to a single viscidium (Fig. 11C), and are therefore carried away together in the
course of pollination. The stamen also is placed so low on the column
that the two stigmas, which in the early purple orchid are joined together in one large cavity, are here separated from one another and
lie one on each side of the lower part of the stamen. As in the early

purple orchid, the flowers are visited for the watery liquid which occurs inside the fleshy walls of the spur, there being no nectar.

The action of the pollination mechanism shows many features in common with that just described, but also some significant differences, which are related to the different types of insects concerned. As before, the insect alights on the convex sloping platform provided by the lip and, unrolling its long proboscis, pushes it into the mouth of the spur, where it is guided by the two converging walls mentioned above so as to enter exactly below the projecting anther. The proboscis hits against and pushes back the bursicle containing the sticky attachment of the pollinia, which, as before, adheres to the object with which it comes into contact. A butterfly's proboscis, however, is very different from the broad head of the bee, being very slender and smooth and, moreover, being continually unrolled and rolled up again. We find, therefore, that the sticky disc of the pollinia is beautifully adapted for attachment to such an organ, being long and narrow, and placed so that it lies at right angles to the proboscis. On making contact with the latter the two ends of the viscidium curl underneath, thus grasping the proboscis tightly and, as in the other examples, becoming firmly attached by the hardening of the cement. This curling action tends to draw the pollinia apart and they swing outwards slightly on their stalks (Fig. 11D). The moth may carry away pollinia from successive flowers, as many as eleven pairs having been observed on the proboscis of a single moth.

As the insect flies away in search of another flower the two pollinia execute a forward pivoting movement in the same manner as in the early purple orchid, but instead of pointing straight ahead along the line of the proboscis, they must of necessity diverge somewhat, one to each side (Fig. 11E–G). When the movement is completed the tops of the pollinia, with their readily detached packets of pollen, are so placed as to come into direct contact with the two laterally placed stigmas of the next flower visited. It is very interesting to note here how the special type of attachment necessary for adherence of the pollinia to a slender proboscis, the subsequent movements of the pollinia, and the position of the separate receptive stigmas, all play their parts in ensuring that pollination is carried out efficiently. As Darwin pointed out many years ago, the pyramidal orchid is a very beautiful example of perfect adjustment in all respects to pollination by butterflies and moths.

The fragrant orchid (*Gymnadenia conopsea*, Pl. 26, p. 211) is another example of an orchid pollinated by these insects. It resembles the pyramidal orchid in flower size and general structure, but its long slender spur is half-filled with nectar. The lip lacks the two wall-like outgrowths just in front of the spur, while there are two viscidia which are not covered by any bursicle. The viscidia are long and narrow, not circular as in the early purple orchid, but they lie one on each side of the centre of the roof of the spur, in the same direction as the insect's proboscis when inserted into the spur. As in the pyramidal orchid, there are two separate stigmas, one on each side of the base of the column.

As the moth inserts its proboscis into the spur in search of the nectar, it comes into contact with one or other (rarely with both) of the viscidia, which adheres firmly along the side of the proboscis. The pollinium then pivots forward, as in the other examples, but its lateral position carries it slightly to one side and thus brings it into contact, in the next flower visited, with that stigma which is situated on the corresponding side, so effecting pollination.

From the examples described we can see how the structure of the flowers of orchids, and the habits of the insects which visit them, are fitted together into an intricate and smooth-working mechanism during the operation of which, on the one hand, the insect's desires are satisfied, while, on the other, the pollination of the orchid is ensured.

INSECT VISITORS

One thing that is noticeable from all the examples described is that usually insects of one type or of one size only carry out pollination of any given species of orchid. Although no doubt other insects may occasionally pay visits to the flowers, they play no part in the mechanism and no provision is made for their wants. For instance, no short-tongued insect would be able to obtain the liquid in the long slender spurs of the pyramidal or fragrant orchids. On the whole, the insects which may be observed visiting any given orchid are usually those which can operate the pollination mechanism.

From the above general principle it may be concluded that any orchid with a long slender spur is pollinated by butterflies and/or moths. In addition to the pyramidal and fragrant orchids, already described, these include the two kinds of butterfly orchids (*Platan-*

thera). *Anacamptis* and *Gymnadenia* have coloured flowers and are visited by both day- and night-flying insects, the former probably being attracted by the colour and the latter by the scent which is usually stronger by night. The butterfly orchids (Pls. 24 and 25, pp. 203 and 210), on the other hand, have greenish white flowers which emit a very powerful odour at night, and these are visited mainly by night-flying moths. White flowers with long spurs are very common throughout the orchid family, being found in the Tropics and in the southern Temperate regions as well as in Europe. So far as is known they are always pollinated by moths and often by large moths at that! Probably the best-known example is the Madagascan orchid (*Angraecum sesquipedale*) with a spur from eight to twelve inches long. In his classic book on the fertilisation of orchids, Darwin predicted the existence of a moth with a proboscis long enough to explore the interior of the spur of this orchid, a prediction which has since been confirmed by the discovery of such a moth. Many other orchids with spurs as much as six inches long have been found on the African mainland, some of which inhabit trees, like the *Angraecum*, while others are ground dwellers like our own butterfly orchids.

Although flies of various kinds are known to visit many of our native orchids, and pollinia have been observed attached to their heads, there seems to be no instance in which they are the sole pollinators of any species. In the Tropics there are numerous kinds of orchids which emit foetid and extremely unpleasant odours, which are evidently attractive to carrion flies. Some of our native species, for example the lizard orchid, give off odours which are unpleasant to man, but we have yet to discover what insects, if any, are attracted thereby. A fascinating field for further investigation exists here, which might possibly yield results of considerable importance.

Many other insects undoubtedly visit the flowers of orchids sporadically and may possibly remove pollinia, but there is no evidence that these visits have any significant effect on fertilisation. Observations have been made of the removal of the pollinia of the man orchid by ants, and it may be that these insects are important agents in the pollination of this plant, but more direct evidence is needed to settle this question. In several sorts of orchids, such as the bird's nest orchid (*Neottia*) and some of the helleborines (*Epipactis* spp.), in which the pollinia are very brittle and when mature tend to break up into fragments, small portions are often carried away on the bodies of the very small insects which are often found crawling over the flowers. This pollen may then be deposited on the stigmas of either the same or other flowers in the spike, but it is hardly likely, though not impossible, that they would be taken to other plants. Where the pollinia are more strongly and elaborately constructed, as in the more highly developed orchids (*Platanthera*, *Orchis*, *Ophrys*, etc.), pieces are carried away only on extremely rare occasions.

MIMICRY AND PSEUDO-COPULATION

The plant-lover, on first hearing the common names of our orchids, is usually struck by the number of cases in which the name of some animal figures, for example, bee orchid, fly orchid, butterfly orchid, lizard orchid, frog orchid, monkey orchid, and even man orchid. It may be added that this practice is by no means restricted to native species, well-known foreign orchids including the dove orchid, swan orchid, butterfly orchid (quite different from our British plant of the same name), pigeon orchid, duck orchids, rabbit's ears, crane-fly, adder's mouth, etc. The flowers in many of these orchids bear only fanciful resemblances to the animals after which the plants have been named, but in other instances, for example the bee orchid and the spider orchids, either the flower as a whole or some part of it resembles in a very striking manner the insect named. Recent observations in Europe and northern Africa on certain relatives of the two orchids mentioned, and also in Australia on quite another group of orchids, have shown that these remarkable resemblances are by no means a mere coincidence. The particular orchids which have been studied most carefully, the mirror ophrys (*Ophrys speculum*) of the western Mediterranean regions and the small tongue orchid (*Cryptostylis leptochila*) of Victoria and New South Wales, are each visited by a single kind of insect and only by the males of that species. In each case the lip of the orchid bears a close resemblance to the females of the insect in question, which at the time of the males' visits have not yet emerged from pupation. From the actions of the male it is evident that he has been deceived by this resemblance into thinking that a female is resting on the flower, and is endeavouring to copulate with her. In the mirror ophrys experiments show that an odour attractive to the male insect is emitted by the flower. During the course of visits the male removes the pollinia and carries them from one flower to another, thus effecting pollination. As soon as the females of the insects emerge the visits of the males cease, the orchid obviously no longer being sufficiently attractive.

Similar observations have been made on other Mediterranean orchids, for example brown ophrys (*Ophrys fusca*) and yellow ophrys (*O. lutea*), and on relatives of the Australian orchid mentioned. In some species the male insect visits the flower head first and removes the pollinia on his head, in others he alights in the reverse position and the pollinia become attached to the tip of the abdomen. These differences can be correlated with the shape and colouring of the lip in relation to the female of the insect concerned. In view of the obvious similarity between these visits and the normal mating behaviour of the insects, the term " pseudo-copulation " has been applied to the phenomenon described above.

It is evident that such a system, which depends on the exact synchronisation of the flowering of the orchid with the appearance of the males of a single kind of insect before the females, may in the course of time break down owing to changes in climate or other external causes. There is reason to believe that this is the explanation of the paucity of insect visitors to our own bee orchid and its allies. Certainly the number of insects which visit the various British species of *Ophrys* (the bee orchid, fly orchid, early and late spider orchids) is very small in each case, and appears to be restricted in each species to the males of one kind of insect only. Here again is a possibly fruitful field for further observations on our own native plants.

SELF-POLLINATION

Wonderful as are the delicately adjusted relationships between orchids and insects, yet this very perfection may have within it the seeds of failure. Any outside influences which reduce the numbers of the special insects available, or change their habits so that they are no longer active when the orchids are in flower, throws the mechanism out of gear ; the production of fertile seeds is then not possible on a sufficiently large scale to offset natural wastage. In some orchids, such as the bee orchid, this difficulty has been overcome by the development of self-pollination, which takes place regularly in all flowers which have not been fertilised already by the appropriate insect. As the flowers mature the stalks of the pollinia shrink in such a manner as to cause the upper club-shaped pollen-bearing part to be pulled out of its bag-like container, and to curve forward in a half-circle until the tops hang in front of the stigmas immediately below, the viscidia meanwhile remaining enclosed in their pouches (Pl. XXIIb, p. 307). The slightest movement shakes the hanging pollinia so that they touch the stigma, to which they adhere. Examination of bee orchid plants which have been in flower for some time will show this to have happened in practically every flower.

Some of the helleborines are also regularly self-pollinated, but in these cases the process is not so spectacular as in the bee orchid. Sometimes parts of the rather friable pollen masses fall from the slightly projecting stamen on to the sticky stigma beneath. In other species the pollen masses swell up and " froth " over on to the edge of the stigma just below ; this happens in a different manner in different species. In these plants the pollination mechanism has not reached such a high degree of complexity as in the bee orchid, the absence of a properly developed rostellum between the stamen and the stigma making self-pollination a comparatively simple process.

The helleborines of the genus *Epipactis* form an interesting series illustrating the stages by which normal cross-pollination by insects may be replaced by self-pollination of the types just mentioned. In this group of plants the pollination mechanism is much simpler than in many of those already described. The anther lies just above the stigma, and in the cross-pollinated forms is separated from it by the rather small rostellum. This consists merely of a sort of very thin-skinned bag containing a viscous liquid which, as in the other examples mentioned previously, hardens on exposure to air, although not so quickly as in the early purple and pyramidal orchids. The pollinia are shed from the anther and come to rest on the rostellum just below. When this is broken by contact with an insect's head, the liquid comes out and attaches the pollinia to the insect in a single rapid process. On the insect visiting another flower, portions of the very fragile pollinia are broken off and left behind on the sticky stigma. This is the normal method in the broad-leaved, violet and dark red helleborines (*Epipactis helleborine, E. purpurata* and *E. atrorubens* respectively), the visiting insects being wasps only in the first two and various sorts of bees in the third. In all these species seed is usually only set in those flowers to which pollen has been brought by the method just described. In the green-leaved or slender-lipped helleborine (*Epipactis leptochila*), however, the rostellum, though present in the bud, dries up at the time of, or soon after, the opening of the flower. Cross-pollination therefore, though possible, and indeed occurring on rare occasions, cannot be the usual means of obtaining fertilisation of the ovules. Self-pollination takes its place in nearly all the flowers, and, judging by the abundant production of seed pods, is evidently an efficient process. It is carried out by the pollen masses swelling and being pushed forward on to the receptive surface of the stigma just below. The reliance on self-pollination is carried a step farther in the dune helleborine (*E. dunensis*), in which the rostellum is only rarely produced, but the pollen masses sometimes break up in the bud and no doubt pieces fall on to the stigma, causing self-pollination even before the flowers open. After the flowers have opened, and in this species they sometimes do not open properly, self-pollination takes place by the swelling of the pollinia, which consequently froth over on to the surface of the stigma.

It should be noticed that in the last two species, as well as in those normally cross-pollinated, the flowers are more or less horizontally placed, so that the visit of an insect is in no way impeded. In the pendulous-flowered and Isle of Wight helleborines (*E. pendula* and *E. vectensis*, Pl. 13b, p. 142, and Pl. 14, p. 143), on the other hand, the flowers hang almost vertically downwards during their whole existence, and are thus not easy of access by any insect. Both species are, so far as is known, always self-pollinated, the rostellum, column and lip withering in the bud or soon after the flower opens. In the Isle of Wight helleborine the visits of insects are rendered even more difficult by the fact that the flowers either do not open at all or at the best only open slightly. In both species seeds are set in practically every flower on the spike. It is possible, however, that these species provide examples of apomixis, that is, a process in which the ovules develop into seeds without fertilisation by the male organs. This is well known in dandelions, hawkweeds and other plants, but our knowledge is not so definite as regards orchids. The Danish botanist O. Hagerup has shown that apomixis can take place during the process of fertilisation in several orchid genera, but we do not know if plants ever develop from the embryos produced in such a manner. The decay of the column at a very early stage in *E. vectensis*, and to a less extent in *E. pendula*, does suggest that some form of apomixis is necessary, since in many flowers normal self-pollination scarcely seems feasible.

FERTILISATION

Whether the flower be cross-pollinated by insects operating one of the many special mechanisms, or self-pollinated as described above, the result is the production of fertilised ovules which on development give rise to the mature seeds. The ovules in most orchid flowers are very numerous, so it might be thought that the fertilisation of such a large number would be an unlikely event. The special nature of the pollen, however, is a provision against such a difficulty. Even a small part of a single pollinium, such as is likely to be deposited on the stigma during one operation, contains an immense number of pollen grains, running probably into thousands or tens of thousands. As each individual pollen grain is capable of fertilising an ovule, the danger of these remaining unfertilised is not very great, provided that pollen is brought to the flower at all. The extent to which this latter event occurs no doubt varies from one species to another, depending on the efficiency of the particular mechanism used in each case. It is probable, however, that the weather conditions at the time that the flowers are opening are even more important. On the whole, insects are more active in fine sunny weather, so the occurrence of such conditions at the right period undoubtedly plays an important part in the production of a good crop of seeds. Observations show that the seed production of a single orchid flower does in many cases far exceed that of flowers of any other plant. Our own native orchids produce comparatively moderate numbers of seeds, ranging from an average of about five hundred to each seed-pod in the common twayblade to an average of over ten thousand in the bee orchid. A large fruit in the latter species may contain over twenty-six thousand seeds, but even these figures pale into insignificance when compared with the seed production of some tropical orchids. The number of seeds in the capsules of some of these have been estimated on different occasions. These vary from 370,000 in the tropical American genus *Gongora* through about 1,500,000–1,750,000 in *Maxillaria* and *Cymbidium*, natives of Brazil and Burma respectively, to the recorded maximum in the remarkable swan orchid (*Cycnoches chlorochilon*) of Central America. In this plant the stupendous number of 4,000,000 seeds was estimated to occur in a fruit six inches long and two inches in diameter.

DEHISCENCE AND DISPERSAL

When the fruits are ripe they split lengthwise into six parts which, however, remain joined together at both ends. Three of the valves, as the parts are called, bear the seeds, while the others are merely narrow strips of the fruit wall, the splitting taking place in such a manner as to expose the seeds most effectively. In dry weather the fruit (capsule) contracts, thus causing the slits to open and allowing the seeds to escape, whereas in damp weather the dry fruit walls absorb moisture, lengthen, and the gaping sides of the splits are drawn together again.

As may well be imagined in view of the large number of seeds, these are usually extremely small and often rather like dust in general appearance. Actually, however, the seeds are rarely globular, but are normally longer in one direction than another, and more or less flattened. There is generally a rather thickened portion in the centre containing the germ, while in most orchids the thinner surrounding portion may be extended to form a kind of flattened wing-like structure. Whether winged or not the seeds are certainly very light, and easily carried for long distances by the wind, but no doubt the wing-like expansions of the seeds render them more buoyant and thus help in their effective distribution. In our native species the dried fruits at the tips of the relatively stiff dried-up stems are moved to and fro by the wind, the seeds are shaken out a few at a time, and are distributed far and wide. These seeds, as is the case with others distributed by the wind, are probably carried upwards, by ascending columns of hot air, to very considerable heights, and then transported long distances in the upper atmosphere before sinking slowly to the earth again. Many of those tropical orchids which grow on trees, where they are often perched in very exposed places, are even more conveniently situated for distribution of their seeds by the wind. The enquirer may wonder why it is necessary for such immense numbers of seeds to be produced, ·but, as has been seen in Chapter 1, the hazards which are encountered during the establishment of new plants render an apparent surplus of seeds quite essential.

CHAPTER 4

DISTRIBUTION,
GEOGRAPHICAL AND ECOLOGICAL

INTRODUCTION

I T IS obvious even to the most unobservant that no species of British plant is found growing universally throughout the country, or in every sort of locality within a more restricted area. Many plants are found only in the south of England, others can be found only on mountains in Scotland, while yet others are restricted to chalk downs or to sand-dunes by the sea coast. It is evident also that it is the climatic conditions, temperature, rainfall, etc., which in the first place determine the general distribution of a plant. However, even when the climate, taken in its broadest sense, is favourable to the species, other circumstances, such as the nature of the soil or the amount of available shelter, may limit the actual locations in which the plant can successfully maintain itself. There is also the past history of a country to be considered in trying to explain the occurrence of a plant in this or that place. The past history of a country includes primarily its past climates and its geological history, such as its fusion with or separation from neighbouring countries, particularly since the last great Ice Age. It is concerned secondarily with human activities in more recent times, such as the felling of forests, the draining of swamps, and the intensity and nature of agricultural practice at different periods, any one of which may have had a profound effect on the present distribution of any given species. These various outside influences may interact with one another in a very complicated way, so that it is extremely difficult in any one example to decide which has been predominant.

The broad outlines of the distribution of a plant are based on a combination of present climate and past history, and constitute its geographical distribution. The detailed occurrence of a species in relation to soil or to different types of vegetation, such as woods, meadows, marshes, etc., constitute its ecological distribution. Examination of the occurrences of many different plants will soon show how much they differ from one another, both as regards their geographical and their ecological distributions ; this is no less true of orchids than of any other family of plants. Some may occur throughout the greater part of our islands, others are known only from the extreme south-east of England or from a few localities in Ireland. Considered ecologically, some orchids, for example the common spotted orchid (*Orchis fuchsii*), may inhabit a great variety of situations, whereas others, such as the violet helleborine (*Epipactis purpurata*) or bog orchid (*Hammarbya paludosa*), can be found only in certain restricted and well-defined habitats, where apparently the conditions are exactly to their liking.

Geographical Elements of the Flora

As might be expected from the geographical position of the British Isles in relation to the European continent, and from their known geological history, the British Flora is predominantly European in character, and this is true of all but one of our native orchids. With this single exception (Irish ladies' tresses, *Spiranthes romanzoffiana*), they either occur elsewhere in Europe or their nearest relations are to be found in that continent. If we examine the distributions of the various species, however, we find that they exhibit the same sorts of differences outside the British Isles as within their boundaries, some species being widely spread over very extensive areas, whereas others are known only from much more restricted regions. It is possible on these grounds to classify our orchids into a series of groups, starting with those with the widest distribution, through species which are found in more and more restricted areas, until at length we come to those which are not known outside our islands, the so-called endemic species of our flora. Apart from the size of the total area in which any species is found, we may also notice that some are predominantly northern in their general occurrence whereas others are more southern in distribution.

More than half the orchids native in this country (31 species) are not only widely distributed in Europe, but also occur in Siberia and Asia Minor, sometimes extending as far east as Manchuria, the western ranges of the Himalayan mountains, or parts of Persia. These form what may be termed the Eurasian element of our orchid flora.

Table I

GEOGRAPHICAL ELEMENTS OF BRITISH ORCHID FLORA

1. **Eurasian Element Proper (7)**

    Cephalanthera longifolia
    Epipactis helleborine
    Platanthera bifolia
    P. chlorantha
    Orchis mascula
    O. morio
    Listera ovata

2. **Southern Eurasian Element (9)**

    Cephalanthera damasonium
    Spiranthes aestivalis
    S. spiralis
    Himantoglossum hircinum
    Anacamptis pyramidalis
    Orchis purpurea
    O. simia
    Ophrys fuciflora
    O. apifera

3. **Central Eurasian Element (8)**

    Cephalanthera rubra
    Epipactis atrorubens
    E. palustris
    Neottia nidus-avis
    Gymnadenia conopsea
    Coeloglossum viride
    Orchis militaris
    O. latifolia

4. **Northern Eurasian Element (7)**

    Cypripedium calceolus
    Epipogium aphyllum
    Herminium monorchis
    Corallorhiza trifida
    Liparis loeselii
    Hammarbya paludosa
    Orchis cruenta

5. **Northern Montane Element (3)**

    Listera cordata
    Goodyera repens
    Gymnadenia albida

6. **European Element (7)**

    Epipactis purpurata
    Aceras anthropophorum
    Orchis ustulata
    O. fuchsii
    O. ericetorum
    Ophrys sphegodes
    O. muscifera

7. **Western European Element (5)**

    Epipactis dunensis
    E. leptochila
    Orchis praetermissa
    O. purpurella
    O. pardalina

8. **Mediterranean Element (1)**

    Neotinea intacta

9. **American Element (1)**

    Spiranthes romanzoffiana

10. **Endemic Element (4)**

    Epipactis pendula
    E. vectensis
    Orchis occidentalis
    O. traunsteinerioides

PLATE 3

Robert Atkinson

Spikes of Fragrant and Spotted Orchids and hybrid (*Gymnadenia conopsea* and *Orchis fuchsii*). From Buckinghamshire; June

PLATE 4

Robert Atkinson

Lady's Slipper Orchid (*Cypripedium calceolus*). In a garden at Kingswood Common, Oxfordshire; May

A small number of these occur throughout Europe and the Mediterranean area, and may be termed the Eurasian element proper. Of these the sword-leaved helleborine (*Cephalanthera longifolia*, Map 3, p. 346), the broad-leaved helleborine (*Epipactis helleborine*, Map 8), the two species of butterfly orchids (*Platanthera bifolia* and *P. chlorantha*, Maps 28 and 29), early purple orchid (*Orchis mascula*, Map 31) and green-veined orchid (*Orchis morio*, Map 30) are found also in North Africa. The common twayblade (*Listera ovata*, Map 17), though absent from the latter area, is distributed through western Asia to central Siberia and the western parts of the Himalayan mountains and may properly be placed in this group. With the exception of the sword-leaved helleborine and green-veined orchid, these species are found throughout the greater part of the British Isles. The former of the two exceptions, though a local plant, has been recorded from as far north as Inverness and Ross-shire, but *Orchis morio* is not known from Scotland ; both are widely spread in Ireland as well as in England and Wales.

The remainder of the Eurasian group (24 species) fall into three groups according as they are more characteristic of the southern, central or northern parts of Europe and Temperate Asia. Firstly, there is the Southern Eurasian group, containing those species which are not found north of Holland or Denmark (or southern Sweden in a few instances), but are characteristic of the Mediterranean region (including North Africa), extending into Asia Minor, Palestine or Persia but not into Siberia. Most of these are also southern in distribution in this country, as, for instance, the summer ladies' tresses (*Spiranthes aestivalis*, Map 14, p. 349), late spider orchid (*Ophrys fuciflora*, Map 42), lizard orchid (*Himantoglossum hircinum*, Map 34), lady orchid (*Orchis purpurea*, Map 38), monkey orchid (*O. simia*, Map 37), and large white helleborine (*Cephalanthera damasonium*, Map 4). Indeed this group includes some of the rarest and most local of our native species, and it is evident that many of them are either decreasing in numbers or only just holding their own. The bee orchid (*Ophrys apifera*, Map 43), autumn ladies' tresses (*Spiranthes spiralis*, Map 13) and pyramidal orchid (*Anacamptis pyramidalis*, Map 33) are found farther north than the others but none occurs beyond southern Scotland.

In the second place we have those species of the Eurasian group which are found either only in the northern part of the Mediterranean region or are restricted to mountains in this area, but at the same time are not especially characteristic of northern Europe. These may be said to form the Central Eurasian element, which consists of eight species, viz :—red helleborine (*Cephalanthera rubra*, Map 2, p. 346), dark red helleborine (*Epipactis atrorubens*, Map 7), bird's nest orchid (*Neottia nidus-avis*, Map 21), fragrant orchid (*Gymnadenia conopsea*, Map 26), frog orchid (*Coeloglossum viride*, Map 24), marsh helleborine (*Epipactis palustris*, Map 5), early marsh orchid (*Orchis latifolia*), and soldier orchid (*Orchis militaris*, Map 36). Of these the red helleborine goes farther south on the whole than the others, and is probably intermediate between this group and the Southern Eurasian species already mentioned. The frog orchid is interesting because in addition to being widely spread in Europe and Asia, it also occurs in Newfoundland and Alaska on the American continent. Throughout northern North America and eastern Asia (China and Japan) there is a closely allied species, which has been considered by some authorities as a variety of the European plant.

As might be expected from their occurrences on the continent the members of this group exhibit considerable diversity in their geographical ranges within the British Isles. The fragrant orchid and the early marsh orchid have the widest distributions, being found commonly throughout the whole of our islands. The frog orchid is nearly as widely spread, but is, on the whole, more frequent in the northern part of the area than in southern England and Wales. The dark red helleborine is definitely northern in distribution, but in contrast to this species are the bird's nest orchid and marsh helleborine, which are commoner in the south and find their northern limit in central or north-central Scotland. Finally there are the red helleborine and soldier orchid, two of the rarest species in our flora and restricted to Gloucestershire and Buckinghamshire respectively.

Finally there is the group of Eurasian species, seven in all, which have a decidedly northern general distribution in Europe. These species usually occur throughout Siberia to Sachalin, northern China or Japan, but are not found south of the Caucasus Mountains or the Caspian Sea. The fen orchid (*Liparis loeselii*, Map 19, p. 350) and common coral-root (*Corallorhiza trifida*, Map 22) are found in North America, while the lady's slipper (*Cypripedium calceolus*, Map 1) has in the same continent several closely similar relatives which by some botanists are considered to be only varieties of the European plant.

The fen orchid is not found so far north as any of the others, and should be looked upon as an intermediate between this group and the Central Eurasian species already dealt with. The bog orchid (*Hammarbya paludosa*, Map 20) and flecked marsh orchid (*Orchis cruenta*), on the other hand, do not occur so far south as the remainder of the species.

Three of the seven species, namely, the spurred coral-root (*Epipogium aphyllum*, Map 23), fen orchid and musk orchid (*Herminium monorchis*, Map 25), are found only in the southern half of England, the first-named being extremely rare and recorded from not more than about five localities. The lady's slipper and the common coral-root, on the other hand, are northern species in our islands, the former being an extremely rare inhabitant of northern England, whereas the coral-root is almost restricted to Scotland. The bog orchid is distributed locally throughout the British Isles, but is more frequent in the north. The flecked marsh orchid provides a marked contrast with the remainder of this group, being found only in three counties in the west of Ireland.

Passing from the northern group of Eurasian species we now come to a small group of species, three only, which are even more northern in their distribution, being characteristic of the mountainous districts of northern Europe, Asia and America. Two of them, namely, the small white orchid (*Gymnadenia albida*, Map 27, p. 352) and lesser tway-blade (*Listera cordata*, Map 18) occur in Greenland, while the latter and the creeping ladies' tresses (*Goodyera repens*, Map 16) are found in Alaska. The plants of this group are found only on mountains in central and southern Europe, and even there they are not common. In view of their distribution they have been termed Northern Montane species.

All three are very definitely northern in distribution in these islands, reaching their greatest abundance in Scotland. The lesser twayblade has been recorded from several southern English counties, but it is certainly rare in southern England. Apart from localities in Norfolk, where it has possibly been introduced with planted pine trees, the creeping ladies' tresses is restricted to the extreme north of England and Scotland. The third member of the group is very rare in England south of the Pennines, but occurs in central Wales.

Seven of our British orchids are less widely distributed than the species included in the Eurasian and Northern Montane groups, although they occur generally throughout Europe. They may therefore be termed European species, in spite of the fact that two of them, namely, the burnt orchid (*Orchis ustulata*, Map 39, p. 355) and the violet helleborine (*Epipactis purpurata*, Map 6), have been found in western Siberia, while the man orchid (*Aceras anthropophorum*, Map 35) occurs in North Africa. As might be expected, these species show much the same grouping into southern, central and northern species as we have seen in the Eurasian group. The man orchid and the early spider orchid (*Ophrys sphegodes*, Map 41) have a markedly southern distribution in Europe, whereas the two spotted orchids (*Orchis fuchsii* and *O. ericetorum*) are more characteristic of northern Europe. The fly orchid (*Ophrys muscifera*, Map 40), burnt orchid and violet helleborine occupy an intermediate position in this respect and may be said to be central in distribution.

These differences in distribution outside the British Isles are on the whole in agreement with those within our islands. The man orchid, early spider orchid and violet helleborine are most abundant in the southern part of England, occurring rarely in scattered localities farther north. The dwarf or burnt orchid extends to the extreme north of England, but is commoner in the south, while the fly orchid is found as far north as Perth and west Ross-shire, as well as occurring in Ireland : both species are local and often found in small numbers. The two spotted orchids, on the other hand, are widely spread throughout the whole of the British Isles, though the common spotted orchid is commoner in the south, while the heath spotted orchid is more characteristic of the west and north. This, however, may be due more to the kinds of soils they prefer than directly to the different climates of the regions concerned.

We now come to two small groups of orchids whose distributions outside this country are more restricted than any already dealt with. The first group, consisting of five species, includes plants which are found in Western Europe only, and may therefore be termed the Western European Element of our orchid flora. The species concerned are the dune helleborine (*Epipactis dunensis*, Map 9, p. 348), green-leaved helleborine (*E. leptochila*, Map 10), common marsh orchid (*Orchis praetermissa*), leopard marsh orchid (*O. pardalina*) and dwarf purple orchid (*O. purpurella*). The first named is rather more widely spread than the others, having been recorded from northern France, Belgium, Holland, and north Germany as far east as Pomerania, always, of course, along the coast. The common marsh orchid has much the same general distribution, though it is not found east of the Rhine basin, while the fourth species is known with any degree of certainty only from Holland. It should be noted that these two species are closely related to other southern European species, of which they may be looked upon as northern representatives. Indeed, some authorities consider that *O. pardalina* is not a good species at all, but merely a series of hybrid populations. The dwarf purple orchid is so far known only from Norway, but it may occur elsewhere in Scandinavia. It is clearly an ally of the widespread European *O. majalis*. The dune helleborine is certainly closely related to the widely spread broad-leaved helleborine (*E. helleborine*) ; perhaps it is a special development of this species suited for growth in sand-dunes. The green-leaved helleborine is recorded from Germany and, more recently, from Denmark.

Within the British Isles, however, the common marsh orchid and dwarf purple orchid are much more widely distributed than the other two species. The former occurs over the whole of the southern half of England, in south and central Wales, and along the eastern part of England as far north as Durham. *O. purpurella* is widely distributed in Wales, northern England, Scotland and in the northern parts of Ireland. The leopard marsh orchid is found locally in various parts of the southern counties from Devonshire to Kent, but the dune helleborine is restricted to the coasts of Lancashire and Anglesey. This is rather difficult to understand in view of its extended distribution along the north-western European seaboard, since there are numerous sand-dunes in many other parts of the country. *E. leptochila* is widely spread in southern England and in South Wales.

The other type of restricted distribution outside our islands is exhibited by the very interesting dense-flowered orchid (*Neotinea intacta*, Map 32, p. 354). This species, which occurs in a number of localities in the western Irish counties of Galway, Clare and Mayo, is otherwise an inhabitant of the Mediterranean region, extending from the Iberian Peninsula, the Canary Islands and Madeira in the west to Cyprus and Asia Minor in the east. There is therefore a gap of about one thousand miles between the Irish localities and the nearest ones outside our islands ; this fact has given rise to a number of interesting speculations as to the cause of such a discontinuous distribution (see also pp. 71 and 231).

Before coming to those species which are not known outside the

British Isles, there is yet one more remarkable example of geographical distribution among our native orchids. This is found in the Irish ladies' tresses (*Spiranthes romanzoffiana*, Map 15, p. 349), which is known from several counties in Ireland (Cork, Armagh, Londonderry, etc.), and also in several islands in the southern Hebrides (Colonsay, Coll). Otherwise the species occurs nowhere else in the Old World, but has a wide distribution in North America from Newfoundland, Labrador and southwards as far as New York, right across the continent to California and northwards to British Columbia and the Aleutian Islands. The whole width of the Atlantic Ocean is therefore interposed between the two areas of distribution of this species, which constitutes the American element of our orchid flora.

Finally there are the endemic species, which are restricted in distribution to our own island group. These number four in all, belonging to the two genera *Orchis* and *Epipactis*, namely, the Wicklow marsh orchid (*Orchis traunsteinerioides*), Irish marsh orchid (*O. occidentalis*), pendulous-flowered helleborine (*E. pendula*, Map 11, p. 348) and Isle of Wight helleborine (*E. vectensis*, Map 12). Of these it is interesting to note that the helleborines are, on the whole, natives of the southern part of England, whereas the *Orchis* species are found chiefly in the north and west of the British Isles, especially in Ireland. Both the latter are undoubtedly closely related to species which occur on the mainland of Europe, and this is probably also true of the helleborines. It is indeed possible that further careful examination of the European orchid flora may yet disclose the occurrence of one or more of the above species in some part of the continent.* We must therefore look upon our endemic species in general as special British representatives of certain continental species. Indeed some of them (e.g. Wicklow marsh orchid) are considered by some authorities not to be true species, but merely sub-species or varieties of European species. The existence of these endemic species is therefore not an indication of differences between the British and general European orchid floras, but rather a further confirmation of the essential unity of the orchid flora over the whole continent, including these islands.

* I find myself quite unable to agree with the Swedish botanist Nannfeldt's identification of *E. vectensis* with species from Iran (Persia) and Cyprus, nor with some of the Danish plants mentioned by him. As regards the Swedish plants he describes, and also some of the Danish, there is a greater resemblance to the Isle of Wight helleborine. Careful examination of all the related forms concerned, including *E. pendula*, is necessary, however, before really reliable conclusions can be reached.

So much for the actual facts regarding the distribution of our native orchids. But the reader will naturally wonder what are the reasons for these differences, particularly as regards such species as the dense-flowered orchid and the Irish ladies' tresses. As mentioned earlier, we may relate the distributions of many of our species to the operation of major climatic influences, temperature, rainfall and the like. This is no doubt the explanation of the different groups termed here Southern, Central and Northern Eurasian and Northern Montane groups. These are evidently adapted to life in increasingly colder regions in the order given above. It is natural that similar differences in the climate within the British Isles will have a corresponding effect, although in such a small area the direct effects of climate tend to be masked by those imposed by soil, altitude or other local factors.

Of course, not all members of the European orchid flora are to be found in this country, even when they appear to be suited by the climate. It is here that the past history of the country has to be taken into consideration. It is generally accepted by geologists and others who have studied this subject, that during the last great Ice Age, approximately 10,000 to 100,000 years ago, the greater part of these islands was covered at one time or another by huge sheets of ice, leaving free only the extreme south and west, and perhaps isolated mountains elsewhere. It is clear that during this period the climate of the ice-free portions must have been very different from conditions to-day, and must have approached that of arctic or almost arctic regions. Under the ice itself nothing could survive, and even where the ground was ice-free the number of species able to survive must have been limited. There are still, however, very great differences of opinion as to which these were. In considering this question it has always to be borne in mind that the glaciation was not continuous, but actually took place in four main periods with warmer, so-called inter-glacial, periods between. The extent of the ice covering no doubt varied from one ice-period to another, thus enabling the plants to survive in different places at different times.

When the ice finally retreated northwards at the end of the Ice Age the climate gradually improved again, and species which had been forced to exist farther south were able slowly to migrate into the areas left free by the ice. But not all species were equally favourably placed for this purpose, nor have all species equal migratory abilities. The result has been that some have occupied all the areas within our islands that are suited to them, others have only progressed part of the way, while others have never got here at all.

Many of the members of our orchid flora, such as the common twayblade, the two butterfly orchids, sword-leaved, large white and marsh helleborines, man orchid, etc., are widely distributed species showing very considerable uniformity over immense areas. These are comparatively stable species which developed their characteristic features a very long time ago. These species have not changed to any appreciable extent during or since their re-occupation of our islands following the glaciation, and the British plants are therefore indistinguishable from those occurring on the mainland of Europe. Other groups of our native orchids, such as the various helleborines belonging to the genus *Epipactis*, and the marsh and spotted orchids (the dactylorchids), are still subject to comparatively rapid evolutionary changes, many of the recognised species even now not being easily distinguishable. The species belonging to these groups probably migrated into this country at much the same time as the more stable species, and in due course became cut off from the mainland individuals of the same species by the geological changes which led to the formation of the English Channel. But whereas the stable species remained more or less constant, the helleborines and dactylorchids continued to change, thus giving rise to new forms which tended to be different from those developed contemporaneously on the mainland. This is no doubt the explanation of some, at least, of our endemic species. It seems very probable that the Irish marsh orchid (*Orchis occidentalis*) has been derived by evolution from the same stock as the continental broad-leaved marsh orchid (*O. majalis*), which is widely spread in central and northern Europe. In the same way the Wicklow marsh orchid (*O. traunsteinerioides*) is apparently related to the northern European narrow-leaved marsh orchid (*O. traunsteineri*), of which, indeed, it may be a sub-species. It is not so easy to suggest parallels for our endemic helleborines, and indeed some of these may yet be found in Europe.

Another explanation, however, of some of our endemics may be based on an alternative conception of the history of our flora. There is very considerable evidence that many plants now occurring in the British Isles were there before the Ice Age and persisted throughout that period in the areas free from ice. As already mentioned in more general terms, these areas comprised England south of the Thames and portions of Ireland. It has often been assumed that nothing but

" arctic " plants survived here, but observations near glaciers and
ice-sheets in other parts of the world show that many other kinds of
species can persist in such places. Some of our peculiar orchids may
therefore have persisted from periods prior to the Ice Age and have
then re-occupied the glaciated areas after the retreat of the ice.

This explanation has the advantage that it also accounts to a
certain extent for the other extraordinary distributions mentioned
previously, namely, those of the dense-flowered orchid and of the Irish
ladies' tresses. It is extremely difficult to see how these two species
can have migrated directly to Ireland from their main centres of
distribution since the Glacial Period. The explanation is much easier
if it be assumed that they have been here all along. There is geologi al
evidence that the western parts of the British Isles were once connected
directly with what is now western Europe, and also possibly with
northern America via the Faroes, Iceland and Greenland. The two
species might therefore have entered Ireland when such connections
existed, the British populations becoming cut off from the remainder
by the vast disturbances accompanying the Ice Ages. There are,
however, a number of different theories in the field, each purporting
to explain these and other remarkable distributions, and the matter
is still under active discussion (see Chapter 12 for further discussion
about the dense-flowered orchid).

ECOLOGICAL DISTRIBUTION

As mentioned at the beginning of this chapter, the ecological distributions of our species show much the same sorts of differences as
we have seen is true for their geographical distributions. We have, on
the one hand, the so-called " tolerant " species, which seem to be able
to live happily in a great variety of different situations, for example
the common twayblade (*Listera ovata*), while in marked contrast to
these there are species which appear to be able to exist only in certain
very special situations or habitats, such as a very shady beech wood or
a wet acid bog, these latter species being termed " exclusive ". Every
species, however, is limited in some respect with regard to where it
can grow, the differences between tolerant and exclusive species being
only of degree. There are some habitats, salt marshes for instance,
where none of our native orchids is to be found, whereas, on the other
hand, our chalk downs are the natural haunts of many of our most

beautiful and rarest species. On the whole, differences in the soil seem to be most important in determining the occurrence of the great majority of our orchids. This is not surprising when we remember the invariable presence of the mycorhizal fungus at some time during the life history of every species. The fungus is a normal inhabitant of many soils, from which it infects the germinating seeds of all species or, in some species, re-infects the adult plant in suitable circumstances. The continued existence of the fungus in the free state is clearly determined by the soil conditions, which may often be completely unfavourable to it. On such soils establishment of fresh orchid individuals is impossible.

The great majority of British orchids are restricted to, or grow much better on, limestone, chalky or other calcareous soils, some of them, such as the rare soldier and monkey orchids, being found only on the chalk. Other species, for example man orchid (*Aceras*), large white helleborine (*Cephalanthera damasonium*) and fly orchid (*Ophrys muscifera*), are found on a variety of calcareous soils, including various limestones as well as the chalk. It is interesting to note that some species, which are confined to limestone soils in this country, may grow indifferently on calcareous and non-calcareous soils on the European mainland. It is generally considered that limestone soils, particularly the chalk, being comparatively dry and warm, help to compensate southern species for the cooler, damper climate of more northern and western regions. This is particularly noticeable in genera or parts of genera, such as *Ophrys* and the *militaris* group of *Orchis*, which are mainly distributed in southern regions, and is possibly connected with maturation of the tubers and the new growing point of next year's aerial shoot. It is noticeable that the soldier orchid is always found on limestone soils in the more northerly parts of its European range, and the same is true of the spider and fly orchids (*Ophrys* spp.) ; farther south these species have a much wider soil tolerance.

Many species, however, although they appear to be more common on calcareous soils, can also grow on soils which are neutral or faintly acid. For instance, the early purple and green-veined orchids (*Orchis mascula* and *O. morio*) are frequently found on clayey neutral soils, and the former also occurs among heathy vegetation on slightly acid soils. Many marsh species do not need soils which are themselves limy, provided the drainage water which flows into or through the marsh contains a sufficiency of lime or other basic substances to neutra-lise the natural acidity of the soil. Thus the early marsh orchid (*Orchis latifolia*) and the marsh helleborine (*Epipactis palustris*) will grow on quite deep peat in which the drainage water is derived from surround-ing or neighbouring calcareous soils.

Some species occur commonly on both calcareous and non-cal-careous soils, examples being the common twayblade, lesser butterfly orchid (*Platanthera bifolia*), fragrant orchid (*Gymnadenia conopsea*) and broad-leaved helleborine (*Epipactis helleborine*). In the fragrant orchid and lesser butterfly orchid, however, there is reason for thinking that the individuals on limy soils and those occurring on heathy places may constitute different varieties of the species, though this has not yet been worked out at all accurately. In the other species mentioned the plants growing on different soils seem indistinguishable from one another, except in so far as the differences are evidently the direct result of the soil conditions themselves.

Finally we have a few species of orchid which are characteristic of acid soils, and occur rarely on those which are at all calcareous. The commonest of these is the heath spotted orchid (*Orchis ericetorum*), which grows on such soils throughout the country, and in many places is the only orchid to be found. Others are the bog orchid (*Hammarbya paludosa*), lesser twayblade (*Listera cordata*) and, less exclusively, the creeping ladies' tresses (*Goodyera repens*).

Apart from the nature of the soil, the occurrence of orchids is often determined by the vegetation occupying the ground, the main types of vegetation, such as woodlands, scrub, and grassland, all possessing their own characteristic orchid species. There is, of course, a close relationship between vegetation and soil type, particularly in the British Isles, the different kinds of woodlands and grasslands being determined by the soil in any given place. Nevertheless other factors of the habitat, such as the amount of shade or the richness of the soil in humus, both of which are directly dependent on the vege-tational covering, are often of great importance to orchid species. Different degrees of tolerance, or of exclusiveness, are shown by dif-ferent orchids with respect to types of vegetation, the more tolerant being able to inhabit a wide range of woodlands, scrub and grassland ; good examples are the common twayblade and common spotted orchid (*O. fuchsii*). The two butterfly orchids are also found in a great range of plant communities, from woodlands and scrubby places to grasslands and damp or swampy places. It is interesting to note that three of the species mentioned have very wide geographical ranges and are therefore very tolerant both ecologically and climatically. So far as *Orchis fuchsii* is concerned, however, it is probable that several varieties are involved, each one characteristic of certain types of vegetation.

It will be of interest, and will help the reader to obtain a general view of the ecological distribution of orchids in this country, if we consider in turn the various major vegetational types, together with the orchids inhabiting them.

ORCHIDS OF WOODLAND AND SCRUB

Many British orchids are found characteristically in woods and forests of different kinds, even if they sometimes occur outside them. Any observer knows, however, that woods in different parts of the country and on different soils are composed of different sorts of trees, such as oaks, beech, ash, birch, Scots pine, etc. This is because the dominant tree species in any wood depend on climate, soil, topography and other factors, some species being more prominent in some circumstances and others predominating where the external factors are different. Different sorts of woodland may therefore be distinguished not only by the tree species present, but in various other respects, depending on the special combination of factors which determine their occurrence. These other differences play their part in the determination of what orchids may be found in the various types of woodland. It will be clear from what has been said previously, that woodlands on calcareous soils may be expected to be richer in orchids than other woodlands, and this proves to be true.

BEECHWOODS

Of all the woodlands in this country beechwoods are far and away the richest in orchid species. This is probably due to two reasons : firstly, they occur in the south-eastern half of England, and secondly, they grow usually on limestone soils, particularly on the various hill ranges formed by the chalk. The soil conditions are consequently such as are known to be favourable for the growth of most kinds of orchids. Beechwoods are also found on the sands and gravels overlying the chalk, or on the flatter summit plateaux where much of the lime has been washed away from the comparatively deep soil. These woods are nothing like as rich in orchids as those on the shallower chalk soil where the underlying rock comes near to the surface. Beech trees cast a very heavy shade, so that shrubby undergrowth and herbaceous plants are reduced to a minimum ; indeed in places there is practically no vegetation at all, only a thick layer of rotting beech leaves.

Characteristic and widely spread beechwood orchids are the large white helleborine (*Cephalanthera damasonium*), broad-leaved helleborine (*Epipactis helleborine*) and bird's nest orchid (*Neottia nidus-avis*). Other species which are not found so constantly, but nevertheless occur in many places, are common twayblade (*Listera ovata*), common spotted orchid (*Orchis fuchsii*), fly orchid (*Ophrys muscifera*), green-leaved helleborine (*Epipactis leptochila*), greater butterfly orchid (*Platanthera chlorantha*) and sword-leaved helleborine (*Cephalanthera longifolia*).

Cephalanthera damasonium is undoubtedly the most typical beech-wood orchid. It occurs in nearly all such woods, and even under isolated beech trees or small groups of trees. It is most common on the drier steeper slopes where the chalk soil is very shallow, and is therefore characteristic of the well-known " hangers " or hanging beechwoods of the North and South Downs and Chiltern Hills. With it is found *Neottia*, the two species often occurring in deep shade where there is practically no other vegetation. Other species occurring here are *Epipactis helleborine* and *E. leptochila* (Pl. 13a, p. 142), especially the latter. The bird's nest orchid is a saprophyte and so, unlike most other species, not dependent on light for food manufacture. It may therefore be found in very dark spots, under tall closely interlacing beech trees (Pl. 20, p. 191), among a thick growth of young trees, or even under the yew trees which so frequently form a sort of second storey in beechwoods. In all these places the ground is bare of vegetation with a thick layer of decaying leaves. In similar dark shady places, but where the ground is flatter and the soil deeper, one finds the violet helleborine (*Epipactis purpurata*, Pl. 12, p. 139) and, in Oxfordshire, the extremely rare spurred coral-root (*Epipogium aphyllum*). This latter species is also a saprophyte and is notable for the irregularity of its flowering. Other species growing in the shadier parts are the two rare helleborines, *Epipactis pendula* in Gloucestershire, Bedfordshire, and Sussex, and *E. vectensis* (Pl. 14, p. 143) in Kent and formerly in the Isle of Wight. These are usually associated with a meagre ground flora of ivy, sterile dog-violets, wild arum, dwarf brambles, etc. The common twayblade may also sometimes be found in quite shady places in beech-woods, though not so much as in oakwoods.

In lighter spots, such as small openings in the tree canopy, along rides or paths, or at the margins of the woods, we find quite a number of other species, as well as some of those already mentioned. The broad-leaved helleborine is really more characteristic of these places than of the shadier parts ; it is often scattered about among the low undergrowth of privet, dogwood and various herbaceous plants which is found in open places. Other widely spread species are *Orchis fuchsii*, *Ophrys muscifera*, the two butterfly orchids (*Platanthera chlorantha*, Pl. 24, p. 203, and *P. bifolia*, Pl. 25a, p. 210), *Cephalanthera longifolia* (Pl. 6, p. 111) and *Listera ovata*. Besides these there are other orchids which, though equally typical of such spots, are found much more locally. The very handsome lady orchid (*Orchis purpurea*, Pl. 34, p. 243) is often abundant in beechwoods in Kent, but does not occur outside that county, while the very rare soldier orchid (*O. militaris*) was once to be found in similar habitats in Buckinghamshire and Hertfordshire. In the extensive beechwoods on the Oolitic limestones of the Cotswold Hills in Gloucestershire we find, in addition to most of the widespread species mentioned above, the beautiful red helleborine (*Cephalanthera rubra*). This is normally an inhabitant of open spots in the woods or even of scrubby places, but it will persist in a sterile condition under the deep shade of large beech trees.

Orchids which are normally looked upon as non-woodland species may sometimes be found in open places in beechwoods, one example being the pyramidal orchid (*Anacamptis pyramidalis*). Another very interesting example is the bee orchid (*Ophrys apifera*), which occurs in a number of beechwoods, or mixed woods of beech and other trees, on the Chiltern Hills, often in quite considerable shade. The bee orchid seems quite at home in these places, but flowers a month later than in the chalk grassland outside.

Closely associated with the beechwoods there are often extensive areas of bushes or young trees forming scrub. This scrub vegetation may sometimes represent the remains of woods from which the large trees have been removed, the area of such scrub having been largely increased as a result of extensive felling during the two wars. Much of the scrub on chalk soils, however, is the result of the opposite pro-cess, that is to say, it represents the invasion of grassland by bush and tree species, and the gradual conversion of downland into woodland. In the present climate of England this is a natural process, which may be happening in many places and not only on chalk or even other limestone soils.

Now it is clear that the past history of any piece of ground is of importance in determining what plants are likely to be found there ; consequently the orchids found on the two kinds of scrub mentioned are either not the same or, if they are, their frequency of occurrence is different in the two. Scrub of the first type, derived from old woods, will tend to contain woodland species, such as the early purple orchid (*Orchis mascula*), helleborines (*Epipactis* and *Cephalanthera* spp.), lady orchid, greater butterfly orchid, common twayblade or even bird's nest orchid where the shade is thick enough. Such species as can adapt themselves to the changed conditions may persist in this scrub for many years, this being especially the case with those species which normally inhabit the more open and lighter parts of the woods. On the other hand, we may expect to find in the other kind of scrub, that on its way from grassland to woodland, orchids which are the ordinary inhabitants of grassland and can still put up with the changes taking place. Scrubs of this type are rarely homogeneous ; usually they consist of alternating patches of taller and shorter growth, with here and there a small enclosure of unaltered grassland. Here the grassland orchids survive, as also among the lower and more distant bushes of hawthorn, blackthorn, dogwood, privet, wayfaring-tree, wild roses and other similar plants. The pyramidal orchid is one which survives in such places, also the common spotted orchid ; other species occurring less frequently here are the man orchid (*Aceras anthropophorum*) and the green-veined orchid (*Orchis morio*). Many of the woodland orchids also become established in these scrubs, particularly the large white helleborine, fly orchid, twayblade, lady orchid and greater butterfly orchid. The rare soldier orchid (*Orchis militaris*, Pl. 33, p. 242) is a characteristic plant of scrubby places.

One of the most interesting members of the chalk and limestone scrub associated with the beechwood community is the rare lizard orchid (*Himantoglossum hircinum*), the great majority of the records of this species being from such spots. I well remember seeing about 40 specimens of this grand orchid in Bedfordshire growing in a low scrub of hawthorn and other bushes (see Pl. 30, p. 227). They were almost invisible at a few yards' distance, and protected from severe grazing by the thorny shrubs all around. Accompanying the lizard orchids were numerous individuals of the pyramidal orchid and the grassland form of *Orchis fuchsii*. Unfortunately this area has since been ploughed up by the farmer on whose land it occurred.

Mention has already been made of beechwoods on sands and gravels, and also on the deep loamy soils of the chalk-hill plateaux. These beechwoods are almost devoid of orchids, although the bird's nest orchid is rarely found in shady spots. Occasional plants of tway-blade and early purple orchid may also be found, but their occurrence may be due to a slightly greater amount of lime in the soil locally.

ASHWOODS

As one travels north and west of the regions where the beechwoods occur, these latter are found to be replaced on limestone soils by woods in which ash in the predominant tree. This is a climatic effect, the beech being characteristic of more continental climates, whereas the ash is more a tree of oceanic regions. The ashwoods are found typically on the geologically older limestones, particularly the Magnesian limestone and Carboniferous or Mountain limestone. These reach their greatest development in and around the Pennine Hills, as well as in smaller areas such as the Mendip Hills in Somerset, parts of South Wales and the Wye Valley. There are also extensive areas of these rocks in Ireland.

Many of the orchids of ashwoods are the same as those occurring in beechwoods, but the specifically south-eastern species are mostly lacking. On the other hand, a few species of more northerly distribution may take their places. These older limestones are relatively harder than those in the south-east, and therefore weather often to form cliffs and screes, particularly where the topography is more broken. These cliffs and steep slopes often support scrub, either of small ash trees, or more frequently of ash, hazel, oaks and other trees, while the gentler or more stable slopes bear mature ashwood. In these woods and scrub we find such orchids as *Orchis mascula, O. fuchsii, Listera ovata, Ophrys muscifera, Platanthera chlorantha, Epipactis helleborine*, all of which we have already found in the beechwoods. The common spotted orchid and greater butterfly orchid are usually found in damper spots or in marshy places near streams. Other less frequent species are *Ophrys apifera, Anacamptis pyramidalis, Platanthera bifolia* and

PLATE V

C. Thomas

a. Flowers from two plants of Broad-leaved Helleborine, *Epipactis helleborine*, to show variation in size, etc. (×4)

E. J. Bedford

b. Front and side views of flower of hybrid between Frog and Fragrant Orchids (× *Gymnaglossum jacksoni*) (×4)

PLATE VI

E. J. Bedford

Flowers of Late Spider Orchid, *Ophrys fuciflora* (top left) and Bee Orchid, *O. apifera* (top right) with (below) flowers from two hybrid plants ($\times 2\frac{1}{2}$)

Cephalanthera longifolia. All these species occur in the more open woods, or in the associated scrubby areas. The bird's nest orchid is a very rare member of the ashwood flora ; this is not surprising in view of the comparatively light shade cast by the ash trees and the scarcity of the accumulated humus soil so necessary for the growth of this saprophyte.

In the Somerset ashwoods we find the southern *Cephalanthera damasonium* (large white helleborine), so characteristic of the beech-woods, but this plant is not found to any extent farther north. In Yorkshire and other northern counties, however, two species find their special habitat in these ashwoods or scrubs, particularly in the dwarf woods clothing the rocky " scars " which are such a feature of the northern limestone valleys. Firstly we have the dark red helleborine (*Epipactis atrorubens*), which is also a plant of rocky cliffs as well as the open scrub or " scar " woods. The most interesting orchid, however, is undoubtedly the lady's slipper (*Cypripedium calceolus*), which is now found in such habitats only in Yorkshire, but used to occur in similar places in Durham and other northern counties. This striking plant was once a characteristic feature of the steep rocky ashwoods on Carboniferous, Magnesian and Corallian limestone in the whole Pennine region, but is now extremely rare.

Woods of ash, or frequently ash and sessile oak mixed, are found in various places in Ireland on limestone rocks, especially around or on islands in some of the lakes. These woods are rich in herbaceous vegetation, including such orchids as common spotted orchid and bird's nest orchid. In rocky places the dark red helleborine is also sometimes found.

OAKWOODS

The most widely spread of all types of woodlands in these islands are those formed of oak trees. There are two species of oak involved, the pedunculate oak (*Quercus robur*) and the sessile oak (*Q. petraea*). The former is relatively eastern and southern in its general distribution, whereas the latter is on the whole northern and western, although both species may form woodlands in some areas. In other places mixed woods occur containing trees of both species, together with hybrids between them. Apart from the effect of climate, which is evidently mainly responsible for the different occurrences of these two types of oakwood, the soil is also an important factor. Pedunculate oakwoods occur usually on soils with more bases present, although these soils may be heavy or light in different places, whereas sessile oakwoods are more characteristic of well-drained soils poor in bases, especially lime. These soil differences, as might be expected, are important in their effects on the distribution of orchids. Taking these woods by and large, those composed of *Quercus robur* are richer in orchid species than those in which *Q. petraea* is the dominant tree, though there may be local departures from this generalisation due to special conditions. These will be mentioned where appropriate.

Pedunculate oakwoods are the commonest type of woodland in the Midlands, southern, and eastern England, except on the exposed chalk soils where, as already mentioned, the beech is the dominant tree. They are especially abundant on clayey or marly soils, including those of clay-with-flints lying on the chalk itself. They are also found on the sandy soils of the Weald, the London Basin and the Hampshire Basin, but from an orchid point of view these more closely resemble the sessile oakwoods. On more marly soils containing an appreciable amount of lime, especially in the west, the oakwoods contain a large proportion of ash, and are evidently transitional to the ashwoods dealt with above.

In southern England, mainly due to former demands for oak in shipbuilding, the oakwoods are mostly in the form of " standards with coppice ". The larger oak trees are spaced out, the intervals being filled with shrubs of hazel, ash and other woody plants, which are cut back regularly at intervals of about fifteen years and allowed to sprout out again. The mature coppice of shrubs so formed is about 15–20 feet in height and casts a very heavy shade. The orchids occurring, like the other herbaceous plants, are therefore subjected to a regular cycle of conditions, from the bright sunny state following cutting to the deep gloom of the mature coppice. The most characteristic orchid of these coppiced woods on clays and marls is the early purple orchid (*Orchis mascula*, Pl. 37, p. 258). This species usually reaches its best development in the years immediately following coppicing, while the shrubs are still only half-grown. It often occurs literally in thousands, usually accompanied by the bluebell (*Scilla non-scripta*), celandine (*Ranunculus ficaria*), dog's mercury (*Mercurialis perennis*) and other woodland herbs. A coppiced wood filled with the reddish purple spikes of this beautiful species is a sight not easily forgotten. In Somerset when a boy I often filled my arms with the flower-spikes, apparently without making the slightest impression on the numbers present. This is, of course, not a practice to be recommended, as this orchid depends mainly on seed for maintaining its numbers, but it gives an idea of the relative abundance of the species. With the early purple orchid, but never so abundant, are found the greater butterfly orchid, twayblade and common spotted orchid ; the latter, however, is usually more abundant in rides or along the wood margins. None of these is able to continue flowering under the growing shrubs for so many years as *Orchis mascula*, and consequently they are usually only to be found in flower for a few years after clearing. Thereafter they may still be recognised in a sterile state, in which state they remain until the wood is again coppiced. Other orchids in these woods are the broad-leaved helleborine in the lighter parts, and the bird's nest orchid and violet helleborine (*Epipactis purpurata*) in the comparatively thick shady coppice. The latter is especially characteristic of hazel-coppice on the deep soils on the tops of the chalk hills, as in Hampshire, Surrey and Kent, but unlike the bird's nest orchid, it does not require a very large amount of humus in the soil. The sword-leaved helleborine and green-leaved helleborine occur very occasionally in pedunculate oakwoods, but can scarcely be said to be true members of the oakwood flora. Where the soil is locally more calcareous, or where the layers overlying the chalk are very thin, orchids belonging to the beechwood flora, such as the large white helleborine and fly orchid, may be found.

As already indicated, the pedunculate oakwoods on sandy soils are much poorer in orchids than those on the clays and marls. The early purple orchid, common spotted orchid and twayblade are to be found very locally in places where the soil is neutral or faintly alkaline. The only regularly occurring species is the heath spotted orchid (*Orchis ericetorum*), which grows usually in grassy spots, among bracken, or the like. Much of the ground vegetation of these woods is of a heathy type, including heather itself ; from such places orchids are usually quite lacking, with the rare exception of the broad-leaved helleborine and lesser butterfly orchid (*Platanthera bifolia*). These heathy oakwoods often alternate with areas of birchwood, or even with true heaths, all very poor as regards their orchid flora.

The sessile oak (*Q. petraea*) is the chief forest-forming tree on the older rocks of the north and west, especially in regions of comparatively high rainfall. Good examples may be found in the Pennines, in many parts of Wales and the Welsh Border, the Lake District, southern Scotland, and scattered over the greater part of Ireland. Sessile oak-woods are found usually on non-calcareous soils, or on limestones where these have been impoverished through the washing-out of soluble bases. These soils are therefore either neutral or more or less acid in nature. Such conditions are not favourable for the growth of orchids, which consequently are decidedly uncommon in sessile oak-woods. Very few of these woods are coppiced, so that the conditions within them are more constant than in the southern pedunculate oak-woods. Much of the ground vegetation is heathy in character with heather, bilberry (*Vaccinium myrtillus*) and similar plants ; orchids are practically absent from such regions. The heath spotted orchid is the only species likely here. The best places for orchids are along the flatter reaches of the stream valleys, where soluble salts have been washed down from above. Early purple orchid, common spotted or-chid, greater and lesser butterfly orchids and twayblade may be found in such situations. The most generally distributed species is the broad-leaved helleborine, which occurs locally in many sessile oak-woods, but prefers those with a neutral reaction. In the damper oak-woods along the bottoms of the valleys in west Yorkshire, where the soil is deeper than elsewhere, we find the violet helleborine (*Epipactis purpurata*) replacing the broad-leaved helleborine.

In Ireland most of the naturally occurring woodland is composed of sessile oaks, good examples being found near Killarney in Co. Kerry, and in counties Mayo, Sligo and Wicklow. Birches, holly, hazel and rowan are common associates, while at Killarney the straw-berry tree (*Arbutus unedo*) occurs in abundance in the oakwoods. Orchids are decidedly rare in the Irish oakwoods, but among others we find the bird's nest orchid and sword-leaved helleborine. Many of the woods are too rocky to be suitable for the growth of orchids, but the broad-leaved helleborine sometimes occurs in such habitats.

Where, of course, the soils have not entirely lost their bases, as on some of the limestones, the orchids mentioned above are more abun-dant, and may be accompanied by the pyramidal orchid and, where the shade is sufficient, by the bird's nest orchid. Sessile oakwoods also occur in southern England in Hertfordshire, Essex and Middlesex on sandy, gravel or clay soils. These woods, which usually have a strong admixture of hornbeam (*Carpinus betulus*) as a lower storey tree, are rather richer in orchid species than those already mentioned, but are poorer than the neighbouring pedunculate oakwoods. Most of the species are decidedly local, and are generally inhabitants of the paths and margins of the woods. They may include, however, the bee and fly orchids as well as those mentioned above.

PINEWOODS

The only genuinely natural coniferous woods in these islands are those formed by Scots pine (*Pinus sylvestris*). There are two distinct types of these, which are very different from one another as regards their orchid flora. In the Highlands of Scotland we find very old pine-woods, which are thought to be direct descendants of much more extensive forests which existed when the climate of Britain was much more continental in character. In southern England, however, we have very recent pinewoods, which have arisen by the direct colonisation of heathy areas by seeds from plantations or isolated planted trees. Very few of these are more than a hundred years of age, as shown by records.

The Scottish pinewoods occur in upland valleys, as much as 1,000 to 2,000 feet above sea level, both south of the Caledonian Canal, as in Aberdeenshire and Perthshire, or to the north in Inverness. Although parts of the forest are well-wooded, there are many open places, while much of the so-called " forest " is really a sort of pine-heath with scattered pine trees among heather and other heath-forming shrubs. Even under the trees the vegetation is of a heath-like nature, including among other plants bilberry or blaeberry (*Vaccinium myrtillus*), cowberry (*V. vitis-idaea*) and various heath grasses. Bracken is also a common plant in parts of these forests. These ancient pine forests are the home of several very interesting orchids. The most characteristic of these is the creeping ladies' tresses (*Goodyera repens*, Pl. 1, p. 46) which, although it occurs occasionally elsewhere, is found chiefly in these forests. This orchid is specially suited by its method of growth for existence in the mixture of pine-needles and moss which covers the ground in the shadier parts. Other species are the lesser twayblade (*Listera cordata*, Pl. 16a, p. 159) and common coral-root (*Corallorhiza trifida*). The former grows at its best in slight openings of the wood or where the canopy is not too thick, and here it may occur in great numbers. The latter, one of our three sapro-phytic orchids, is found under fairly dense shade where there is a thick layer of rotting leaves, especially where there is an admixture of birches or perhaps alders with the pines. Other orchids which may occur in the larger openings are heath spotted orchid (*Orchis ericetorum*), lesser butterfly orchid (*Platanthera bifolia*) and fragrant orchid (*Gymnadenia conopsea*), but these are scarcely forest species and more of the nature of invaders from the heathy areas outside. The small bog orchid (*Hammarbya paludosa*) may also be found in local bogs within the forest, but again is not a true member of the forest flora.

The southern pinewoods have no special orchids associated with them, but this is hardly surprising in view of their recent formation. Most of the orchids of heathy areas occur occasionally in the openings, particularly *Orchis ericetorum*.

Extensive areas throughout the British Isles have been planted with conifers, often Scots pine, in the past, and in recent years the immense afforestation schemes of the Forestry Commission have added thousands of acres. These now support young forests of Norway or Sitka spruce, Japanese larch, Douglas fir, Scots pine and many other exotic trees. In these the close initial planting kills off all the ground vegetation, and most of the forests are hardly old enough to have developed a new flora, especially of orchids, which take some time to recolonise an area.

The older coniferous plantations, however, often contain a well-developed ground flora including various species of orchids. In many Scottish plantations *Goodyera repens* is well established, and this is also true of certain pine plantations in Norfolk. It is thought that the orchid was introduced to this latter region in the soil with the seedling trees. Other species growing in northern plantations are lesser and common twayblades and broad-leaved helleborine. Where pines have been planted on calcareous soils, which is sometimes the case, the orchids of the chalk woodlands may be found growing in the plantations. I have seen early purple orchid, fly orchid, common spotted orchid, common twayblade, bee orchid, broad-leaved helleborine and many other species growing quite happily under young pines where not planted too close, or in open more mature plantations. An interesting occurrence of another kind is that of two species of helleborine (*Epipactis pendula*, Pl. 13b, p. 142, and *E. dunensis*), which are found growing in young pine plantations on the sand dunes of the Lancashire coast. The former species seems quite at home in this habitat, but the latter is usually a species of the open dunes.

On the whole, it appears that many orchids can grow under conifers provided these are not too close growing. It will be interesting to see if the new exotic forests covering so much of our hilly country develop an orchid flora in the future. The common practice of clear-felling and block replanting may prevent any orderly and gradual development, but if the alternative system of selective felling be adopted on any large scale we may yet see the slow building up of new types of forests with their associated orchids and other herbaceous plants.

BIRCHWOODS

Birchwoods are found closely associated with both the oakwoods and pinewoods already described. They are frequent on the sandy and gravelly soils of southern England, and also form an upland forest belt above both the oakwoods and pinewoods in northern England, Wales, Scotland and Ireland. Many birchwoods represent the remnants of oakwoods which have degenerated owing to selective cutting or heavy grazing by stock, rabbits, etc. Increasing acidity of the soil, due to washing out of soluble salts, may also lead to replacement of oakwoods by birchwood, or even by heath vegetation. In most places the birchwood is associated with heathy vegetation and contains a heathy ground flora, the exact composition of which varies with the past history of the wood, the topography and the nature of the soil. Orchids are uncommon in most birchwoods, since the majority of species dislike acid soil conditions. The heath spotted orchid is probably the most generally distributed, while on neutral or almost neutral soils we find broad-leaved helleborine and common spotted orchid. Other species are common twayblade and lesser butterfly orchid, the latter usually occurring in more open places. In the Scottish birchwoods the lesser twayblade is a common orchid species, while in areas formerly inhabited by pines the creeping ladies' tresses not infrequently survives for some time under birches. The common coral-root also occurs locally in Scottish birchwoods, usually in shadier and damper situations. Another rather local birchwood orchid is the early purple orchid, but it is probable that this again is a survivor from former oakwoods, as in places on the Pennines. An extremely interesting recent discovery is that of the Isle of Wight helleborine (*Epipactis vectensis*) growing under mature birch trees in Berkshire. The accompanying vegetation suggests a neutral soil, and this may explain the occurrence here of a plant known otherwise only from beech or similar woods on chalky soil.

ALDER-WILLOW WOODS

Unlike all the other woods already dealt with, those formed of alder or willows, or more frequently a mixture of the two, are almost invariably found on soils which are very wet. This wetness may be due to defective drainage on slopes, or the woods may occur in flat valley bottoms along slowly moving streams or rivers. The woods are composed of the common alder (*Alnus rotundifolius*) with several species of willow, of which grey sallow (*Salix atrocinerea*), goat sallow (*S. caprea*), white willow (*S. alba*), crack willow (*S. fragilis*) and osier (*S. viminalis*) are the commonest. Birches and poplars are often frequent members of the woodland flora. The soil may be mainly mineral with a high proportion of humus, or it may consist of peat, originally formed under fen conditions. In many cases the woodland is the last of a series of plant communities formed successively following the gradual filling-up of lakes by peat formation or the deposition of silt. Good examples of these will be found in the Norfolk Broads and the Lake District.

As might be expected from the past history of the sites of many of the woods, as well as from the present soil conditions, the orchids are mostly those characteristic of swamps. The ground surface varies much in actual dampness, however, and permits a greater variety of species to flourish than would otherwise be the case. Orchids found very generally in the lowland woods are common spotted orchid (*Orchis fuchsii*), common twayblade, and fragrant orchid, the latter usually in more open spots. Other less common species are broad-leaved helleborine (*Epipactis helleborine*) and, in some Scottish woods of this type, common coral-root. In English alder-willow woods the common marsh orchid (*Orchis praetermissa*) is not infrequently found, especially when these woods have arisen on old reed-swamp or fen. As might be expected from their origin, the woods vary much in density and often enclose small open marshy areas in which the original marsh or fen vegetation persists. The woods occurring on badly drained slopes are found mainly in regions of high rainfall, as in Wales and Scotland. They contain fewer orchids than the lowland ones, but *Orchis fuchsii* and *Gymnadenia* occur occasionally, also the heath spotted orchid (*O. ericetorum*), especially on poorer soils.

ORCHIDS OF GRASSLANDS

Apart from arable ground, a high proportion of non-wooded country in these islands is occupied by grasslands of different types. These vary from those with high agricultural usage, such as meadows regularly cut for hay or constantly grazed pastures, through the variously used rough hill-pastures, to the wild practically unused grass-land on moors or mountains. As a general rule the more a grassland is interfered with by man, the less suitable it is as a habitat for orchids, since these plants are slow growing and do not like their roots dis-turbed. Heavily grazed fields or other areas rarely yield any orchids, due to the double effect of trampling and actual biting of the plants. Ley farming is particularly destructive, and leads to the virtual extinc-tion of orchids in the fields concerned. As pointed out later in Chap-ter 5, the great majority of our orchid species are inhabitants of open grassy places, the general habit (structure) being suitable for growth among grasses or plants of that type.

LIMESTONE AND CHALK GRASSLAND

Much of the higher limestone areas is occupied by grassland, partly because the overlying soil is too shallow to allow of the proper development of trees, and partly because historical reasons have led to the choice of these areas for grazing domestic animals. Large stretches of the chalk hills (Downs) of the south-east support such grassland communities, and also extensive areas on the older limestones in the west, Midlands and north of England, as well as in parts of Scotland and Ireland. These grasslands show close resemblances to one another as regards general floristic composition, though naturally climatic and other factors often determine the exact species present in different areas. This applies also to the orchids, but many species are to be found in these habitats almost throughout our islands.

In general, grasslands on limestone soils can be divided into two main groups, depending upon the size of the grasses. Tall grasslands, in which the grasses reach an average height of about a foot, with the flower-spikes standing even higher, are formed by erect brome (*Bromus erectus*), false brome (*Brachypodium pinnatum*), false oats (*Arrhenatherum elatius*), oat grasses (*Helictotrichon pratense* and *H. pubescens*) and others.

On the other hand, we find much shorter turf (two to six inches in height) composed mainly of sheep's fescue (*Festuca ovina*), red fescue (*F. rubra*), crested dog's tail (*Cynosurus cristatus*), *Koeleria cristata*, *Sesleria caerulea* and other similar plants. With each of these are associated numerous characteristic flowering herbs, including various species of orchids. Although these two types of grassland often exist in extensive stretches, yet in many places they may alternate with one another in small patches, depending upon the soil and other local conditions. Some species of orchid may be found growing in both types, such, for instance, as *Orchis fuchsii*, *Listera ovata*, *Platanthera chlorantha* and *Orchis mascula*. Others, such as *Anacamptis* (Pl. 29, p. 226), *Gymnadenia* and *Aceras* (Pl. 31, p. 234), seem to grow better in the taller types of grassland. An even greater number, of which *Ophrys apifera*, *O. sphegodes* (early spider orchid, Pl. 46, p. 287), *Herminium* (Pl. 22, p. 195), *Coeloglossum*, *Spiranthes spiralis* (Pl. 16b, p. 159) and *Orchis ustulata* (Pl. 35a, p. 250) are good examples, are nearly always found growing where the turf is shorter. This is apparently because they are either small plants, or their leaves form a sort of rosette on the surface of the ground. In either case were they surrounded by tall grasses much of the light they need would be kept from them.

Of calcareous grasslands those covering the chalk downs of southern and eastern England are by far the richest in orchid species. In addition to all the species mentioned above, we find the lesser butterfly orchid (*Platanthera bifolia*), monkey orchid (*Orchis simia*), green-veined orchid (*O. morio*), fly orchid (*Ophrys muscifera*), late spider orchid (*O. fuciflora*, Pl. 47, p. 302) and, rarely, the lizard orchid (*Himantoglossum hircinum*). Sometimes many of these species are to be found growing within quite a small area ; in fact, it is well known among orchid enthusiasts that when you find one orchid species on the downs there is a very good chance of finding several more near by. Some of the species are extremely abundant. Often the tall waving areas of erect brome grass are coloured pink or lilac with the innumerable spikes of fragrant orchid or common spotted orchid. Elsewhere the deeper pink spikes of the pyramidal orchid impart their own tinge to the vegetation. In the shorter turf we may sometimes find the musk orchid almost covering the ground with its pale yellow-green spikes, while in yet another place the deep or paler magenta spikes of the green-veined orchid stud the ground in all directions. Much less conspicuous are the early spider orchid, fly orchid, frog orchid and autumn ladies' tresses. The downs are at their best in June when the great majority of species are in flower.

Old chalk pits or diggings seem to provide especially favourable habitats for orchids, possibly because the great local variation in conditions as regards drainage, slope, nature of soil, etc., must somewhere provide a suitable niche for each species. Be that as it may, such places often yield many kinds of orchid, especially where the turf is short, and not absolutely continuous. In particular the bee orchid, early and late spider orchids and musk orchid are frequently found in old chalk pits or the irregular ground associated with past superficial digging of chalk.

Apart from the species already mentioned, which all grow naturally in dry places, and are therefore at home on the downs, one may occasionally come across others which normally inhabit wetter places. The marsh helleborine (*Epipactis palustris*), for instance, has been found growing in quite dry spots high up on the downs in Wiltshire and Kent, while several species of marsh orchid have been recorded from similar places. These plants, including such species as *Orchis praetermissa* and *O. latifolia*, are probably derived from odd seeds blown up from damper habitats in the valleys below. There is no evidence that the marsh orchids can persist in these places ; on the other hand, the marsh helleborine, owing to its well-developed vegetative means of spreading, is a decidedly persistent plant.

Closely allied to the chalk grassland are the similar areas on Oolitic, Liassic and similar limestones to the north and west of the chalk areas. These are slightly less rich in orchid species, but those which occur may be very abundant. Good examples may be found on the Purbeck Hills in Dorset, the Polden Hills and elsewhere in Somerset, the Cotswolds in Gloucestershire, and the neighbourhood of Barnack in Northamptonshire. *Orchis fuchsii*, *Anacamptis*, *Gymnadenia*, *Listera ovata*, *Platanthera chlorantha*, *Spiranthes spiralis* and *Ophrys apifera* are common in most of the areas mentioned, while many of the other chalk orchids occur more locally. The early spider orchid (*Ophrys sphegodes*) is especially abundant on parts of the Purbeck limestones (Pl. 2, p. 47).

Farther north we find extensive grassland areas on the Carboniferous and Magnesian limestones on and near the Pennines of Derbyshire, Yorkshire and Lancashire, and also in the Lake District and Durham. The grass species are similar to those farther south with the addition of *Sesleria caerulea*. A striking feature in the Derbyshire Dales is the occurrence of *Orchis mascula*, the early purple orchid, which in June often tints the steep grassy limestone slopes with its purple spikes. The orchid species mentioned just above are all found in these grasslands, as well as *Orchis ustulata*, *Platanthera bifolia*, *Ophrys muscifera* and *Coeloglossum viride*. An interesting additional species, which occurs occasionally, but becomes more abundant on similar soils farther north and in Scotland, is the small white orchid (*Gymnadenia albida*, Pl. 23b, p. 202). This species is also to be found on the limited areas of limestone grassland in Wales. In all these regions, as indicated earlier, orchids are best developed where grazing is at a minimum ; consequently the enclosures preserved for hay often yield the finest displays of orchid species. It may be possible to find seven or eight different species growing more or less together in quite a small area. On the higher more exposed regions orchids do not flourish to the same extent, but this may be due to the washing of soluble salts from the soil.

Limestone Pavements and Cliffs

The hard rock of the Carboniferous limestones, both in the Pennines and in Ireland, often weathers slowly to form steep cliffs, or in places more or less flat rocky areas with little or no overlying soil, that formed being carried away by water action. Soil is retained only in small pockets in the rock, or in the vertical joints between the individual rock masses. These so-called limestone pavements cover extensive stretches in the Ingleborough region of Yorkshire and elsewhere in the Pennines, and, in perhaps even greater extent, in the western Irish counties of Clare, Galway and Mayo. The latter forms part of the Burren Hills, which is one of the most interesting botanical regions in the British Isles. The vegetation of these pavements consists of a mixture of woody plants and herbs, the former predominating in protected places or where there is more soil, the latter in more exposed situations. This herbaceous vegetation has features in common with the limestone grassland on the one hand, and the ashwoods on the other, the proportion of grasses being lower than in true grassland. Most of the common orchids of the limestone grassland are to be found in the rock crevices and patches of soil, such as *Orchis mascula*, *Spiranthes spiralis*, *Ophrys apifera* and many others. In the Pennine region we find also the dark red helleborine (*Epipactis atrorubens*, Pl. 11, p. 138) and broad-leaved helleborine (*E. helleborine*) in such places. The former is characteristic of limestone cliffs and rocky slopes, where it occurs both in the open and in the scrubs already described. Both species also occur locally on the extensive rock screes below the limestone cliffs, once these have become more or less stable. Other orchids are extremely rare on such screes as their rooting systems are not suitable for growth in this type of habitat. The tough rhizome and comparatively long roots of the helleborines enable them to establish themselves in these loose stony soils.

In the Burren region of western Ireland, in addition to the fly orchid, bee orchid, fragrant orchid, autumn ladies' tresses, dark red helleborine and early purple orchid, there are two especially interesting orchids. The common spotted orchid is replaced in this region by its Irish sub-species *o'kellyi* (Pl. 40, p. 267), which is a characteristic plant of the limestone grassland and pavements of this region. Even more remarkable is the little dense-flowered orchid (*Neotinea intacta*, Pl. 28, p. 219), which is not found elsewhere in our islands. Indeed the limestone flora in this region is extremely rich and varied, in other species as well as orchids, and worthy of a visit by all nature-lovers.

OTHER GRASSLANDS

There are many kinds of grasslands on non-calcareous soils, depending on the dampness or dryness of the soil, the degree of acidity of the soil, the depth of peat developed, and, superimposed on all the other variations, the extent of man's interference, mainly in terms of grazing, manuring and cutting.

As already mentioned, the greater the interference by man, the fewer the orchids which may be found. It must also be remembered that orchids mostly prefer less acid soils. Consequently the grasslands richest in orchids are those on neutral or faintly acid soils, in which grazing and trampling are at a minimum. Cutting for hay is less destructive, since the plants may have set some seed at least by the time mowing takes place, while the base of the plant is not much injured. The occurrence of orchids in most of these grasslands is often determined by the past history of each area concerned. Where woodland formerly covered the ground, as in many places, one may find orchid species persisting from earlier woodland conditions. This is true of both lowland and upland grasslands, and on many types of non-calcareous soils.

In the south there are large stretches of what is termed neutral pasture or grassland on the clay and silty soils. The grasses here are of moderate size, consisting of soft brome (*Bromus hordeaceus*), cocksfoot (*Dactylis glomerata*), Yorkshire fog (*Holcus lanatus*), meadow foxtail (*Alopecurus pratensis*), red fescue (*Festuca rubra*) and many others, together with a varied series of flowering herbs. The green-veined orchid (*Orchis morio*) is a common though local plant in such places, being especially partial to fields containing cowslips. Other orchid species are common spotted orchid, both the butterfly orchids and, where the turf is shorter, the autumn ladies' tresses. Where the drainage is not very good rushes may occur, and with them the common marsh orchid (*Orchis praetermissa*). Large areas of neutral grassland are also to be found in central Ireland, especially on glacial deposits. Lighter, particularly sandy, soils are usually rather more acid in nature, and here we find a grass-heath type of community, which contains very few orchids apart from *O. ericetorum*. This grass-heath often passes over to true heath vegetation with heather and similar plants.

In the hilly country of the west and north there is usually a belt of grassland between the more intensively cultivated ground in the valleys, and the moorland vegetation above 1,000 ft. altitude or so. This grassland region is more or less grazed or grown for hay, and provides the best ground for orchids off the limestone rocks. The rough pasture, especially at a higher level, consists largely of bent-grasses (*Agrostis*), *Sieglingia decumbens*, fescues (*Festuca*), etc., and is rather poor in orchids, especially where sheep are the animals concerned ; cattle are not so destructive although they do much damage to orchids by their treading. In Wales, northern England and parts of Scotland the small meadows attached to outlying farms at about 600 to 900 feet above sea level, or perhaps higher in the more elevated mountain areas, are comparatively rich in orchid species, which often occur in immense numbers. Among these we find fragrant orchid, heath spotted orchid, common spotted orchid, greater and lesser butterfly orchids, frog orchid, small white orchid, early purple orchid, common twayblade and, in wet spots, the dwarf purple orchid and early marsh orchid. The soil in these meadows is neutral or slightly acid, but there is considerable variation in different places owing to the irregular topography of many of the fields. Where the soil becomes more acid, and especially where bog-moss becomes at all common, the number of orchids present is much reduced.

The damper grasslands on peaty soils, composed either of mat-grass (*Nardus stricta*) or of purple moor grass (*Molinia caerulea*), are very poor in orchid species. The same is true for the most part of the high-level hill pasture or open grasslands above 1,500 feet altitude in Wales and elsewhere. The heath spotted orchid (*Orchis ericetorum*, Pl. 41, p. 274) is the sole species to be found in extensive stretches of such grasslands, but some of the other species mentioned already may occur locally in favourable situations.

ORCHIDS OF HEATH AND MOORLAND

The plant communities here dealt with are developed on non-calcareous soil covered with a variable depth of raw-humus or peat. In the drier parts of the British Isles the thickness of peat is not great, and these areas support heath vegetation. Where the rainfall is higher the peat formation as a general rule is much more extensive and deeper, leading to the development of moorlands. It should be understood, however, that there is no hard and fast line of division between the two types, which may often, due to local topography or other factors, occur in close proximity or may pass gradually into one another.

Heath and moorland vegetation is composed mainly of dwarf shrubs belonging mostly to the family *Ericaceae* (heather, heaths) on the one hand, and coarse grasses and sedges (cotton grasses, deer grass, purple moor grass, etc.) on the other. All types are comparatively poor in orchids, it being possible to walk for miles over such vegetation without seeing a single orchid. This is particularly true where the peat is deep and cotton grasses (*Eriophorum* spp.) are the chief plants.

There is a great variety in moorland and heath vegetation, depending upon the degree of development of peat, the topography of the land, or the underlying rock, among other factors. Perhaps the most abundant plant is the common heather (*Calluna vulgaris*), which is found in areas with shallow or deep peat, and is as characteristic of the dry heaths of eastern and southern England as of the extensive moors of the north and west. The heather often covers extensive areas with scarcely any admixture of other species, except for mosses and lichens covering the ground between the individual heather plants. Very few orchids occur in pure heather, a notable exception being the tiny lesser twayblade (*Listera cordata*). This very interesting, but extremely inconspicuous orchid is usually to be found growing in the moss cushions, and is only visible when the heather bushes are parted. As it is a northern species it has only rarely been recorded from southern heaths and moorlands.

Very often, however, heather is mixed with heaths (*Erica cinerea* and *E. tetralix*), bilberry (*Vaccinium myrtillus*) and various heath or moorland grasses. In such places the heath spotted orchid is not infrequent, while other orchids occurring here are lesser butterfly orchid (*Platanthera bifolia*, Pl. 25b, p. 210), fragrant orchid (*Gymnadenia conopsea*) and common twayblade. The early purple orchid and greater butterfly orchid may also be found occasionally, but the former usually indicates the previous occurrence of woodland.

Other types of moorland, such as the extensive moors of cotton grass and deer grass (*Scirpus caespitosus*) on deep peat, and the higher altitude moors of crowberry (*Empetrum nigrum*), bilberry and cowberry (*Vaccinium vitis-idaea*), are practically devoid of orchids except for the ubiquitous *Orchis ericetorum*.

In damp situations on moorlands and heaths, both in the south and north, the deep coloured variety of the early marsh orchid (*Orchis latifolia* var. *pulchella*) is an abundant species locally. It favours wet hollows where the heather is mixed with cross-leaved heath (*Erica tetralix*), or not too acid bogs. In the south the common marsh orchid (*O. praetermissa*) is sometimes found in similar places among heath vegetation on sandy soils, but it is more properly an inhabitant of marshes and fens.

ORCHIDS OF FENS, MARSHES AND BOGS

To many people the terms marshes, fens and bogs are more or less interchangeable, merely indicating very wet places with tall rushy or grassy vegetation. Botanically, however, the terms are applied much more exactly to describe plant communities growing under quite different conditions from one another. Two factors are important, firstly, the presence or absence of peat in any quantity, and secondly, the nature of the drainage or ground water, whether it be acid, neutral or alkaline.

The term bog should be applied only to places where the ground water is more or less acid and there is a marked development of peat.

PLATE VII

E. J. Bedford

Flowering stems of Red Helleborine, *Cephalanthera rubra*, from Gloucestershire ($\times \frac{2}{3}$)

PLATE VIII

C. Thomas

a. Side view of column and ovary of Violet Helleborine, *Epipactis purpurata* (left) and Broad-leaved Helleborine, *E. helleborine* (right) (×3½)

C. Thomas

b. Front, back and side views of column and ovary of Slender-lipped Helleborine, *Epipactis leptochila*. Note the distinct stalk to the anther in the right-hand picture (×3½)

Such communities are only found on non-calcareous soils, and usually in regions of high rainfall, although they may occur locally, where the drainage is bad, in drier regions, as for example the New Forest in Hampshire and Ashdown Forest in Sussex. Bogs are therefore usually associated with the moorlands and heaths of acid soils, occurring where the drainage is defective. In Ireland, owing to the consistently damp climate, bogs may cover large areas of land, even on slopes or hills.

In contradistinction to the acid bogs associated with moorlands and heaths, marshes and fens occur where the drainage water is either neutral or distinctly alkaline. This may be due to the limy nature of the soil where the marshes are situated or, on the other hand, the water may have been brought by streams or rivers from calcareous soils although the marsh itself is not on such. Marshes usually occur on mineral soils, whereas fens are formed on peat of varying depth. In these latter the natural acid nature of the peat is neutralised by the calcareous drainage water, producing a type of vegetation quite unlike that of acid bogs. There are all intermediates between marshes and fens, depending upon the degree of peat formation, and the orchids are usually common to both types of vegetation. Normally marshes and fens are wet for the greater part of the year, but they may dry out in dry summers and some nearly always do.

Fen communities are best developed in lowland areas, because it is usually only there that suitable conditions exist for their formation. They may, however, be formed in lakes at higher altitudes. The formation of peat is normally associated with continuous wet conditions, such as exist at the edges of lakes, by the lower courses of rivers and in similar places. Marshes are rather more widely distributed, either in the lowlands, or in upland regions where the drainage is defective ; that is, usually by streams, at the edges of lakes, or at the bottoms of valleys. Good examples of fens are found in the region of the Norfolk Broads, in the Somerset Levels, in parts of northern Lancashire and in many parts of the central Irish plain. The area of fen and marsh land is continually shrinking, owing to more efficient drainage and more intense agricultural exploitation of the country.

FENS

These are developed on peat where the drainage water is either

W.O.B.

neutral or alkaline in nature. In the most typical examples, as in East Anglia, the drainage is from the highly soluble chalk rocks, and the water is very calcareous. The vegetation in fens consists of a mixture of tall grasses, rushes, sedges and mixed flowering plants. There is a great variety in the vegetation, depending on the level of the water, different species being more abundant in drier or wetter places respectively. Common grass-like plants in the fens are the tall sedge *Cladium mariscus*, tussock sedge (*Carex paniculata*), soft rush (*Juncus effusus*), blunt-flowered rush (*J. obtusiflorus*), common reed (*Phragmites communis*), reed meadow grass (*Glyceria maxima*), reed canary grass (*Phalaris arundinacea*), and purple moor grass (*Molinia caerulea*). Among other plants are meadow-sweet (*Filipendula ulmaria*), yellow flag (*Iris pseudacorus*), marsh marigold (*Caltha palustris*), royal fern (*Osmunda regalis*) and horsetails (*Equisetum*), but the fen vegetation is very rich and varies considerably from one district to another.

The commonest orchids belong to the group known collectively as marsh orchids. These are often very abundant, occurring in such numbers as to colour the vegetation locally. The most widespread is the early marsh orchid (*Orchis latifolia*, Pl. 42, p. 275), which is found in such habitats throughout the British Isles. The pale yellow variety *ochroleuca* is a true fen plant, being confined to the East Anglian fens so far as Britain is concerned. In the south the common marsh orchid (*O. praetermissa*, Pl. 44a, p. 283) is also abundant, the two species not infrequently occurring together, though they are not usually in full flower at the same time. A less commonly occurring marsh orchid is the Wicklow marsh orchid (*O. traunsteinerioides*, Pl. 38b, p. 259), which is found in some fen areas in England as well as in eastern Ireland ; some authorities think that this is merely a variety of some other species. Another orchid widely distributed in fens is the marsh helleborine (*Epipactis palustris*, Pl. 8, p. 127), which is a characteristic plant of reed-swamps and similar types of vegetation ; it is especially common in the fenny marshes of the central Irish plain. *E. palustris* is usually a rather local plant, but is often abundant where it does occur owing to its creeping mode of growth. In the East Anglian fens we find the very rare and rather inconspicuous fen orchid (*Liparis loeselii*, Pl. 48a, p. 303), which occurs only in the peaty soil of true fens, though it prefers some admixture of sand. In the Irish fen areas around Lough Neagh the rare Irish ladies' tresses (*Spiranthes romanzoffiana*, Pl. 18, p. 175) is an interesting plant ; it can, however, also occur in marshes or bogs with neutral or slightly acid ground water.

As might be expected from the nature of the distinction between fens and bogs, we not infrequently find regions where the vegetation is intermediate in character. Indeed even in the fen areas proper, bog conditions may be set up when the natural growth of the peat carries the ground surface above the level of the alkaline drainage water. The upper peat layer becomes acid and supports a bog vegetation, including such orchids as lesser butterfly orchid and heath spotted orchid. In other places, where the soil water is neutral or perhaps slightly acid, we do not find true bogs, but rather a mixed vegetation which possesses some of the features of both fen and bog. The common plants are sweet gale (*Myrica gale*), purple moor grass, meadow-sweet, sedges (*Carex panicea, C. pulicaris*, etc.), and the larger cotton grasses (*Eriophorum latifolium* and *E. angustifolium*). Common orchids here are heath spotted orchid, lesser butterfly orchid, fragrant orchid, and early marsh orchid, especially the deep coloured variety (*Orchis latifolia* var. *pulchella*). In Ireland we sometimes find the Irish ladies' tresses and Irish marsh orchid (*O. occidentalis*) in such localities. The very rare summer ladies' tresses (*Spiranthes aestivalis*) occurs in several such intermediate areas in the New Forest. In the north and west we also find the dwarf purple orchid (*Orchis purpurella*) growing on deep peat with *Molinia* and *Myrica*, but this species is usually an inhabitant of marshes.

BOGS

In very acid conditions the peat is formed almost entirely by bog-mosses (*Sphagnum* spp.) and here we get true bogs. These are frequently actively growing in height and often very soft and treacherous. With the bog-mosses are sedges (*Carex* spp., *Rhynchospora* spp., *Scirpus caespitosus*), cotton grasses (*Eriophorum* spp.), heather (*Calluna*), heath (*Erica tetralix*), cranberry (*Oxycoccus*), bog asphodel (*Narthecium ossifragum*) and other dwarf shrubs and flowering herbs.

The characteristic orchid of such bogs is the tiny bog orchid (*Hammarbya paludosa*, Pl. 48b, p. 303), which grows on the surface of the sopping *Sphagnum* cushions, often accompanied by such plants as sundews (*Drosera* spp.) and butterworts (*Pinguicula* spp.). The lesser twayblade (*Listera cordata*) is also sometimes to be found in these bogs. In the drier parts we find the heath spotted orchid and lesser butterfly orchid, but orchids are not so abundant here as in less acid-loving vegetation.

MARSHES

Marshes differ from the two types of habitat just described in the complete absence or poor development of peat. There are, however, places where marshes pass into fens on the one hand, and into bogs on the other, depending on the nature of the drainage water. Marshes occur on any soils where the drainage is defective, especially on heavy soils such as clays and marls. They are also to be found along valleys of streams or rivers, either in the lowlands or in upland regions. Naturally there is a great variety of marshes, depending on the soil, the amount of lime in the water, the nature of the drainage, etc.

The simplest type of marsh is just a damp hollow in a field occupied by rushes, either hard rush (*Juncus inflexus*) or soft rushes (*J. effusus* or *J. conglomeratus*), together with other damp-loving plants such as lesser spearwort (*Ranunculus flammula*) and cuckoo flower (*Cardamine pratensis*). At the other extreme are extensive marshes covering many acres and often passing almost imperceptibly into fens or, more rarely, bogs. These marshes are very rich in species, for although rushes are usually the most abundant plants, we also find yellow flag, meadow-sweet, great hairy willow-herb (*Epilobium hirsutum*), marsh marigold, horsetails, cuckoo flower, ragged robin (*Lychnis flos-cuculi*), water mint (*Mentha aquatica*), as well as various kinds of sedges and grasses.

The marsh orchids are again the commonest orchids to be found in these habitats, the two most widespread being the common marsh orchid (*Orchis praetermissa*), which is a frequent inhabitant of marshy fields or meadows in southern England, and the dwarf purple orchid (*O. purpurella*, Pl. 43b, p. 282), which is characteristic of upland marshes in Wales, Scotland and parts of Ireland. In western Ireland the Irish marsh orchid (*O. occidentalis*) replaces these two species in marshes and also in fen vegetation. In the limestone region of Mayo, Galway and Clare the flecked marsh orchid (*O. cruenta*) occurs in the marshes at the edges of the highly calcareous lakes, usually with the black bog-rush (*Schoenus nigricans*). The early marsh orchid (*O. latifolia*) is not so common in the absence of peat, but it occurs locally in marshes in various parts of the country. In marshes in southern England, especially in the south-west, we find the so-called leopard marsh orchid

(*O. pardalina*, Pl. 44b, p. 283), a tall plant with brilliantly coloured flowers, usually occurring with *O. praetermissa*. Apart from marsh orchids there are the spotted orchids (*O. fuchsii* and *O. ericetorum*), the former usually on more alkaline soils, the latter on slightly acid soils, but sometimes both together. Where either of these is present numerous hybrids between them and the various marsh orchids are almost invariably to be found, some of them being very tall and vigorous. In the upland marshes in Wales, northern England and Scotland hybrids between *O. purpurella* and *O. ericetorum* are very common, being present in practically every marsh where the dwarf purple orchid grows. The marsh helleborine (*Epipactis palustris*) is sometimes found in marshes, though it is really a fen plant ; it occurs frequently in the limy grassy marshes of the central Irish plain. The dense-flowered or marsh fragrant orchid (*Gymnadenia conopsea* var. *densiflora*, Pl. 27, p. 218) is another characteristic inhabitant of marshes. Less frequently one comes across twayblade and greater butterfly orchid, but these are scarcely true marsh plants.

ORCHIDS OF SAND DUNES

The extensive sand-dune areas around our coasts, though looking rather unpromising as habitats for orchids, are nevertheless often quite rich in these plants. This is no doubt because sea-sand frequently, if not invariably, contains large numbers of the shells of marine animals, and is consequently comparatively rich in lime. It therefore provides a habitat which in many respects is similar to that of limestone soils, both where dry and where wet.

Most sand-dune systems consist of series of higher ridges alternating with low valleys (slacks), though the regularity of the arrangement of ridges and valleys varies much in different systems. The vegetation of the ridges and the slacks is very distinct in most cases, the former consisting of various types of grassland, whereas the latter often takes the form of marshes of various kinds.

The flora of sand-dune ridges, the actual dunes themselves, depends upon their age, the most recently formed dunes nearest the sea carrying a very sparse vegetation, whereas the older ones farther inland are consolidated to varying degrees, and bear an often dense grassy turf. In general, we may say that the more stabilised the dune is the more orchids we are likely to find on it.

The seaward less stabilised dune ridges usually bear an open vegetation of marram grass (*Ammophila arenaria*) accompanied by varying amounts of other grasses and flowering herbs, these increasing in quantity and species with greater shelter and stabilisation. On such dunes we find few orchids, among them the bee orchid (*Ophrys apifera*), which I have seen in Wales high up among relatively sparse marram grass and other plants, and the pyramidal orchid. In some Scottish dune systems we find the coral-root (*Corallorhiza trifida*, Fig. 19b, p. 190) in rather similar habitats.

It is, however, the landward lower and much more stabilised dunes that provide the most favourable spots for orchids. These dunes are usually covered with a more or less dense turf of dwarf grasses, though marram may still occur in isolated tufts or stems. Fescues (*Festuca* spp.) and bent grasses (*Agrostis* spp.) are abundant, together with common meadow grass (*Poa pratensis*), sea timothy (*Phleum arenarium*) and other dwarf species. Flowering herbs include rest harrow (*Ononis repens*), bird's foot trefoil (*Lotus corniculatus*), hemlock stork's bill (*Erodium cicutarium*), and many others. Where the grasses are less continuous numerous dwarf annual plants are abundant. The orchids in such habitats include frog orchid (*Coeloglossum viride*), bee orchid, autumn ladies' tresses (*Spiranthes spiralis*), pyramidal orchid (*Anacamptis pyramidalis*), early purple orchid, twayblade, and sometimes other species. The frog orchid is often abundant on these stabilised dunes, exhibiting great variety in size, colour, the length of the bracts and other features. Two rare orchids occurring locally in such places are the lizard orchid (*Himantoglossum*), of which there was formerly a large colony on dunes in Somerset and which was even more abundant this summer in a similar habitat in Kent, and the dense-flowered orchid (*Neotinea*), which has been recorded from calcareous dunes in western Ireland.

On the landward side sand dunes often abut on to vegetation developed on other soils, and in this region, which is often intermediate in character, we may find other orchids. For instance, where heathland adjoins dunes, the heath spotted orchid may be found on the innermost dune areas. In many of the Hebridean islands the most stabilised inner portions of the sand dunes are the special habitat for the local sub-species of spotted orchid, the Hebridean orchid (*Orchis fuchsii* sub-sp. *hebridensis*, Pl. 39, p. 266), which is much more abundant here than anywhere else. The deep indian-red form of the early marsh orchid (*O. latifolia* var. *coccinea*) may also be found in such places, though it is more common in the dune slacks.

In the valleys or slacks conditions are much damper than on the ridges, so much so that extensive marshes are often formed. Elsewhere there may be coarse grassland or even scrub. A special feature of dune valleys, and also even of the more stabilised flatter areas, are the low secondary dunes formed around the plants of creeping willow (*Salix repens*). These are in the form of low mounds a foot or so in height due to the accumulation of sand among the much branched stems of the willow. They are much damper than the *Ammophila* dunes and harbour many other plants among the willow. A common plant on these dunes is *Orchis latifolia* var. *coccinea*, which seems to be able to grow in drier places than the ordinary forms of the species. Other orchids here are common spotted orchid, twayblade and marsh helleborine. On the Lancashire dunes and also in Anglesey we find the dune helleborine (*Epipactis dunensis*, Pl. 10, p. 131), the creeping willow dunes being its usual habitat there. The dwarf purple orchid is also found on such dunes in Wales and Scotland, particularly in the damper parts.

The marshes in the slacks are often very extensive. The soil may be entirely sandy, but more frequently there is a proportion, sometimes high, of mud or silt, due to the fact that the dunes were originally formed by the deposition of blown sand on former salt or freshwater marshes. Owing to the admixture of sand, especially in the surface layers, the habitat in these marshes is rather different from that in ordinary freshwater marshes. Often maritime species are present (species of *Juncus* and *Scirpus*), remnants from brackish conditions, as well as true freshwater species. The vegetation varies very much from place to place. The most frequent orchids are the marsh helleborine and early marsh orchid (usually the variety *coccinea*). Others are common marsh orchid (*Orchis praetermissa*) in southern localities, including South Wales, and dwarf purple orchid in the north and in other parts of Wales. In the Hebrides the Hebridean orchid is also found in the dune marshes, though it is more abundant in drier places. In several localities in South Wales a special western form of the rare fen orchid (*Liparis loeselii* var. *ovata*, Pl. XXIVa, p. 315) occurs in the dune slacks. Altogether the flora of these marshes has many features in common with that of fens, the orchid species being mostly found in both types of vegetation.

CHAPTER 5

CLASSIFICATION

IN COMMON with other groups of plants the Orchids are classified chiefly on the basis of the structure of the flowers, and particularly of the male and female reproductive organs. These, it will be remembered, are joined together to form the column, the female organs also including the ovary, which is below the rest of the flower. The ovary itself shows little variation, having usually a single cavity with the ovules borne on three ridges along the walls. In the tropical Asiatic lady's slippers, however, there are three separate cavities. The stigmas, which are also part of the column, are on the other hand modified very considerably, and exhibit great diversity in different orchids. In most cases only two of them are fertile, the third stigma, which is placed in the median plane of the flower (the plane running from the front to the back), being usually modified to form a special structure or rostellum. The fertile stigmas may be separately placed one on each side of the flower, as in the pyramidal orchid (*Anacamptis*, Fig. 11A, p. 50) or the fragrant orchid (*Gymnadenia conopsea*), or they may be joined together to form a single stigma of varying shape (Fig. 7B, p. 33). In the large tropical genus *Habenaria*, in which many of our orchids have been erroneously placed, the stigmas are in the form of stalked structures projecting from the front of the column. These different arrangements of the stigmas are, however, of only secondary importance in the general classification of the family. The modifications of the rostellum are of much greater importance, because this structure plays a direct part in most of the pollination mechanisms, either as a separate entity, or by producing, in conjunction with the stamen, the pollinarium or pollen-conveying apparatus.

It is, however, the male organs which provide the most satisfactory means of primary classification, both the stamens themselves and the pollen which they produce. As mentioned earlier on, there are only one or two stamens in each flower in the orchid family instead of the six found in the allied lily family. The occurrence of one or two stamens determines the two main divisions in the family, those species possessing two stamens, such as the lady's slipper (*Cypripedium*) and its relatives, forming the sub-family *Diandrae* (Fig. 7 A, p. 33), whereas the vast majority of orchids, in which there is only one stamen, constitute the *Monandrae* (Fig. 7 B).

The stamens in the *Diandrae* resemble much more in appearance those found in the lily family than does the single stamen of the *Monandrae*, and this relationship is underlined by the nature of the pollen in the two groups. In the *Diandrae* the pollen grains are all separate, though buried in a sticky paste so as to make them adhere to the stigma of another flower, whereas in the *Monandrae* the pollen is aggregated to form the variously shaped pollinia. For these reasons the *Diandrae* is considered to be less highly evolved than the other sub-family, and to occupy a more or less intermediate position between the *Monandrae* and the lily family. The hundred or so species of the *Diandrae* are widely spread in the north temperate zone, including both Old and New Worlds, and also in the tropics of America and Asia extending as far east as New Guinea, but do not occur in either Africa or Australia. The tropical types, especially those native in Asia, are very commonly cultivated, and include some of the most popular of hothouse orchids. All the species have the lady's slipper sort of lip (Fig. 8, p. 43), but the tropical ones have very different leaves and general method of growth. One of the Central American species (*Selenipedium chica*) has the distinction of being the tallest of orchids (excluding certain climbing varieties), the slender cane-like stems reaching the astonishing height of 10–15 feet, at the top of which is borne the flower-spike.

The two stamens in the *Diandrae* are placed one on each side of the column (Fig. 7 A, p. 33), whereas the single stamen of the *Monandrae* occupies a more or less central position (Fig. 7 B) towards the true front of the flower. It should be pointed out that the flowers in most orchids are twisted through half a circle (180 degrees) by the spiral twisting of the flower stalk or ovary, so that the true back of the flower, where the lip is situated, is brought to the front (Fig. 5 B, p. 30; Pl. I, p. 18). By the same process the real front of the flower is carried round to the back, and consequently the stamen is usually to be seen in this position. In some orchids, for example the spurred coral-root (*Epipogium*), no twisting has taken place, and consequently the lip is uppermost at the top or back of the flower. In the bog orchid (*Hammarbya*) also the lip is uppermost, but in this instance the flower stalk has twisted through a whole circle (360 degrees), so as to bring the lip back to its starting point ! In both these plants the stamen is towards the apparent front or bottom of the flower, which is really its correct position. It will be seen that there are only a few examples of British orchids in which the lip is uppermost, but, on the other hand, this type of arrangement is not uncommon in orchids growing in other parts of the world, and is found in genera which are very diverse as regards both floral structure and general appearance.

The single stamen of the *Monandrae*, which consists almost entirely of the pollen-bearing portion (anther), there being no very obvious stalk (filament), is always borne near the top of the column. It may, however, be attached to the latter either by its bottom or by its top, this apparently trivial difference being actually of fundamental importance, and distinguishing the two main divisions of the *Monandrae*.

That group (*Basitonae*) in which the anther is attached by its front or base includes more than half the total number of our native orchids, such as those belonging to the genera *Orchis* and *Ophrys* and the butterfly orchids with their allies. In these plants the stamen occupies the front of the column, usually in an upright position, and is attached so firmly and intimately to it that it cannot be separated (Fig. 10 A, p. 48). The sticky discs (viscidia), by means of which the pollinia are removed, are at the bottom of the stamen and just above, or on each side of, the entrance to the spur when such is present.

The pollinia in the *Basitonae* are rather complicated in structure (Fig. 5 C, p. 30). The viscidium is at the end of a stalk (caudicle) which is slender below, but is thickened in a club-shaped manner in the upper part. The numerous pollen masses radiate out from this thickened part, to which they are each attached by a very slender elastic thread or threads. The stalk is in all cases a part of the stamen itself, though the disc, on the other hand, is a detached portion of the third stigma or rostellum and therefore not derived from the stamen. With very few exceptions the members of this group are terrestrial plants rooted directly in the soil, being in this respect in striking contrast to the predominantly epiphytic *Acrotonae*. Saprophytic forms are also very rare in the *Basitonae*, although a few such are known among exotic species. Including thirty British species, the *Basitonae* number about 1,500 species altogether, spread throughout the world, though commoner in the north than in the south temperate regions.

Those orchids which have the stamen attached by its top or apex constitute the *Acrotonae*. This group is much larger than the *Basitonae* (about 16,000 species), and there is a correspondingly greater variety in the detailed structure of the stamen and of the pollinia. In the helleborines (*Epipactis* and *Cephalanthera*), ladies' tresses (*Spiranthes* and *Goodyera*), twayblades (*Listera*, Fig. 9B, p. 45), etc., the stamen is usually found on the back of the column, the viscidia, where present, being at its summit. As the stamen is only attached by a narrow stalk, it can easily be separated from the remainder of the column, though it does not fall off naturally. The pollinia here are rather soft and readily break up to form a powdery mass, while there are no central stalk or special attachment threads.

In the fen orchid (*Liparis*), bog orchid (*Hammarbya*) and coral-roots (*Epipogium* and *Corallorhiza*), on the other hand, the stamen is perched on, or not very far from, the very tip of the column. In most of these genera the anther forms a sort of little cap covering the pollinia, attached by a very short stalk and readily falling off when the stamen is mature. The pollinia in these plants are rather variable, but agree in being of a waxy consistency. They may possess caudicles, and sometimes viscidia, but in none of our native species is the structure so complicated as in the *Basitonae*. Although there are only a few orchids with this second type of stamen, termed operculate, among our native representatives of the *Acrotonae*, the great majority of exotic species, including the beautiful cultivated *Cymbidiums*, *Cattleyas* and *Odontoglossums*, come into this category. In many of the exotic members of the group the pollinia are very remarkable, rivalling those of the *Basitonae* in the complexity of their structure.

The *Acrotonae* undoubtedly contain orchids with the simplest and most primitive type of flower structure, such, for instance, as is found in the genus *Cephalanthera* and its allies. These plants possess comparatively simple pollination mechanisms, while their vegetative parts also show few, if any, of the special features found elsewhere in the family, for example, stem or root tubers. It is very interesting to note that vegetatively many of these orchids closely resemble tropical plants belonging to other families, and it is evident that we have here indications of the general course of evolution of the orchid family from plants with flower structure very similar to that in the daffodil or lily families. From such simply organised forms we may trace various lines of evolution leading to the highly developed members of the *Basitonae*, on the one hand, and the more specialised groups of the *Acrotonae*, on the other.

On the whole the former group is best suited for growth in grasslands, and is therefore well represented in our temperate grasslands. Its members are, however, also common in grasslands in tropical countries, particularly the numerous species of the genus *Habenaria*, in which some of our British plants have been included in the past. The orchid flora of the more temperate parts of the Union of South Africa also includes numerous representatives of the *Basitonae*, which in floral complexity can vie with, or perhaps even surpass, any species among the north temperate species of the group. The members of the *Basitonae* are, however, by no means precluded from growing in woods or other shady places, as a cursory glance at the list of our British representatives will readily prove. The early purple orchid (*Orchis mascula*) and greater butterfly orchid (*Platanthera chlorantha*) are two common species which frequently occur in woods, often in considerable shade. Nevertheless there are very few exotic species epiphytic in habit, and even these exhibit no special characters fitting them for life in such a remarkable situation.

The *Acrotonae*, on the other hand, although they also include a number of highly developed terrestrial species, particularly in Australia, contain numerous genera which have become specially adapted to an epiphytic existence in the extensive forests of the tropics, where the group reaches its greatest development. The British species of this group are all terrestrial plants, though they exhibit a tendency to grow in woods, some of them in very dense shade. The great majority of saprophytic orchids belong to the *Acrotonae*, our orchid flora containing three saprophytic species among the twenty-three members of this group. In view of the absence of the highly evolved epiphytic types from these islands, it is not surprising that the British species which exhibit most complexity are all to be found among the *Basitonae*, the *Acrotonae* being represented by relatively simply organised species.

The following synopsis shows the relationship of our British orchids to the scheme of classification discussed above, and indicates the affinities of the various genera and species. The scientific and English names of each species are given.

SYNOPSIS OF CLASSIFICATION OF BRITISH ORCHIDS

SUB-FAMILY A. Diandrae

TRIBE. Cypripedieae

1. *Cypripedium calceolus* L. Lady's Slipper

SUB-FAMILY B. Monandrae

DIVISION A. Acrotonae

TRIBE 1. Neottieae

Sub-tribe i. Cephalantherinae

2. *Cephalanthera damasonium* (Mill.) Druce
   Large White Helleborine
3. *C. longifolia* (L.) Fritsch Sword-leaved Helleborine
4. *C. rubra* (L.) Rich. Red Helleborine

Sub-tribe ii. Epipactinae

5. *Epipactis palustris* (L.) Crantz Marsh Helleborine
6. *E. helleborine* (L.) Crantz Broad-leaved Helleborine
7. *E. dunensis* (T. and T. A. Steph.) Godf. Dune Helleborine
8. *E. atrorubens* (Hoffm.) Schult. Dark Red Helleborine
9. *E. purpurata* Sm. Violet Helleborine
10. *E. leptochila* (Godf.) Godf. Green-leaved Helleborine
11. *E. pendula* C. Thomas Pendulous-flowered Heleborine
12. *E. vectensis* (T. and T. A. Steph.) Brooke and Rose
    Isle of Wight Helleborine

Sub-tribe iii. Listerinae

13. *Listera ovata* (L.) R.Br. Common Twayblade
14. *L. cordata* (L.) R.Br. Lesser Twayblade
15. *Neottia nidus-avis* (L.) Rich. Bird's Nest Orchid

Sub-tribe iv. Spiranthinae

16. *Spiranthes spiralis* (L.) Chevall. Autumn Ladies' Tresses
17. *S. aestivalis* (Lam.) Rich. Summer Ladies' Tresses
18. *S. romanzoffiana* Cham. Irish Ladies' Tresses

Sub-tribe v. Physurinae

19. *Goodyera repens* (L.) R.Br. Creeping Ladies' Tresses

Sub-tribe vi. Epipogiinae

20. *Epipogium aphyllum* Sw. Spurred Coral-root

TRIBE 2. Epidendreae

Sub-tribe Liparidinae

21. *Hammarbya paludosa* (L.) O. Kuntze	Bog Orchid
22. *Liparis loeselii* (L.) Rich.	Fen Orchid

TRIBE 3. Vandeae

Sub-tribe Corallorhizinae

23. *Corallorhiza trifida* Chatel.	Common Coral-root

DIVISION B. Basitonae

TRIBE Ophrydeae

Sub-tribe i. Gymnadeniinae

24. *Gymnadenia conopsea* (L.) Rich.	Fragrant Orchid
25. *G. albida* (L.) Rich.	Small White Orchid
26. *Coeloglossum viride* (L.) Hartm.	Frog Orchid
27. *Platanthera bifolia* (L.) Rich.	Lesser Butterfly Orchid
28. *P. chlorantha* (Cust.) Rchb.	Greater Butterfly Orchid
29. *Herminium monorchis* (L.) R.Br.	Musk Orchid

Sub-tribe ii. Serapiadinae

30. *Neotinea intacta* (L.) Rchb. f.	Dense-flowered Orchid
31. *Anacamptis pyramidalis* (L.) Rich.	Pyramidal Orchid
32. *Himantoglossum hircinum* (L.) Spreng.	Lizard Orchid
33. *Aceras anthropophorum* (L.) R.Br.	Man Orchid
34. *Orchis simia* Lam.	Monkey Orchid
35. *O. militaris* L.	Soldier Orchid
36. *O. purpurea* Huds.	Lady Orchid
37. *O. ustulata* L.	Burnt Orchid
38. *O. morio* L.	Green-veined Orchid
39. *O. mascula* L.	Early Purple Orchid
40. *O. fuchsii* Druce	Common Spotted Orchid
41. *O. ericetorum* (Linton) E. S. Marshall	Heath Spotted Orchid
42. *O. latifolia* L. sec. Pugsl.	Early Marsh Orchid
43. *O. praetermissa* Druce	Common Marsh Orchid
44. *O. purpurella* T. and T. A. Steph.	Dwarf Purple Orchid
45. *O. occidentalis* (Pugsl.) Wilmott	Irish Marsh Orchid
46. *O. cruenta* O. F. Muell.	Flecked Marsh Orchid
47. *Ophrys muscifera* Huds.	Fly Orchid
48. *O. sphegodes* Mill.	Early Spider Orchid
49. *O. fuciflora* (Crantz) Rchb.	Late Spider Orchid
50. *O. apifera* Huds.	Bee Orchid

Subspecific Groups

In Chapter 2 it was pointed out that all species vary to some extent, and some of the types of variations existing in certain British orchids were described and discussed, especially colour forms. The degree of variability in different genera, or even in different species of the same genus, is markedly different, so that some species, for example the greater butterfly orchid (*Platanthera chlorantha*), the common tway-blade (*Listera ovata*) and the musk orchid (*Herminium*), are relatively constant as compared with the great degree of variability shown by such species as the Irish marsh orchid, common spotted orchid and broad-leaved helleborine.

Sometimes, as, for instance, in the Irish marsh orchid and broad-leaved helleborine, there seems to be very little relation between the different variants and the habitat, on the one hand, or the general geographical distribution of the species, on the other. The different forms in such cases seem to be merely combinations in a purely for-tuitous manner of all the possible varying characteristics, except perhaps anthocyanin, of which the development is usually related to the amount of shade available.

This is not true, however, of the common spotted orchid (*Orchis fuchsii*), the lesser twayblade (*Listera cordata*) and the fragrant orchid (*Gymnadenia conopsea*) among others. In all these species we find forms, differing from one another in various features, which may be related to the nature of the habitat or, alternatively, may occupy distinct geographical areas within the general area of distribution of the species. *Listera cordata* and *Gymnadenia* provide examples of the former, while within the highly polymorphic *Orchis fuchsii* we find forms falling into each of these two categories. In *Listera* there are two forms, one of which is characteristic of heather moors, whereas the other is found in pine and birch woods. In the fragrant orchid there seem to be distinct races characteristic of chalk downs, heathy country and swamps respectively, the last mentioned (var. *densiflora*) being a very striking plant with broader leaves, a denser spike of differently scented flowers and flowering about a month later than the dry land types.

In *Orchis fuchsii* similar ecological races are found on chalk downs and in woods, and perhaps also in damp places in the more hilly regions of the north and west. Apart from these, however, we find also marked geographical races, best called subspecies, which more or less replace the normal types in certain regions. For instance, the subspecies *hebridensis* (Pl. 35b, p. 250) entirely replaces *O. fuchsii* proper (Pl. 38a, p. 259) in the outer Hebridean Islands, while the subspecies *o'kellyi* (Pl. 40, p. 267) is much the commonest and most widespread form in north-western and western Ireland. Little is known of the reasons for these segregations within the common spotted orchid, but as pointed out in Chapter 4, the species belongs to a group still in the process of active evolution, and the corresponding European species, *O. maculata*, shows the same development of local races in many parts of the continent.

In cross-pollinated species the development of local races is, of course, very considerably hindered, unless there is some kind of isolation of different groups, either geographically or through incompatibility during pollination and fertilisation. When we come to self-pollinated species, however, no such hindrance exists. This is well shown in the helleborines of the genus *Epipactis*. The cross-pollinated species, *E. helleborine*, *E. purpurata* and *E. atrorubens*, although exhibiting considerable variability from one individual to another, show little sign of the production of local forms or geographical races. On the other hand, in the self-pollinated *E. leptochila*, which usually occurs, like many other orchids, in well-defined populations at some distance from one another, there are many indications of the arising of local races due to the isolation imposed by self-pollination. The populations of this species occurring in Surrey, on the Chiltern Hills and on the Cotswold Hills all differ slightly from one another in various respects, particularly the shapes of the lip and other perianth members. Even separate populations within the same general region show much greater individuality than similarly placed populations of *E. helleborine* or *E. purpurata*. This tendency reaches its maximum development in the Isle of Wight helleborine, where the various populations so far discovered all seem to be different from one another, so much so that their discoverers doubted at first the identity of the plants with those already recorded. Among the self-pollinated *Epipactis* species several local races have become so divergent from any other form that they are considered by some authorities to be distinct species. Examples of this are the recently described *E. cleistogama* from the Cotswold Hills, clearly a close relative of *E. leptochila*, and an interesting plant occurring on sand dunes in south Wales, which possesses many features distinguishing it from *E. dunensis* of the north Wales

PLATE 5

Robert Atkinson

a. Large White Helleborine (*Cephalanthera damasonium*). Chiltern Hills, Oxfordshire; June

A. U. Däniker

b. Red Helleborine (*Cephalanthera rubra*). Schaffhausen, Switzerland

PLATE 6

Robert Atkinson

Sword-leaved Helleborine (*Cephalanthera longifolia*). Hampshire; May

and Lancashire coasts. It is evident that in these self-pollinating groups the status of a " species " is widely different from that obtaining in the cross-pollinated groups.

HYBRIDS

Anyone who begins to take an interest in our native orchids, and in particular attempts to identify them by comparisons with descriptions in " Floras " or other books, sooner or later finds a specimen (or perhaps several specimens) which does not seem to agree properly with any of the descriptions or illustrations available, but appears to possess the qualities of more than one species. The probable explanation is that any such specimen is a naturally occurring hybrid between two different species, and consequently will have inherited features from both its parents. Hybrids between species seem to be commoner among orchids than in many other families of plants ; at least that is the impression gained by the ordinary field botanist. This may be merely because the markedly individual structure of the flowers in different species of orchids makes any departure from the normal very noticeable, thus enabling hybrids to be detected readily. There is some evidence, however, in particular that furnished by the numerous artificial hybrids produced by the large commercial orchid-growers, that species of orchids do indeed hybridise more easily with one another than do members of other families. It also seems true that the off-spring so produced are usually capable of producing fertile seed, and so of giving rise to further hybrid forms. Most of the large and beautiful orchids sold by florists are hybrids of very complex parentage, some containing " blood " (genes) from as many as four or five different species.

The degree to which such crossing takes place in nature varies considerably from one genus of orchids to another, some groups, such, for instance, as the helleborines, providing very few examples of hybrids, whereas in the genus *Orchis* numerous hybrids have been recorded. On the whole, crossing is found to take place more frequently between species which are closely similar in flower structure, the probability decreasing as the resemblances in the floral parts become less. This is no doubt partly due to the adaptation of most orchid flowers to pollination by a special group of insects, which naturally usually only visit flowers with a similar structure. It may be, however, that on rare occasions an insect for some reason visits successively flowers of different structure, and there is then the possibility of a hybrid between such dissimilar species.

Dissimilarity between species, and the consequent improbability of cross-pollination by insects, is only one of the factors preventing the production of hybrids. Differences in the time of flowering may be a complete bar to the formation of hybrids, notwithstanding the species concerned are very similar florally. Even when species flower together and are similar in flower structure, so that the same insect visits them, there is always the possibility that the pollen deposited may be incapable of fertilising the ovules in the species pollinated.

Nevertheless it seems that among our orchids such cases are uncommon, hybrids having been recorded between most pairs of species which fulfil the conditions already mentioned. Hybrids between some pairs of species, such, for instance, as that produced by the crossing of the early purple orchid (*Orchis mascula*) and green-veined orchid (*O. morio*), or those between the various species of *Ophrys* (Pl. VI, p. 79), occur usually as isolated specimens or perhaps in very small numbers. The position is quite otherwise with the various marsh and spotted orchids. Nearly all these plants hybridise very freely with one another, and where two or more species occur together in any quantity it is the exception not to find at least one plant which exhibits intermediate characters. Sometimes the hybrids are very abundant, and in great variety, possessing the features of the accompanying parents in almost all possible permutations and combinations. Many of the specimens may best be interpreted as the result of back-crossing of the primary hybrids with one or other of the original parent species. Such a hybrid-swarm, as it is termed, is very difficult to understand and to recognise unless one is well acquainted with the pure species from which it has sprung. In some localities only one true species can be found apart from the hybrids. This may be because the original cross was effected by pollinia brought by an insect from some distance away or, on the other hand, the missing species may have died out in the locality since the hybrids were first produced. Since hybrids in orchids, as in many other plants, are often much more vigorous than their parents, their persistence under conditions which lead to the dying out of one or other of the parents is not so surprising as it might appear on first consideration. The virtual " extinction " of one or perhaps of both of the original species may also be the direct result of the greater vigour of the hybrids formed. As these increase in numbers the chances of further crosses between them and the remaining " pure " plants becomes progressively greater, and each time the offspring consist of more hybrids. At the same time the chances of fertilisation of individuals of pure species by pollinia from other plants of the same species decreases proportionately, and so the number of individuals of the species slowly decreases whereas that of the hybrids increases. Since most of the marsh and spotted orchids are perennial plants of some years' duration, this process of replacement of species by hybrids is of necessity slow, but it is all the more certain. This is because populations of perennial plants are, on the whole, not subject to such violent fluctuations in numbers as is the case with annuals and other monocarpic types which flower only once in their lifetime.

The situation becomes even more complicated when more than two allied species occur together, as is not infrequently the case. More than one series of hybrids may then be formed, and these are apparently quite capable of crossing with one another or with any of the species present. The welter of forms produced under such conditions may readily be imagined, but must be seen to be properly appreciated. The interpretation of many individual specimens becomes a task which can only be attempted successfully by a person with considerable experience both of the species themselves, and of the main combinations of qualities which are found in any single hybrid series. Even with this knowledge there are many single plants which defy accurate placing.

It must be clearly understood that the hybrids in practically all the above-mentioned cases are " putative " hybrids, that is to say, there is no actual proof of their nature, but in view of their floral and vegetative characters, and the presence usually of the two supposed parents, their hybrid nature is almost certain. In very few instances have corresponding hybrid forms been produced by artificial means. This is partly because it is extremely difficult to raise our native orchids from seed, and partly because the seeds take so long to produce a flowering plant that the process of hybridisation is necessarily a very slow one. In those few cases in which hybrids of known parentage have been raised, they agree very closely with naturally occurring plants which had been considered on circumstantial evidence only to have the same parentage.

The interest attaching to hybridisation in the marsh and spotted orchids is, however, far from being merely that it makes identification of specimens difficult. As in many genera in other families, it has been, and no doubt still is, an important means for the production of new species. An examination of *Orchis* populations throughout the British Isles, and also elsewhere in Europe, shows clearly the segregation of local races (or perhaps merely populations) differing from all other orchid species in the combination of features which they exhibit. These may well be the result of some past hybridisation of which there is now no other evidence. If for some reason the main basic character-combination produced is comparatively stable, and especially if the population is more or less isolated (by whatever means) from all others, the special features of these populations become accentuated, and finally justify considering them as distinct species. It has been suggested that some of our commonest British palmate orchids may be of this nature, such, for instance, as the common marsh orchid (*O. praetermissa*). This resembles very closely plants in Europe which the evidence shows to be hybrids between the early marsh orchid (*O. latifolia*) and the spotted orchid (*O. maculata*, in the wide sense), and it is possible that *O. praetermissa* also originated from crosses between these two species. Even if this be true, it is clear that by now *Orchis praetermissa* has developed all the characters of a good species, at least in our islands. On the other hand, an active controversy is still being waged as to the nature of the leopard marsh orchid (*O. pardalina*), which some authorities consider to be a distinct species, whereas others look upon the plants referred to it merely as a series of hybrids between *O. praetermissa* and the common spotted orchid (*O. fuchsii*). Maybe the leopard marsh orchid, if not a true species yet, is on the way to becoming one, and perhaps gives us an idea of the situation during the early stages of the history of *O. praetermissa* itself.

Bigeneric Hybrids

The hybrids referred to so far have all been between species belonging to the same genus, such as those between various species of *Orchis* or of *Ophrys*, although the species concerned may be either closely similar to one another, or less frequently considerably different in flower structure. Every now and then, however, the seeker after orchids will encounter a plant which, in view of its general features, and taking into consideration the orchids nearby, can be interpreted only as being a hybrid between species belonging to two different genera, a so-called bigeneric hybrid. Often the mixture of characters derived from the two parents is quite evident (Pl. Vb, p. 78), as, for instance, in some hybrids between the fragrant orchid (*Gymnadenia conopsea*) and the common spotted orchid (*Orchis fuchsii*, Pl. 3, p. 62), the suspected hybrids possessing the characteristic sweet scent of the former and the spotted leaves of the latter. In other cases the evidence has to be built up from the examination of numerous small features, in which the hybrid is found to be intermediate between the two supposed parents.

As in the hybrids previously mentioned, there may be considerable variation in bigeneric hybrids derived from the same two parent species, depending on how the features inherited are combined in the offspring. It is rare for the hybrid to be intermediate in all the more obvious parts of the plant ; more frequently it seems to agree almost entirely with one or other of the parents in some of its features, and its hybrid origin may be suspected only on account of the abnormal colouring or the strange shape of the lip. In such cases, however, it is usually found that there are numerous less conspicuous parts of the plant which in their shape or colour are intermediate, and indicate the hybrid origin of the individual in question. When the two parents are markedly different in appearance, as, for instance, such pairs as the frog orchid (*Coeloglossum*) and common spotted orchid (*Orchis fuchsii*), or the fragrant orchid (*Gymnadenia conopsea*) and common marsh orchid (*Orchis praetermissa*), the blending of such incongruous elements often produces a distinctly bizarre effect, which may appear to the inexperienced observer to be due to disease or some other external agency. Indeed such bigeneric hybrids do not appear to be very satisfactory, on the whole, many of the flowers not being properly formed, and probably not capable of pollination or the production of seeds. We do not know to what extent these hybrids are capable of reproducing themselves, but it would appear that in this respect they fall a long way behind those produced within a single genus. Many cultivated tropical orchids have been artificially crossed to produce bigeneric hybrids, while there are even more complex types in the formation of which species from three or four genera have been employed. These hybrids are evidently fertile, at least to a certain extent, and they are certainly often very beautiful and not in any way deformed.

A few words of warning must, however, be given in connection with supposed bigeneric hybrids. Orchids are extremely prone to the production of abnormal individuals or " sports ", and it is unwise to jump to the conclusion that plants apparently intermediate in flower colour, length of spur, etc., are hybrids, particularly between two different genera. Such plants should always be seen, preferably in a fresh state, by an experienced botanist ; finders of any specimens suspected of being such hybrids are asked to communicate with the author or with any competent orchid specialist. Botanists still know very little about them and would welcome the opportunity of studying as many specimens as possible.

In animals, particularly in the higher animals, the ability of two species to cross is always considered a sign of close relationship, that is, that the species in question have been derived from some common ancestral form during no great period of geological time, and have not diverged from one another to any great extent. In plants it appears that crossing is possible between species showing greater divergence in structure, even though these may usually be placed in the same genus. At the same time, as has already been noticed, crossing occurs more frequently between those species of a genus which show the closest similarity in general structure, and are probably most closely related, whereas it may be very uncommon between members of dissimilar groups.

The great frequency of recorded hybrids between species belonging to different genera of European orchids has led to the suggestion that many of these species are more nearly related to one another than their position in different genera would seem to imply. It is argued that these genera have been separated from one another on characters of insufficient importance, and should therefore be combined to form one or more larger genera as, indeed, was done by the older botanists. A consideration of the numerous artificial hybrids, often between most diverse parents, which have been produced by orchid cultivators, will show that the above view is untenable, since its logical application would result in a general lumping together of easily recognisable groups of species into large genera very difficult to describe or to characterise.

Nevertheless, a careful examination of the bigeneric hybrids which have been recorded may give useful indications of affinities between genera or groups of species. For instance, many hybrids have been noticed between the marsh and spotted orchids, on the one hand, and the members of the *Habenaria* group (*Platanthera*, *Gymnadenia* and *Coeloglossum*), on the other. Contrasting markedly with this state of affairs is the extreme paucity of similar hybrids between the *Habenaria* group and the remainder of the genus *Orchis*. It has consequently been suggested that the marsh and spotted orchids, dactylorchids as they are called in allusion to their finger-like lobed tubers, are more closely related to *Gymnadenia* and its allies, which also have forked tubers, than to the other species of *Orchis*, which have globose or egg-shaped tubers. The Dutch botanist Vermeulen, on the above and other evidence, has indeed recently separated the dactylorchids into a distinct genus *Dactylorchis*.

CHAPTER 6

THE LADY'S SLIPPER

THERE ARE few of our native orchids which arouse greater interest than this beautiful species, partly because of the remarkable shape and appearance of its flowers, but partly, no doubt, owing to its great rarity in the wild state. Luckily plants are not infrequently cultivated in rock gardens, so the orchid enthusiast may have the chance of familiarising himself with the species even if he never sees it growing wild. There is little danger of confusing the lady's slipper (*Cypripedium calceolus*) with any other British orchid, since, in addition to the very striking slipper-like lip, the flower is more than twice as large as that in any other species.

In the early stages after germination of the seed development is rapid, the first foliage leaf being produced in the fourth year. From then onwards the leaves produced in successive years gradually increase in size, and the plant becomes independent of the mycorhizal fungus with which the seedling is first infected. Flowering, however, is usually delayed until the plant is about sixteen years old. In the mature plant the above-ground stems arise from a branched creeping underground stem or rhizome, which is somewhat similar to that in the common twayblade (*Listera ovata*). From this rhizome spring a number of relatively slender roots, there being no tubers of the type characteristic of many other British orchids. The simple unbranched aerial stems bear several (up to five) rather broad leaves somewhat resembling those of the lily of the valley, and terminate in a large solitary, or more infrequently two, nodding flowers (Pl. 4, p. 63). The sepals and petals are usually brownish purple or claret coloured, forming a very pleasant contrast with the yellow lip. It is interesting to note that the two " lateral " sepals in this plant, instead of being separate and on each side of the lip, are almost completely joined together to form a single sepal with only two small teeth at the tip to indicate its dual origin, this combined sepal being placed immediately behind the lip. The petals are often more or less spirally twisted, but may sometimes be almost straight. The lip is bag-like, resembling a rather bloated slipper, with a comparatively small opening on the upper side near its base, which opening is partially blocked by the column and its associated reproductive organs. Quite a number of colour forms have been recorded in Europe, including plants with entirely yellowish or greenish flowers. So far there is no certain record of a complete albino with quite white flowers, but this is not surprising as species of plants with yellowish or brownish yellow flowers rarely produce pure white forms.

Formerly the lady's slipper grew wild in the three northern counties of Yorkshire, Durham and Westmorland (Map 1, p. 346). There were apparently three well-known regions, the first being the region of Ingleborough in the West Riding of Yorkshire, and the neighbouring valleys of the upper Wharfe and its tributaries round about Litton, Kettlewell and Grassington. Here the habitat of the lady's slipper is the oak-hazel woods and thickets which are found on, or more frequently on the screes below, the steep rocky slopes (scars) of the Carboniferous limestone, which are such characteristic features of these upland valleys. The second area of distribution is to be found on the southern slopes of the Cleveland Hills in the North Riding, especially the valley of the River Rye and its tributaries north and west of Helmsley. Here again the species is an inhabitant of the woods and thickets occurring on the rocky steep-sided valleys cut out of the Corallian or Middle Oolite limestone rocks. These woods are of mixed oak and ash with a considerable admixture of hazel, and are very similar to the ones already mentioned from western Yorkshire. Thirdly, the lady's slipper at one time occurred in southern Durham not far north of Hartlepool at Castle Eden Dene. This is a thickly wooded picturesque craggy ravine extending inland from the coast for a distance of about five miles. There are similar ravines to the north and south, and in all probability the species also occurred in these, though we have no records. The rock here is the Magnesian limestone, a relatively soft and pure limestone, and the woodlands are also of much the same type as those already mentioned. The similarity of the habitats in these three centres of distribution is quite remarkable, open and rather scrubby woods of oak, ash and hazel on steep rocky limestone slopes. Evidently the lady's slipper is a plant which requires very special conditions for growth in the British Isles.

Apart from these main areas in which the plant was at one time frequent, and perhaps abundant locally, there are a number of records of its occurrence in scattered localities in Cumberland and Westmorland. Here it appears never to have been common ; at least only a few specimens have been recorded on any one occasion. So far as can be gathered from the scanty records available, the species occurred in rocky woods on Carboniferous or Magnesian limestone, that is to say, in much the same sort of places as in the three chief areas.

The history of the plant seems to have been very similar in all its stations. It was first recorded in 1640 from a " wood called the Helkes in Lancashire neere the border of Yorkeshire " by Parkinson, a London apothecary, in his *Theatrum Botanicum*, an account of all the plants then known. The species was no longer to be found in Helks Wood, which is near Ingleborough, in 1796, it having been eradicated by a gardener at Ingleton who apparently found a ready sale for it. The lady's slipper continued to be found at other localities in the Ingleborough district, but was " rarely met with " in 1838, and by 1888 was said to be very rare. It may perhaps still survive here, but there are no recent records.

The species seems to have been commoner and more widely distributed in the valley of the Upper Wharfe. Although it has been rare there since the first half of the nineteenth century, it has flowered at intervals in various localities since then, the most recent record in print being for 1937 from the vicinity of Grassington. As many as six flowers were cut from one place near Kettlewell in 1911.

In the North Riding of Yorkshire the species may still survive in some of the more inaccessible valleys, but here again it has not been seen in any quantity since about 1850. In Durham, from which it was first recorded in 1777, it was almost completely extirpated by 1868, but a few plants may still linger on in sheltered situations. There is no evidence that the lady's slipper still survives anywhere in Cumberland, Westmorland, or the Furness region of Lancashire.

It is clear from all the records that the lady's slipper has been a rare plant for the last hundred years, during which time it has apparently been disappearing from more and more known stations. This has no doubt mainly been due to the rapacity of collectors and others, who have dug the plants up and transplanted them to gardens. Although it is possible to grow the species successfully if the proper treatment is given, its uprooting and transplanting is definitely a practice to be condemned. In most of Europe the plant has decreased greatly for the same reasons, and in certain areas (e.g. parts of Switzerland and Austria) it is protected by legislation. Luckily in England it is being carefully preserved in the few places where it is known to occur and its special interest is appreciated.

As regards its distribution outside the British Isles, the species comes into the Northern Eurasian group of species, being found right across Europe and Asia to Sachalin on the Pacific Ocean. It is not known, however, in the Mediterranean region proper, but only on mountains to the north of that sea, and also is absent from south-west Asia. The plant does not occur at high altitudes in this country, but this is probably because the woods which the species inhabits do not occur in northern England at altitudes above about 1,000 feet, the hills above this bearing grassland or moorland. On the European continent, however, it inhabits a greater variety of woods (beech, larch, fir, etc.), but almost invariably on calcareous soil, or occurs in rather open scrub as in this country. In the much larger mountain areas of central Europe such woods reach a much higher altitude than in Britain, and consequently our species has been recorded at altitudes of as much as 5,000 to 7,000 feet, as for instance in Switzerland or the Tirol. On the whole it appears that too great exposure to the sun is disadvantageous, as the plant favours north-facing slopes on moist soil with a certain amount of shade. In the central European woods the lady's slipper is accompanied by other orchids such as bird's nest orchid (*Neottia*), sword-leaved helleborine (*Cephalanthera longifolia*), twayblade (*Listera ovata*), greater butterfly orchid (*Platanthera chlorantha*) and fly orchid (*Ophrys muscifera*), all of which have been recorded from the woods in which it occurs in England.

It is interesting to note that in Canada and the United States of America there is a kind of lady's slipper (*Cypripedium parviflorum*) which very closely resembles our British species, and indeed is considered by some orchid specialists to be merely a variety of it. But the American variety is characteristically a native of peat bogs or moist woods on rather rich soil, and evidently has quite different habitat requirements from those of the European plant.

The lady's slipper usually flowers during the latter part of May and the beginning of June. Like other members of the sub-family *Diandrae*, the individual flowers remain open for a considerable time. Flowering can take place only during periods when an individual is actively manufacturing its own food by means of its leaves. In very shady situations the plant can maintain an entirely underground existence nourished by the mycorhizal fungus, which becomes more active under such conditions. However, no flowers are produced in such cases until after the leaves have again developed properly following an increase in the light reaching the spot where the plant grows.

In an earlier chapter (pp. 41–43; Fig. 8, p. 43) an account was given of the pollination of the flowers of the lady's slipper. The general principle involved is that the slipper-like lip acts as a temporary trap for suitable insects, which eventually escape in such a manner that *firstly* pollen from the last flower visited is deposited on the stigma, and *afterwards* more pollen is carried away for pollinating another flower. The correct sequence of events is ensured by the relative positions of the male and female organs, the insect having to pass the latter first and being forced into close contact with one of the stamens at the very moment of escape. The insects concerned are small bees of the genus *Andrena*, the females of five species having been recorded as visiting the flowers. The visits are apparently to obtain the nectar, which is secreted from small hairs on the floor of the slipper. It is also possible that in cold weather the bees use the enclosed lip as a refuge in which to pass the night, as they have been found inside the lip very early in the morning in a semi-torpid condition. Other insects have been found in the slippers, such as various sorts of flies and some small beetles, but the former usually cannot escape, and eventually die, whereas the beetles are able to creep out without taking any part in the pollination of the flowers. It is clear that the mechanism is so adjusted as to allow the unconscious co-operation of the bees, but that the other insects are merely intruders whose presence is usually neither harmful nor of any advantage to the plant.

Apart from new plants arising from seeds, multiplication of individuals may take place following branching of the rhizome and the dying off of the rearward parts. This is, however, a comparatively slow process, since the rhizome grows a very short distance in each year.

CHAPTER 7

THE HELLEBORINES

T HE ORCHIDS forming this group, eleven in all, provide a great contrast in appearance, including, on the one hand, some very striking and beautiful species, and on the other, some of the least attractive of our native orchids. With respect to their frequency in nature they also show great diversity, ranging from the very rare red helleborine (*Cephalanthera rubra*) to the comparatively common and widely spread broad-leaved helleborine (*Epipactis helleborine*). The species are classified into two genera, *Cephalanthera*, containing the larger flowered more attractive types, and *Epipactis*, in which most of the species have small rather dull coloured flowers. The lip (Fig. 6F, p. 31), or modified lower petal, in both genera consists of two readily recognised parts, of which the lower (*hypochile*) is more or less boat- or cup-shaped, while the upper (*epichile*) is flat or even curved forwards and convex. In *Cephalanthera* the lower part is placed parallel to the vertical column, producing a more or less tubular flower, whereas in *Epipactis* it stands out from the column nearly at right angles, and the inner part of the flower is therefore quite open. On the whole, the flowers are more numerous and smaller in *Epipactis* than in the other group.

Usually the helleborines have rather tall slender stems with a number of relatively thin crinkly leaves distributed more or less evenly all the way along, but in less well-grown and somewhat stunted specimens the leaves may be packed more closely together. They never form a basal rosette of leaves, however, such as is found in many of our native orchids, the base of the stem being always more or less bare or enveloped in several sheaths (the bases of undeveloped leaves).

CEPHALANTHERA

This genus contains three British species, viz. large white helleborine (*C. damasonium*, Pl. 5a, p. 110), sword-leaved helleborine (*C. longifolia*, Pl. 6, p. 111) and red helleborine (*C. rubra*, Pl. 5b, p. 110), all of which are widely distributed throughout Europe and also in parts of Asia. It may be looked upon as one of the most primitive types of single stamened (*monandrous*) orchids as regards the vegetative characters, the floral structure and the method of pollination. So far as the general method of growth is concerned, the type of rootstock and the leaves, there is a striking resemblance between the *Cephalantheras* and the lady's slipper. Very similar vegetative growth is also found in members of the lily family, and in tropical members of other families. We may reasonably assume that the *Cephalantheras* still retain what can be looked upon as ancestral vegetative features, although in their flowers they have developed most of the special characters of the orchid family. The peculiar method of pollination provides additional evidence for the above view. In *Cephalanthera* there is no rostellum or specialised stigma as in most other monandrous orchids, but instead of this the ordinary stigma is covered with a very sticky secretion. While penetrating the relatively narrow tubular cavity between the lip and the column, the insect is forced against the stigma and some of the viscous liquid adheres to the thorax. On leaving the flower the insect brushes against the protruding pollinia, which adhere to the sticky material on its body and are carried away to another flower. It is interesting to note that in the sword-leaved and red helleborines the anther is furnished with an elastic hinge, so that on being pushed back by an insect it always returns to the original position, thus ensuring that the pollinia are always maintained in their projecting position. When the insect arrives at the next flower, portions of the pollinia become dragged off by the sticky stigma and pollination takes place. This is clearly a very simple method, in which there are very few special structures and no elaborate mechanism, but it will be seen that even here the stigma has taken on the function of providing the means of attachment of the pollen, if only in a primitive way.

Observations have shown that small bees of various kinds (species of *Halictus* and *Andrena*) are the usual agents of pollination, but although cross-pollination is invariable in the sword-leaved and red helleborines, it is much less common in the large white helleborine, which is normally self-pollinated.

LARGE WHITE HELLEBORINE (*Cephalanthera damasonium*)

This species is much the commonest of the three members of this group, occurring abundantly on the chalky soils in the south and south-east of England. It is often almost the only plant to be seen in shady places under clumps or rows of beech trees, particularly where the ground is rather stony or mossy (Pl. 5a, p. 110). A curious feature of the species is the impression one gets that the flowers never properly open, but this is chiefly due to their shape, the petals keeping rather close together and only the two side sepals spreading at all widely.

The underground perennial part of the plant consists of an erect, rather deeply situated rootstock, from which arise a number of rather thick roots, usually between one and two feet in length, which grow vertically downwards. These roots, of which there may be as many as 95 in a single plant, often penetrate deeply into the soil, this, no doubt, being the reason why the species frequently occurs on relatively dry soils or on quite steep and obviously well-drained slopes. Each plant usually produces only one aerial stem, which bears several somewhat scattered leaves, and terminates in a rather loose spike of comparatively large but not particularly showy flowers. When the aerial shoots first appear in the spring the leaves are often reddish or purplish, but those of the mature plant are of a deep rather dull or greyish green. There may be as many as sixteen flowers in the spike, but this is exceptional, the number usually varying between three and eight. Unfavourably situated or otherwise weak plants may have only one or two flowers, while one can always find a number of stems without any flowers at all. Fine plants may reach a height of eighteen inches or more, but the great majority of flowering stems are between six and fifteen inches high. Some of the sterile stems are no doubt young plants which have not yet flowered, as the seedling does not produce aerial shoots until it is eight years old, and for two or three years these bear leaves only, flowers not appearing until the tenth or eleventh year.

In the large white helleborine the lowest bracts (the leaves occurring with the flowers) are very similar to the ordinary foliage leaves just below, being often much longer than the flower next to them.

In this respect the species differs from the sword-leaved helleborine in which most of the bracts are quite small and all of them almost invariably shorter than the adjacent flower. The flowers themselves are pure white or creamy white in colour, except for several deep orange-coloured ridges on the lip, and as mentioned previously, usually appear to be more or less closed, so that they are almost globular or egg-shaped. One can, however, usually find plants in which the sepals are spreading and the yellow or orange-coloured ridges clearly visible. According to some authorities, the two differently coloured forms (white or cream) are mutually exclusive, only one or the other occurring in any given place.

With respect to its general distribution *Cephalanthera damasonium* belongs to the group of Southern Eurasian species, reaching its northern limit in the British Isles, Denmark, southern Sweden and Lithuania. It is found throughout central Europe and the Mediterranean region, extending into Morocco and Algeria in the south, and to the Caucasus Mountains, Asia Minor and Palestine in the east.

The large white helleborine is characteristically a plant of southern England, particularly in the Home Counties (Map. 4, p. 346). As you go north and west from this region it becomes progressively less common, but it has been found as far west as eastern Dorset and the northern half of Somerset. In the north the species occurs at the extreme southern end of the Yorkshire Wolds to the west of Hull, and is also known from Nottinghamshire, Warwickshire and Worcestershire. Records of its occurrence anywhere north of these counties are very doubtful, and are probably due to confusion with the sword-leaved helleborine, which is found much farther north. It is, however, possible that *C. damasonium* once occurred in places north of its present whereabouts, but that it has become extinct there. Where a species is growing at the edge of its known area of distribution a small change in the habitat may easily result in its dying out, since in such places it is clearly only just able to maintain itself even when the conditions are all favourable to it.

In the British Isles the large white helleborine is almost always found on limestone soils, being especially characteristic of the chalk regions of the south-east, but in Europe it grows in a greater variety of habitats. On the whole, the species seems to prefer spots where there is a certain amount of shade, but rarely plants may be found right out in the open, particularly on north-facing slopes where, of course, the

PLATE 7

A. U. *Däniker*

Red Helleborine (*Cephalanthera rubra*). Schaffhausen, Switzerland

PLATE 8

Robert Atkinson

Marsh Helleborine (*Epipactis palustris*). Hampshire; July

effect of the sun's rays is not so marked. A specially favourable situation for it in the Home Counties is provided by the steeply sloping beechwoods or "hangers" found on the escarpments of the North and South Downs, Chiltern Hills and elsewhere. Here the plants are frequently found in large numbers dotted all over the almost bare ground beneath the trees, but usually attaining their greatest size in places where the tree canopy is not quite so thick and rather more light penetrates. In such places it is often accompanied by the bird's nest orchid (*Neottia*), or more rarely by the fly orchid (*Ophrys muscifera*). In a few localities the two white-flowered helleborines may be found growing together, as in some woods in Hampshire.

On the European mainland the species inhabits a much greater variety of woods than in this country, and also may be found at altitudes of over 4,000 feet in the Alps. The comparatively low altitudes of the hills in southern England prevent it from reaching anything like comparable heights in the British Isles. Although it is in the beech hangers already mentioned that the species occurs most abundantly, yet it is interesting to note in lightly wooded country how almost every isolated beech tree or small group of beeches often has a few plants growing beneath its shade. Plants may also often be found in comparatively dense thickets, or among bushes in more open scrubby places. It is not at all necessary for the soil to contain much in the way of humus ; in fact, the species often appears to prefer rather bare stony or mossy places, though it is also found in soil covered with quite a thick layer of dead beech leaves.

The roots produced in the early stages of the seedling's growth are infected by the usual fungus associate. These roots grow horizontally in the leaf mould, etc., from which food is obtained by the fungus for the young plant. The deeply penetrating roots, which are produced later, are usually quite free from infection, the mature plant being thus entirely fungus-free. It is therefore easy to see why the species usually occurs on soils rich in soluble plant food.

The best time to find the species in flower is during the last week of May and the greater part of June, but it naturally varies a little according to season. Early flowering plants may be opening as early as the middle of May, while on the other hand, it is sometimes possible to find individuals still in flower towards the middle of July.

The narrow more or less tubular shape of the inner part of the flower in *Cephalanthera* is connected with the visits of insects and the

W.O.B. K

fertilisation of the flowers which follows. The other two British species (*C. longifolia* and *C. rubra*) are entirely dependent upon insects for pollination of the flowers and subsequent fertilisation, but this is not the case with the large white helleborine. Various sorts of bees and humble-bees have been observed to visit the flowers, and there can be no doubt that the flowers are occasionally pollinated in this way. Indeed, it is possible to remove the whole or part of the pollinia on a fine camel's hair brush if it is first drawn over the sticky surface of the stigma just below. Darwin showed many years ago that insects visit the flowers to feed on the orange ridges on the lip, which are said to taste like vanilla, and from which small fragments are bitten off.

It seems quite clear, however, that the majority of the flowers are self-pollinated, the bases of the pollinia becoming attached to the uppermost edge of the stigma of the same flower and fertilisation following. This can easily take place as the anther leans forward in such a manner that the pollinia rest on the upper edge of the stigma. That this self-pollination is an extremely effective process may be gathered from an examination of plants some time after they have finished flowering. A comparatively large green seed-pod or capsule will be found to have developed from almost every flower in the spike, it being possible to find fruiting plants bearing as many as sixteen almost ripe capsules. In such a plant the numerous large intensely green seed-pods must contribute to quite a large extent in the production of food for the ripening seeds, acting almost like a number of additional leaves.

Apart from seed production, which normally is evidently very efficient in the species, the large white helleborine multiplies by the production of underground buds on the mature roots (see p. 22). These root-buds are not produced so frequently as in the red helleborine, nor is there much likelihood that they can maintain an underground existence independently as in that species. Nevertheless this method enables the plants to multiply in situations where the production of flowers and seeds is at a minimum.

SWORD-LEAVED HELLEBORINE (*Cephalanthera longifolia*)

There is little doubt that the majority of people, on comparing this species with its relative, the large white helleborine, would consider it much more attractive (Pl. 6, p. 111). There are several reasons for this. In the first place, the flower-spike is quite distinct from the rest of the plant, and the flowers closer together, while secondly the flowers themselves are purer white in colour and open much more widely. The contrast between the white flowers and fresh green leaves produces a charming effect, which is much enhanced if, as is sometimes the case, there are several plants growing together. Unfortunately the sword-leaved helleborine, although widely distributed in the British Isles, is a decidedly uncommon plant, and it is therefore not often that one is able to enjoy its beauty. In this respect it is intermediate between the comparatively common *C. damasonium* and the extremely rare and local *C. rubra*.

The rootstock in *Cephalanthera longifolia* is similar to that in *C. damasonium*, but is not usually quite so deeply situated. It bears two different sorts of roots, that is, a small number of thick ones of various sizes, and a considerably greater number of quite thin wiry ones. The shorter of these thicker roots may serve as storehouses for food, much as in many of our other orchids, while the longer ones penetrate more deeply into the soil, where they absorb mineral food ; all of these are quite free from fungal infection. The thin roots, on the other hand, are heavily infected with fungus, and spread out horizontally into the more superficial layers of the soil, where there is a greater amount of humus or perhaps a considerable layer of dead and decaying leaves. Usually each plant has only one leafy stem, which may be from six inches to as much as two feet in height, but in some individuals there may be more than one. The growth is similar in general features to that in the large white helleborine, but the leaves are narrower and more pointed and generally in two distinct opposite ranks.. The rather dense and short flower-spike bears up to twenty or more flowers, the usual number being about ten. The bracts are very small, except for those associated with the lowest flower or flowers, in this respect providing a marked contrast to the spike of *C. damasonium*. As in the latter, the flowers are entirely white except for the orange parallel ridges on the upper part of the lip, but this coloured region is more easily visible in the sword-leaved helleborine owing to the flowers opening out more.

C. longifolia has much the widest distribution of all the species of the genus, being one of the seven species which constitute the true Eurasian Element of the British Flora. It is found throughout Europe, in Morocco and Algeria in North Africa, and eastwards to western

Siberia, the Himalaya mountains and even western China (Szechwan).

In agreement with its very wide distribution outside our islands, the species has a much wider distribution within the British Isles (Map 3, p. 346) than its nearest relative, the large white helleborine, extending as far north as Perthshire, Inverness and Ross, and also occurring in western, central and southern Ireland. In spite of this the species is nowhere common, the localities where it occurs being generally more or less spaced out and usually not of any great extent. All the records suggest, however, that it was at one time considerably more abundant, or at least it could be found in a much greater number of localities, than is now the case.

Like its relative the large white helleborine, the sword-leaved helleborine is usually found growing on calcareous soils, of such diverse types as the chalk of southern England, the Magnesian and Mountain limestones of the North, and even on glacial drift, boulder clay or in blown sand overlying peat in parts of Ireland. On the whole, it appears to be able to grow in a wider range of conditions as regards moisture than *C. damasonium*, since it may be found on relatively dry slopes in some of its English localities, whereas in Ireland it favours damp woods or even shady swampy places. In the great majority of its stations the sword-leaved helleborine is found growing in woods, or at any rate bushy places, and it therefore appears that some shade is necessary for its continued growth. On the other hand, the species seems to prefer more open spots than the large white helleborine ; it may often be found growing among low bramble bushes or herbaceous vegetation, although it also occurs in places where the ground is almost bare (see Pl. 6). In southern England the species is characteristic of beechwoods or at least woods with a considerable admixture of beeches, but in the north, for example Yorkshire, the Lake District, Durham, etc., it occurs in the ash-oak woods of the limestone areas. In these latter regions the sword-leaved helleborine was once common in the same woods as the lady's slipper, but both species are now almost extinct. In Ireland it has been recorded from oak or mixed oak and birch woods. Praeger has suggested that the restricted distribution of the species in western Ireland is due to the greater part of the country being covered by peat, which renders the ground unsuitable for its growth. The present habitats in this district represent the sole surviving relics of a much more extensive area of woodland, in which the sword-leaved helleborine was probably an abundant species.

PLATE 9

Robert Atkinson

Broad-leaved Helleborine (*Epipactis helleborine*). Oxfordshire; August

PLATE 10

Robert Atkinson

Dune Helleborine (*Epipactis dunensis*). Lancashire; August

Recently a remarkable occurrence of the plant has been recorded from western County Mayo. Here the species grows abundantly in blown calcareous sand overlying damp peaty soil on a rocky ridge near the sea, both among a rather stunted scrub of hazel and dwarf oak and on the exposed summit. Among the bushes the plants may be 9–12 inches in height with a fine spike of flowers, whereas on the open ridge they are only 2 or 3 inches high with one or two flowers !

It will be seen that it is difficult to say exactly what are the conditions which determine the occurrence of the species in any given spot, but it would appear that it is usually found in places where there has been woodland for a long time in the past, if no longer at the present day. The plant seems to be capable of hanging on in a locality for a long time provided the conditions do not change too profoundly, but it seems incapable of colonising new localities. The number of plants visible fluctuates considerably from year to year, it being sometimes difficult to find any flowering individuals for several successive years, and only careful search will reveal the rather inconspicuous sterile aerial stems.

The species flowers from the middle of May to the middle of June, being a little earlier on the average than the large white helleborine, though there is a considerable overlap in the flowering periods. This difference is also found in Europe, where in the south *C. longifolia* may flower as much as a fortnight earlier than *C. damasonium*.

The method of pollination in the sword-leaved helleborine has already been described when dealing with the whole genus *Cephalan-thera*. So far as is known only cross-pollination takes place, this being carried out by small bees or perhaps by other hymenopterous insects. The elastic hinge to the anther, which maintains the pollinia in a prominent position just above the stigma, can be easily demonstrated in this species. Unlike those of the large white helleborine, the pollinia never become attached to the stigma below, and thus self-pollination can only occur by some mischance. Fertilisation and seed-production are nothing like so efficient as in *C. damasonium*, only a few seed-pods being usually produced by quite long spikes of flowers. Presumably there are not enough insects available in most places to enable more than a small proportion of the flowers to be pollinated, though there are evidently occasions when circumstances are more favourable, since Godfery records the removal of 13 pollinia from a spike bearing 17 flowers.

RED HELLEBORINE (*Cephalanthera rubra*)

There can be few of our native orchids which are more attractive than a well-flowered plant of this beautiful species (Pl. 5b, p. 110, and Pl. 7, p. 126), but it is now so rare, and moreover, is such a shy flowerer, that it is only a fortunate person who is able to see it in its full beauty. It can immediately be distinguished from the other British *Cephalantheras* by the bright rose-coloured flowers ; even if the flowers are faded it can still be recognised by the velvety hairy ovary, this being quite hairless in the large white and sword-leaved helleborines. In view of the ease with which it can be recognised, it is somewhat surprising that there are so many doubtful records of its occurrence in various parts of the country. Perhaps some of them are examples of wishful thinking on the part of people who would naturally like to discover one of the rarest of our native plants. In view of our knowledge of the species' method of life, it seems probable, however, that some of these records are genuine, and that the red helleborine still grows in more places than most recent authorities and books suggest.

The rootstock is fairly deeply seated, but the roots in this species show two differences from those of the two white-flowered species, being mostly quite slender and spreading horizontally. From this rootstock the single aerial stem arises, rather slender with comparatively few narrow, and usually not very stiff, leaves scattered almost all along it (Pl. VII, p. 94). The height of the stem varies according to the habitat, being shorter in open places and often much drawn up when the plant occurs in shady or bushy spots. In the latter case it may reach the height of nearly 3 feet, but this is certainly exceptional, a foot to eighteen inches being more general. The flower-spike, which may consist of as many as fifteen flowers, but in this country is usually few-flowered, is rather loose, the lower flowers being accompanied by long narrow bracts often much longer than themselves, in which respect the species resembles the large white helleborine. Although the sepals and petals are of a beautiful rose-pink, sometimes with a lilac tinge, the lip is white with a violet-rose tip, and several yellow raised ridges on its inner surface quite comparable with those in the white-flowered species. As is usually the case in species with pink flowers normally, plants have been found occasionally on the Continent bearing white flowers, but these are merely albino forms.

The red helleborine has not such a wide geographical distribution as the sword-leaved helleborine, being absent from North Africa, northern Asia and the Himalaya mountains. It is characteristically a plant of Central Europe, and although it does occur throughout the Mediterranean region, it is clearly more generally distributed in the east than in the west. On the whole it seems most suitably placed among the Central Eurasian Element of our orchid flora. It appears to be more adapted to life in a moderately continental climate with greater summer and winter extremes than in the more oceanic climate of western Europe.

This is more or less in agreement with its occurrence in this country, as the species has been recorded only from that part of England east and south of a line connecting the Bristol Channel with the Wash (Map 2, p. 346). This half of England is recognised as having a more continental climate than that of the rest of the British Isles. In this region it is now known only from the Cotswold Hills in Gloucester-shire, but there are records of varying credibility from Somerset, Sussex and Kent. In the Cotswolds it has been found at quite a number of spots, although never very abundantly at any given locality. Speci-mens collected in the other counties mentioned have been seen by knowledgeable persons in all cases, but none of them seems to have been preserved, so unfortunately the records rest on the authority of the persons referred to. An interesting example is mentioned in the *Flora of Sussex*, according to which several specimens were seen in 1921 in the hands of a woodcutter in the Arundel district by a per-son who knew the species well in its Gloucestershire stations. The plant is, however, not known to local botanists, and this record, like the others, requires confirmation. Nevertheless the species is so dis-tinctive that it is difficult to conceive what other species could have been confused with it.

Although *Cephalanthera rubra* is not confined to calcareous soils in Europe, it evidently prefers these soils, and it apparently occurs on such in all its recorded English localities. In the Cotswolds, for in-stance, it is confined to Oolitic rocks, which are rich in lime. The exact habitats where the species occurs are rather variable, ranging from somewhat open beechwoods to scrubby places with blackberries and other bushes. Even in woods the plant may occur along paths among tall grass and mixed undergrowth rather than in more shady places. But the searcher can never be certain of finding it flowering, as even when quite a number of plants are present very few may be in flower in any given year. For instance, according to one observer, out of 50 or 60 plants seen in one locality only 10 were in flower. Often plants may remain in a sterile condition for many years until some change in the surroundings enables flowering to take place, while in some places the plants may apparently disappear entirely. On the other hand, individuals may appear where none has been observed for a long time.

There seems little doubt that this curious habit of the species of appearing and disappearing, and of varying in numbers from period to period, is not related to the varying conditions governing establishment of new plants from seed as in other orchids, such as the bee orchid and fragrant orchid. On the contrary, it is a result of its remarkable method of nutrition, and very efficient multiplication by vegetative means. Mycorhizal activity in the red helleborine is nearly always at a comparatively high level, the plant almost always depending to a large extent on the food supplied by its fungal associate. The seat of this activity is in the roots, where the surplus food is stored. Should the wood in which the plant is growing become so overgrown or dense that little light can reach the leaves, these become reduced in size or even disappear altogether. Food supplied by the fungus, however, is sufficient to keep the roots alive for a long period. In fact the plant behaves temporarily as a saprophyte, living entirely on decaying plant remains in the soil, and is thus comparable with the bird's nest orchid and coral-roots. Examination of the roots of plants growing in shady places reveals small outgrowths which are buds, and which eventually extend upwards to reach the surface of the soil (Fig. 3B, p. 23). Here they form several narrow leaves, but usually no flowers so long as the shady conditions persist. These root-produced plants have been found attached to actively growing roots which had lost all connection with any leafy shoot. Should the trees later on be thinned out and the light increased, these plants will rapidly develop into normal flowering ones, and in this way a number of new plants may appear in a comparatively short time. It is undoubtedly this power of multiplying the plants in favourable conditions by means of buds developed from the roots which explains the sudden increases in the numbers of individuals recorded by some observers.

In this country the red helleborine flowers during June and July, the exact time depending upon the situation of the plants. Fertilisation of the seeds is always the result of cross-pollination by insects, the mechanism being the same as that in the sword-leaved helleborine (see p. 124). In Europe a number of species of bees, including humble-bees, have been recorded as visiting the flowers ; no doubt such insects are also the pollinating agents in Britain. It is probable, however, that to maintain its numbers over a long time, the species depends more on its powers of persistence under unfavourable conditions, and on its method of vegetative multiplication, than on seed production.

EPIPACTIS

This genus is evidently closely related to *Cephalanthera*, as is shown by the similarity in growth and general appearance and the structure of the lip, which consists of two distinct parts in both genera. Most of the species have rather small and dingy flowers, but when the flowers are larger than usual, as in the marsh helleborine (*E. palustris*), and the large flowered American species (*E. gigantea*), the more open type of flower renders them almost as attractive as the *Cephalantheras*. It will be remembered that in *Epipactis* the lip spreads out almost at right angles from the column, the lower portion forming a bowl-like or boat-shaped hollow, which is usually differently coloured from the rest of the flower (Fig. 6F, p. 31).

So far as pollination is concerned, *Epipactis* is more highly developed than its sister genus, as there is usually a distinct rostellum (or third sterile stigma), although in some species this may soon disappear after the flower opens. It is, however, a rather primitive apparatus, consisting only of a very thin-skinned bag containing a very sticky liquid which sets hard on exposure to air. The pollinia fall from the anther so as to touch this rostellum, where they remain until the flower is visited by an insect. In the latter event the insect's body contacts and breaks the rostellum, the sticky liquid from within adhering simultaneously to the insect and to the pollinia resting on the rostellum. As the insect flies away it therefore carries the pollinia with it, these adhering to the sticky stigma of the next flower visited. There is at least one European species in which there is no rostellum, while in several of our British species, for example the green-leaved helleborine (*E. leptochila*) and the dune helleborine (*E. dunensis*), the rostellum dries up so soon after the flower opens that the pollination mechanism described above can hardly ever be effective. These species are either entirely or in most cases self-pollinated.

Unlike *Cephalanthera*, where the few species are readily distinguishable from one another, the more numerous species of *Epipactis* (with the exception of *E. palustris*) are very similar in appearance. Indeed they can only be distinguished by careful examination and comparison with illustrations and with one another. Although most of them are undoubtedly quite clear-cut species with definite characters, both structurally and in their habitat preferences, there is still some doubt as to the exact nature of one or two species which have been recognised only during the last ten years or so. The species vary greatly in distribution and abundance, from the widely spread and often quite common broad-leaved helleborine (*E. helleborine*), on the one hand, to species like the dune helleborine (*E. dunensis*), pendulous-flowered helleborine (*E. pendula*) and Isle of Wight helleborine (*E. vectensis*), which are known from a few localities only, and even there may be quite scarce.

MARSH HELLEBORINE (*Epipactis palustris*)

It is convenient to deal with this species first because it is markedly different from the other British members of the genus ; also because in some respects it is intermediate between those species and the genus *Cephalanthera* which has already been described. In the first place, the marsh helleborine is undoubtedly a more handsome plant than any other *Epipactis* (Pl. 8, p. 127), the flowers being considerably larger and more attractively coloured, although there are not so many of them in the flower-spike. More important than this from a botanical standpoint is the different structure of the flowers, particularly the lip. In the marsh helleborine the basal portion (*hypochile*) is distinctly longer than broad with two ear-like flaps, one on each side. The upper portion of the lip (*epichile*) is attached to the hypochile by an elastic joint, so that when it is depressed by any weight (such as an insect) it returns to its original position as the weight is removed. Just in front of this joint is a bright yellow erect plate, which is comparable with the yellow ridges on the inside of the lip in the *Cephalantheras*. Another distinctive feature in this species is its creeping method of growth (Fig. 12, p. 137), rather similar to that of the lily of the valley or the garden mint.

The underground stem or rhizome, which is usually creeping in habit, is quite thin and much branched, so that a single plant may

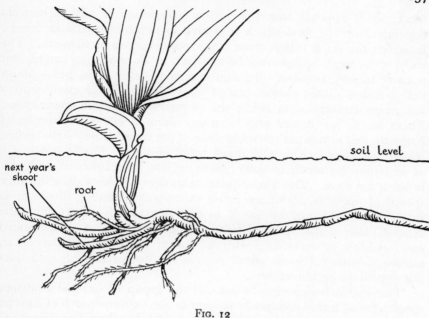

FIG. 12

End of vegetative growth of marsh helleborine, *Epipactis palustris*
Note horizontal underground rhizome, erect leafy flowering stem and
new sections of rhizome growing out. ($\times \frac{2}{3}$)

inhabit quite a large patch of ground. This rhizome lies only an inch
or so below the surface, this being chiefly due to the scarcity of oxygen
in the very damp ground or swamps in which the species is usually
found. Growth is carried on much as in the lily of the valley, the tip
of the rhizome growing upwards each year to form the aerial flowering
stem (Fig. 12), while the horizontal growth is continued by a new bud
which springs from the base of the upright portion. If more than one
bud develops, which may happen if enough food is available, two
new rhizomes are formed from this point. By repetitions of this process
a plant may eventually produce quite a number of widely spaced
leafy (and perhaps flowering) stems, each one being at the end of one
of the branches of the rhizome. Roots develop from many places along
the rhizome, so that all parts of the plant are well supplied with water
and mineral food from the soil. Fungal infection of the roots is very

weak, so it appears that the marsh helleborine is almost entirely dependent on the food which it is able to manufacture in its leaves, in which respect it differs from many other species of *Epipactis*. The leafy aerial stem, which may be as much as three feet in height, but is more usually between nine and eighteen inches high, bears about half a dozen rather closely placed leaves in the lower part, with a few more scattered ones below the comparatively short flower-spike. These leaves are longer and narrower than in any other species of *Epipactis*, and somewhat resemble those of the sword-leaved helleborine, which, however, are usually much more pointed. The lowest leaves or leaf may be much broader, more or less funnel-shaped and embracing the stem. The flower-spike bears fewer flowers than in other species of *Epipactis*, about ten being the average number, although as many as twenty may be found in fine specimens. Apart from the central plate of the lip, the flowers are generally more or less tinged rosy, reddish or brownish, with a whitish lip, but a variety (var. *ochroleuca*) with yellowish white flowers has been recorded, and does not appear to be uncommon.

The marsh helleborine belongs to the group of Central Eurasian species, being found commonly neither in the extreme north of Europe nor in the Mediterranean region proper, but distributed eastwards as far as Persia, Turkestan and the region of Lake Baikal in Siberia. Generally speaking, it is commonest in the lowland regions, but in the Alps it has been found at altitudes of as much as 5,000 feet. The distribution of *E. palustris* in the British Isles is in conformity with that outside Britain (Map 5, p. 347), the species being found throughout England and Wales, and less commonly in the southern half of Scotland as far north as Perth and the island of Mull on the west coast. In Ireland it is widely distributed, but is now extinct in the northeast, although it formerly occurred in Antrim and Down. In the British Isles it is also a lowland plant, not being found in mountainous areas except in the wider valleys. Throughout the region in which it occurs the marsh helleborine is a local plant, although as a result of its creeping method of growth you will often find many apparent " plants " (really flowering stems) growing together.

With rare exceptions the species, as its name indicates, occurs in marshy or other wet places, but a special and very characteristic habitat is that provided by the damp hollows or " slacks " which are to be found in almost every large system of sand dunes. This is one of the

PLATE II

Robert Atkinson

Dark Red Helleborine (*Epipactis atrorubens*). North Wales; July

PLATE 12

Robert Atkinson

Violet Helleborine (*Epipactis purpurata*). Hampshire; August

favourite localities for the marsh helleborine, which has been recorded from such places along the coasts of all parts of the British Isles within its general distribution area. It appears to favour, both here and in Europe, habitats in which either the soil or the water supply contains a considerable amount of lime, and to avoid those which are at all strongly acid. This is especially noticeable in central Ireland, where *E. palustris* is a characteristic member of the extensive limy marshes which are covered to a great extent with coarse vegetation of sedges and other similar plants. The conditions in the sandhill localities are not so different as might appear at first sight, since sea-sand very frequently contains a relatively high proportion of lime in the form of fragments of marine shells. Owing to the comparatively tall stems and the leaves being borne some way above the base, the marsh helleborine is able to maintain itself in quite rank vegetation, such as the common reed. On the whole, the sand-dune individuals are shorter and stockier, and bear fewer flowers, than those growing in other places, a difference which is related to the more exposed position of the plants. Some people maintain that some of these dune plants constitute a special variety which has become adapted to living in these rather special conditions, but so far no experiments have been carried out to test this view.

A very exceptional habitat for the species is in Wiltshire not far from Calne, where it occurs near the top of the chalk downs. The exact spot is where a series of old chalk diggings have left a very irregular surface with a number of hollows and mounds. The orchid is found both in some of the hollows and on the adjacent low mounds, as well as on the slopes between. The ground here is not very damp, the other plants being normally inhabitants of moist or dryish localities. The marsh helleborine is known to be very persistent once it becomes established, so this curious occurrence may represent merely a hanging-on from what was originally a damper habitat. A similar state of affairs has been recorded recently from Kent, where very dwarf plants of *E. palustris* occur in a disused chalk pit near Greenhithe. The ground here was dry when the plants were flowering, but the presence also of hybrids between the common marsh and common spotted orchids suggests that it may be damper at other times.

Unlike most other helleborines, the marsh helleborine appears to avoid shady places, and is usually to be found well out in the open. Indeed all the habitats of the plant are in harmony with the fact that the species usually maintains an almost independent existence, and relies very little on its fungus partner for food. This is in striking contrast with many other helleborines, which depend on their fungal associate for a good deal of their nourishment, and consequently are commonest in habitats which favour the growth of the fungus.

Epipactis palustris has a comparatively long flowering period, lasting from the end of June to the early part of September, but the middle part of this period, from about July 15th to August 15th, is the best time to see the species. The method of pollination of the flowers, which is carried out chiefly by hive bees, is not found in any other species of *Epipactis* and is another example of a beautifully contrived mechanism.

Although both in bud and after fertilisation the flowers are hanging, when ready for pollination each flower assumes a horizontal position, the lip being then also more or less horizontal. It will be remembered that the two parts of this structure are joined by an elastic hinge. Bees visit the flower for the nectar, which is produced from the curious yellow upright plate and flows into the cup-like hypochile. The insect alights on the platform-like epichile, which is depressed by its weight, and crawls forward to obtain the nectar. On leaving the flower after feeding, the upward pressure of the hinged epichile almost compels it to fly upwards in order to escape. As it does this the back of its head comes into contact with the projecting rostellum, which has the usual structure found in *Epipactis*, that is, it is a thin-skinned bag containing a very viscid sticky liquid. This bag is ruptured and the liquid attaches the pollinia, which lie on the top of the rostellum, to the insect's head. The pollen masses, however, are held rather tightly in the anther, and can only be entirely released if the anther is pushed upwards, this being achieved in the course of the bee's upward flight. On visiting the next flower, the pollinia carried on the bee's head come immediately into contact with the adhesive stigma below the rostellum and are removed, thus effecting pollination, while afterwards the insect again carries away further pollinia by the process already described. The whole mechanism is designed to be operated by an insect of the right size with highly developed instincts, for although a smaller insect can rupture the rostellum, and carry away parts of the pollen masses, it will probably not strike the anther and ensure that the whole of the pollinia is liberated. Larger insects, such as humble-bees, which would be unsuitable, do not seem to be attracted by the flowers. Smaller insects, or insects other than bees, although they may occasionally carry out pollination, are neither regular nor entirely satisfactory agents.

Although cross-pollination is the normal state of affairs in the marsh helleborine, observations, both in the laboratory and in the field, have shown that self-pollination does sometimes take place. Unless the pollinia are taken away cleanly by a visiting insect, they are so fragile that pieces often fall down on to the rostellum, and may come into contact with the edge of the stigma below, fertilisation following. On the whole, fertilisation and seed production seem quite effective, since observations have shown that on an average over 80 per cent of the flowers produce ripe fruits. Nevertheless there appear to be grounds for thinking that *Epipactis palustris* maintains itself and multiplies chiefly by the production of underground runners from the much branched and always extending rhizome. Probably the function of the seeds is to enable the species to become established in new localities. Unfortunately, owing to the extensive drainage which is now being carried on throughout the country, there is less and less land suitable for the marsh helleborine. Records show that the species was much commoner in the past, and there is little doubt that at the present time its stations are slowly decreasing in number. Unless, however, there is a very marked change in the habitat conditions, the perennial type of growth enables the species to persist for a long time in a locality, and probably also to tide over temporarily unfavourable periods.

BROAD-LEAVED HELLEBORINE (*Epipactis helleborine = E. latifolia*)

This is undoubtedly the commonest and most widely spread member of the genus *Epipactis*, occurring throughout the greater part of the British Isles (Pl. 9, p. 130), and also being found in a great variety of localities. In addition, it is much more variable than any of the other species, so much so that it is not always easy to recognise that the different individuals seen do all belong to the same species. Some botanists have considered that there are more than one species, the more strikingly different forms of the broad-leaved helleborine having been given different names in the past. This is now known to be due partly to confusion with some of the distinct species dealt with later on, for instance, the green-leaved helleborine (*E. leptochila*, Pl. 13a,

p. 142) and the violet helleborine (*E. purpurata*, Pl. 12, p. 139). The size of the plants, shape of the leaves and colour and size of the flowers all show great variation (Pl. Va, p. 78), different combinations of these producing plants very unlike one another at first sight. Many of these variants may be found growing quite close to one another, but, on the other hand, in some localities all the plants will be found to fall within a comparatively small range of variation. Differences in the vegetative parts of the plant, for instance, bunching or spacing-out of the leaves, are probably due to the nature of the habitat, but there appears to be little relation between the colour of the flowers and the surrounding conditions.

In the broad-leaved helleborine the rootstock is very short and thick, and grows upwards very slowly, in contradistinction to the widely creeping rhizomes of the marsh helleborine. A number of rather thick roots penetrate deeply into the soil, and thus enable the species to grow in comparatively dry spots, such as open banks or steep slopes. There is a very great deal of difference in the degree of fungal infection of the roots in different individuals, plants growing in soils rich in humus, leaf-mould and the like being heavily infected, whereas when the species grows on bare mineral soil the roots are often entirely free from fungus. From the rather woody rootstock a single aerial stem usually arises, although two stems may be produced at the same time, and less frequently five or six or more. The aerial stem, which is generally about one or two feet in height, but which in really robust specimens may reach as much as four or five feet, bears a number of rather broad crinkly leaves in the lower half, the upper half being the flower-spike. Although the stem is frequently purplish towards the base and the leaves may be quite deeply tinged purple, particularly in plants in rather exposed places, the general colour of the leaves is a rather deep dull green, quite different from the purplish-grey colour so characteristic of the violet helleborine. Among the flowering plants of the species many sterile shoots will usually be found, although these are not very obvious at first sight. These represent plants which are not strong or healthy enough to produce flowers, or young plants which have not yet flowered. At least eight or nine years elapse after germination of the seed before flowers are produced, several sterile annual leafy shoots being produced first.

The flower-spike is very variable in the broad-leaved helleborine, not only as regards the number of flowers, which may vary from a

PLATE 13

Robert Atkinson

Robert Atkinson

a. Slender-lipped or Green-leaved Helleborines (*Epipactis leptochila*). Oxfordshire;
July

b. Pendulous-flowered Helleborine
(*Epipactis pendula*). Bedfordshire;
August

PLATE 14

Robert Atkinson

Isle of Wight Helleborine (*Epipactis vectensis*). Kent; August

dozen to over fifty and occasionally reaches the remarkable total of a hundred, but also in its density. Frequently the spikes are rather loose-flowered, each flower standing out clearly from its neighbours, but in other plants the flowers may be so close together that it is extremely difficult to distinguish the individual flowers in what is almost a solid mass. Such dense-flowered plants are usually to be found in more open situations, while those growing in shady places bear the looser spikes, but there are numerous exceptions to this. It is probable, however, that *Epipactis helleborine* exhibits the greatest and most puzzling dif-ferences in the colour of the flowers. The sepals and petals in different plants may show all gradations between pale or even yellowish green, on the one hand, and a deep wine-colour, on the other, while the outer part of the lip (*epichile*), which is usually redder than the rest of the flower, shows an equally striking range of colours, though these may not always parallel those of the other perianth members. For instance, a deep pinkish red lip may be associated with almost green sepals, while, on the other hand, a flower bearing reddish sepals and petals may have a lip of a delicate greenish pink. A marked variety bearing yellowish white flowers has been recorded from Gloucester-shire as well as parts of Wales, and may have a wide distribution in this part of the country. The cup-shaped part of the lip (*hypochile*) is almost invariably darker than the rest of the flower, being frequently of a deep maroon colour. A good deal has been written about the small humps which are found at the base of the lip epichile, these being variable in number, smooth or wrinkled, and often differently coloured from the remainder of the lip. There seems to be no real evidence justifying the separation from *E. helleborine* of distinct species based on the differences shown by these humps. Another feature, which is often very noticeable, is the extent to which the epichile is curved underneath (recurved), so that the point itself is invisible from the front. On the whole the lip epichile is comparatively broad, blunt and practically always recurved to some extent. In these respects the broad-leaved helleborine differs clearly from the green-leaved or narrow-lipped helleborine (*E. leptochila*).

Epipactis helleborine is one of the seven species forming the Eurasian Element Proper of the British orchid flora. It has a very wide dis-tribution throughout almost the whole of Europe and the Mediter-ranean regions of Northern Africa, extending eastwards to Lake Baikal in Siberia and the Himalayas. The Indian plants have been considered by some authorities to belong to distinct species, but this is still an open question. It is quite evident, from the accounts of orchids of other countries, that the broad-leaved helleborine is as variable and puzzling throughout its extensive geographical range as it is in this country.

In agreement with this wide distribution outside the British Isles, we find an almost equally wide range within our own shores (Map 8, p. 347). Indeed the species is found in 91 out of the 112 divisions (vice-counties) into which the country is divided for recording purposes. The only extensive area from which the species is absent is Scotland north of Perthshire ; even here it has been found in the extreme west in West Ross and West Sutherland. In Ireland the broad-leaved helleborine is generally distributed, although it is not recorded from all the vice-county divisions. The earliest record of its existence in Britain is that in Turner's *New Herball*, published in 1562, where it is stated to grow in pastures at Digswell in Suffolk.

Although *E. helleborine* occurs so widely in our islands it could scarcely be termed a common plant, as on many occasions only one or two specimens can be found. Nevertheless, there are places where the species occurs abundantly though never in such large numbers as our more gregarious species, such as the fragrant orchid, early purple orchid or bee orchid. On the other hand, the broad-leaved helleborine probably grows in a greater variety of situations than any other British orchid, except possibly the common twayblade and the common spotted orchid. It is one of the very few of our orchids which appears to flourish on both calcareous (alkaline) and acid soils, as on heaths, though perhaps it is a little more at home on the former.

In the great majority of cases the species grows in more or less shaded spots, though it may be found right out in the open. It is very characteristic of the beechwoods of the Home Counties, but also occurs in oakwoods on lighter soils, and not infrequently in pine plantations provided they are not too thick. In woods it is commonest near the margins, along rides, or in small openings, all places where there is most light, but it may also be found where the shade is so great that there are very few other plants present. Among these are sometimes the green-leaved and large white helleborines, both of which, however, prefer such conditions to the lighter spots. It is frequently possible to find plants in bushy or scrubby places, or even on banks by the side of the road. On the more acid soils the species occurs commonly under birches and mixed up with bracken, being very difficult to see in the latter situations until the flowers open. In northern regions, for instance the Lake District, the broad-leaved helleborine has been recorded from such varied places as dry rocky slopes, around the margins of lakes, or in shady places by river banks. In these districts it is not uncommon also on steep, not very stable, scree-slopes, which usually form one of the characteristic habitats of the dark red helleborine (*E. atrorubens*). From this species it may be distinguished by the several-ranked larger leaves, the hairless ovary, and the larger greenish rather than red flowers.

Rarely *E. helleborine* is found in damp hollows among sand dunes, as in places in Ireland and Wales, but this is not one of its usual habitats, as in the case of the marsh helleborine. Owing to its deeply seated woody rootstock the species is decidedly persistent. It has been known to maintain itself for some years in raspberry beds in gardens, and to come up among heaps of stones, or through newly made gravel paths or drives.

In the broad-leaved helleborine the rostellum is well developed and the pollination mechanism, as described in the introductory remarks to the genus *Epipactis*, is extremely efficient. It is interesting to note that the nectar in this species is apparently attractive to wasps, but not to bees or humble-bees, which have not been recorded as visiting the flowers. Unless the flowers are cross-fertilised by means of insect visits, the ovaries wither away, since there is no self-pollination as in other species. However, it is not difficult to find wasps crawling about on the spikes, while usually a high proportion of the flowers set seed. The flowering period lasts from the beginning of July until late in August.

DUNE HELLEBORINE (*Epipactis dunensis*)

As the name implies, this species is always, so far as is known, an inhabitant of coastal sand dunes (Pl. 10, p. 131). It is one of the less attractive species of *Epipactis* owing to its small rather dingy flowers, which do not open out to anything like the same extent as those of the broad-leaved, violet or green-leaved helleborines. It is, however, a decidedly local plant, not known to occur in many of the large dune areas around our coast.

The rootstock is rather deep-seated, probably owing to the frequently dry superficial layers of the dunes in which the plant grows, consisting at the most of a small irregular woody mass. The roots are few in number, though as many as ten may sometimes be produced. The usually single rather wiry and slender stem reaches a total height of nine inches to as much as two feet, but is often much shorter. A distinctive feature is provided by the rather loose funnel-shaped sheaths surrounding the base of the stem, in which respect it differs from the broad-leaved helleborine. The comparatively few rather small leaves grow in two rows, thus resembling those of the dark red helleborine (*E. atrorubens*), and, like the stem, are stiff, returning quickly to their original position if bent. At the top of the stem is a somewhat narrow open spike of from ten to twenty, or in smaller specimens even fewer flowers. The flowers spread out horizontally at first, but hang in the later stages and after fertilisation. They are small even for an *Epipactis*, rather dull yellowish or pinkish green, their dinginess being enhanced by the fact that they rarely open widely. The lip is the brightest part, being usually pinkish with a greenish tip, while the cup-like hypochile is darker pink, though nothing like as dark as frequently in *E. helleborine*.

Although the distribution of the dune helleborine outside the British Isles is not completely known, owing to its having been confused with other species of *Epipactis*, it has been recorded from a number of localities along the western and northern European seaboard, from western France through Belgium and Holland to near the mouth of the River Oder in Germany. All its known localities are from coastal sand dunes as in this country. Owing to the species being restricted to a special habitat of this sort, the geographical distribution of the dune helleborine is unlike that of any other British orchid. However, it clearly has a generally western distribution in Europe, and may there-fore be included in the Western European element of our orchid flora. Curiously enough, its stations in this country bear much the same relation to Great Britain as the European ones do to the Continent, the species being recorded so far only from the west coast in Lancashire and Anglesey (Map 9, p. 348). It is doubtful if any of the South Wales plants referred to this species are the same as those from the other two localities.*

Even within its chosen habitat the dune helleborine is not to be found everywhere. It does not favour, on the one hand, the higher

---

* This plant has recently been described as a new species, *E. cambrensis* C. Thomas.

more open dunes covered with the coarse marram grass (*Ammophila arenaria*), nor, on the other, the damp hollows between the sand ridges so beloved by the marsh helleborine. Instead it is nearly always found on the lower rather compact little sandhills built up around the dwarf willow bushes (*Salix repens*). However, in some places in Lancashire, portions of the dunes have been planted with Scots pine trees, and in such regions the dune helleborine maintains itself in the shelter of the trees, which here provide conditions more in line with those favoured by most other species of *Epipactis*. It is interesting to note that in at least one of the continental localities, the dune helleborine was found growing among pine trees, in this case maritime pines (*Pinus pinaster*). All this suggests that although *E. dunensis* has become adapted to living in practically open localities, it still retains the faculty of prospering in what might be looked upon as the ancestral home of the genus, namely woodland. Indeed, the plants growing under the trees look healthier, and are better grown, than those on the open dunes. Recently the dune helleborine has been studied more closely by Mr. C. Thomas and Dr. D. P. Young, especially as regards the plants growing under the shelter of the planted pine trees on the Lancashire sand dunes. Under the shade of these trees the dune helleborine grows much taller, and the leaves are less stiff and of a darker green colour. The flower spikes may bear up to twenty-five flowers. Indeed under these conditions the species more closely resembles the broad-leaved helleborine, on the one hand, and the pendulous-flowered helleborine, on the other.

Unlike the two species of *Epipactis* already described (*E. palustris* and *E. helleborine*), the dune helleborine is almost always self-pollinated and fertilised. The rostellum is only rarely developed, but in such flowers, at least during the early stages, the pollinia can be carried away by visiting insects operating the usual mechanism, as in the broad-leaved helleborine. Generally, however, no rostellum is produced, and consequently self-pollination is the only possible method in the great majority of flowers. In the early stages of development the pollinia easily break up, while even in the bud small portions may fall on to the stigma and effect pollination. Usually, however, self-pollination is achieved by the pollinia, which normally fall out of the stamen on to the top of the column, swelling and being pushed over the edge on to the surface of the stigma just below. The dune helleborine flowers rather earlier than most other species of *Epipactis*, starting as early as the third week in June. Plants may still be found in flower during the early part of August, although in some years flowering may have finished before the end of July.

It is still a moot point which other of our helleborines is most closely related to the dune helleborine. On the whole, it seems to resemble most closely the broad-leaved helleborine, which has rather similar flowers and lip. As has already been pointed out, this latter species exhibits much greater variation than any of the other species, and also is found growing in a much greater variety of situations. In many ways *E. dunensis* gives the impression of being a small-flowered form of *E. helleborine*, which has become adapted to life in sand-dune conditions, and in which self-pollination has replaced the usual cross-pollination mechanism of the genus. It should be pointed out, however, that some authorities have considered that self-pollination was the original method in *Epipactis*, and that the more elaborate cross-pollination mechanism has been developed subsequently. A good deal more study is necessary before it is possible to give a firm opinion one way or the other. It is, nevertheless, probably significant that the species in which cross-pollination occurs normally have the widest distribution, whereas, so far as we know at present, all the self-pollinating species are limited or local in distribution.

Dark Red Helleborine (*Epipactis atrorubens*)

Here again is a species which can usually be more easily recognised on account of the situations in which it grows, than by the technical features which distinguish it from its allies. The dark red helleborine, in this country at least, is almost invariably found on bare limestone rocks, growing in the crevices of cliffs or on open stony scree slopes, usually in full sunshine (Pl. 11, p. 138). It is, however, by no means a common plant, although it occurs in fair numbers in a favourable spot. As both the common and Latin names indicate, the flowers are often dark wine-coloured or blackish red, the species being the darkest coloured of all our helleborines, although individuals of both the marsh helleborine and the broad-leaved helleborine may sometimes have flowers nearly as dark.

The underground parts of the dark red helleborine are well designed for growth in the rocky situations in which it occurs. There is a short rather thick rootstock which produces usually one, or sometimes more,

leafy stems ; from this a large number of rather long thin roots arise.
These spread in all directions, penetrating into cracks and crevices
in or between the rocks, and absorbing food from as large an amount
of soil as possible. Quite a small plant will possess as many as forty
or fifty roots, which may be up to a foot in length. Fungal infection of
the roots is on a very small scale, and indeed the habitat and general
appearance of the plant suggest that it normally depends on the food
it can make itself, and is not to any significant extent dependent on
its associated fungus.

In this country the stems are usually single, but on the European
mainland, where the species often grows in more favourable localities,
as many as six flowering stems may be formed on a single plant. Here
the stem is short and stumpy, bearing about half a dozen leaves in two
distinct rows.   These leaves are rather short and broad, stiff, often
folded, rather dark green in colour, and tinged reddish beneath ;
they provide one of the best ways of distinguishing this species from
E. helleborine, in which the leaves are more numerous and borne all
round the stem.   The stiff rather open flower-spike consists of up to
twenty rather small, relatively blunt, brick-red, deep red or wine-
coloured flowers, which are said to have a vanilla scent. The bosses
or projections on the outer part of the lip (epichile) are very prominent
and wrinkled, or have folds rather reminiscent of molar teeth ; they
are often the brightest coloured portion of the flower. Sometimes the
flowers are paler red, or may even be greenish, but there is always an
admixture of darker red.   From the broad-leaved helleborine (Pl. 9,
p. 130), which sometimes occurs in the same places, and with which
the dark red helleborine may most easily be confused, the latter may
be distinguished by the small size and stiff growth, the short folded
leaves in two rows, the short and broad red sepals and petals, the
hairy ovary, and the ridged bosses on the lip. Plants of *E. helleborine*
growing in exposed dry situations may simulate *E. atrorubens* in general
appearance, and perhaps in flower colour, but never possess all the
features mentioned above. On the Continent, however, the dark red
helleborine often grows much taller, with larger leaves and paler
pinkish or greenish red flowers, and it then resembles the broad-
leaved helleborine more closely. Similar larger plants are also known
from the borders of Westmorland and Lancashire, in the neighbourhood of Arnside and Silverdale ; these plants, like the larger European
individuals, are not found in quite such exposed places as the more

dwarf plants. Even these specimens, however, differ from *E. helleborine* in the two-ranked leaves, the blunt sepals and petals, the rough bosses on the lip, and the hairy ovary. In fact, in spite of its resemblances to other species, *E. atrorubens*, once its characteristic features are recognised and appreciated, is a species which can readily be distinguished from all other British helleborines. For the benefit of those who may consult other books, it may be mentioned that the dark red helleborine has been given by various authorities quite a number of different Latin names, including *E. atropurpurea*, *E. rubiginosa*, *E. media* and *E. ovalis*. According to the rules which govern the use of scientific names of plants, the name used here, namely, *E. atrorubens*, is the correct one.

The dark red helleborine belongs to the Central Eurasian Element of the British orchid flora, being distributed throughout Europe, and extending eastwards to Tomsk in Siberia, Turkestan and the Altai Mountains in central Asia, as well as across Asia Minor to Persia and Syria.

In the British Isles the species is rather scattered (Map 7, p. 347), occurring in widely separated localities as far north as Banff, Skye and West Sutherland. It is, however, very rare in the south of England, becoming more frequent in the north, especially in western Yorkshire and the southern parts of the Lake District. *E. atrorubens* has been recorded from quite a number of counties in the south of England, but all these records seem extremely doubtful ; it is probable that dark flowered and rather stunted individuals of *E. helleborine* have been mistaken for the dark red helleborine. The most southerly really authenticated records appear to be from Derbyshire and some of the southern Welsh mountains, but the species may occur in the Wye Valley and in Herefordshire. In Ireland it is found only in the extreme west, in the " Burren " country of Clare and Galway. Although usually a lowland plant, it may be found at altitudes of between one and two thousand feet in Ireland and Scotland, while in the Alps and Central Asia it has been recorded at heights of 7,000 to 9,000 feet above sea-level.

Epipactis atrorubens is almost invariably found growing on soils rich in lime. Indeed, as mentioned earlier, it frequently grows in the cracks of limestone cliffs or among boulders, where its roots ramify deeply between the rock particles or slabs. In Britain it usually occurs in the open, but in Europe it may be found in a variety of woods composed of beech, oak, spruce or pine, or in scrubby places or thickets. It is also known from sand dunes in some parts of Germany, but this is not one of its British habitats. One of the most interesting localities in our islands for the dark red helleborine is provided by the remarkable range of hills in Galway and Clare known as the Burren Mountains. Here there are extensive stretches of more or less bare limestone rock, forming pavement-like or hummocky surfaces with deep crevices and depressions between the slabs or blocks. In these crevices are found not only the dark red helleborine, but also the dense-flowered orchid (*Neotinea intacta*), which occurs nowhere else in our islands.

The dark red helleborine flowers in June and July, depending upon the nature of the situation ; those plants in less exposed places usually flower rather later than the others. Like the broad-leaved helleborine, the present species depends entirely upon cross-pollination by insects for fertilisation, those flowers not visited not setting seeds. From observations on the Continent it appears that a greater variety of insects visit the flowers than in the case of *E. helleborine*, where only wasps carry out the pollination. Quite a number of sorts of humble-bee are known to visit the flowers of the dark red helleborine, as well as species of wasp. From this fact it has been suggested that the nectar produced by *E. atrorubens* is different from that in *E. helleborine*. The actual pollination mechanism is the same as that described in the general introductory remarks on the genus, and also found in the broad-leaved helleborine.

Hybrids between the above two species have been recorded both from Europe and less frequently from this country. This is not surprising in view of the similarity of the flowers, the similar method of pollination, and the fact that the species sometimes grow together, though there is normally not much overlap in their flowering periods. Such plants are usually intermediate in vegetative and floral characters, and can only be recognised with any certainty by an expert.

The long creeping roots sometimes form irregular swellings which give off smaller roots, and may also form buds from which new plants arise. Such buds may also sometimes be produced by the tip of the main root, but at present little is known of the circumstances leading to the production of new plants by these vegetative means. On the whole, it seems probable that new plants usually arise from seeds.

Violet or Clustered Helleborine (*Epipactis purpurata*)

This helleborine contrasts markedly with the dark red helleborine just mentioned, for whereas that species is a lover of sunlight and open places, the violet helleborine appears to shun the light, and usually reaches its best development in the interior of shady beechwoods where very few other plants can flourish (Pl. 12, p. 139). Here it is sometimes accompanied by the green-leaved helleborine (*E. leptochila*) or even by the broad-leaved helleborine, each of which, however, may readily be distinguished from it. Its characteristic features are the frequent clustering of the stems (Pl. IX, p. 162), the narrow greyish purplish leaves, and the colouring of the flowers, which is quite different from that of any other helleborine. The structure of the column is also quite distinct (see Pl. VIII, p. 95).

The rootstock of the violet helleborine is vertical in position, rather deep-seated and evidently very slow growing. It usually produces only one or two fresh roots each year, but as the roots have a long life, a moderately large plant may possess as many as fifty. These grow down vertically or in a steep incline, and may penetrate the soil to a distance of about a yard (Fig. 13, p. 153). Here they are able to absorb mineral food from the soil, a task for which they are comparatively efficient. So far as observations go the roots are never infected by the usual mycorhizal fungus. The rootstock produces only one flowering stem at first, but with increasing maturity more than one bud is produced each year, resulting in a group or cluster of aerial stems from the same point. It is quite common to find groups of six to ten in number, while as many as 38 have been found in old individuals. This clustering of the stems, which is also found to a much less degree in most *Epipactis* species, is, however, one of the characteristic features of the violet helleborine ; it is always very evident where the habitat is congenial and there are a number of plants.

E. purpurata is one of the finest of our helleborines, the stems reaching a height of nearly a yard in robust specimens, although the average height is probably one to two feet. In Europe the average height may be as much as three feet. Each stem bears from five to ten rather narrow leaves, which are usually of a peculiar purplish greyish green, the amount of purple or red colour varying considerably from plant to plant. These leaves look very different, owing to the grey tinge, from the violet or purple tinged leaves which may sometimes be found in

the broad-leaved helleborine. Rarely
the leaves of the violet helleborine
are rosy tinted, or as described by
the discoverer (the Rev. Dr. Abbot)
" when fresh glowing with a beautiful
red-lilac colour ". It should be noted
that the stem is almost always greyish
purple, even when the leaves are
comparatively green.

The flower-spike, which is usually
between 6 inches and a foot in length
and may be 15 inches long in large
specimens, bears a large number of
rather closely placed flowers (Pl. X,
p. 163). The rather pointed sepals
and petals, which spread widely to
give a very open relatively large
flower, are of a pale whitish-green
colour. The lip is pale green, with
the basal cup more or less purplish
inside, while the broadly triangular
pointed epichile, which is whitish, is
usually delicately tinged with pink,
especially on the rather low bosses or
hunches just in front of the cup. The
colour scheme is one rather difficult
to define in a few words, but very
characteristic of the species, and quite
different from that of any other helleborine.

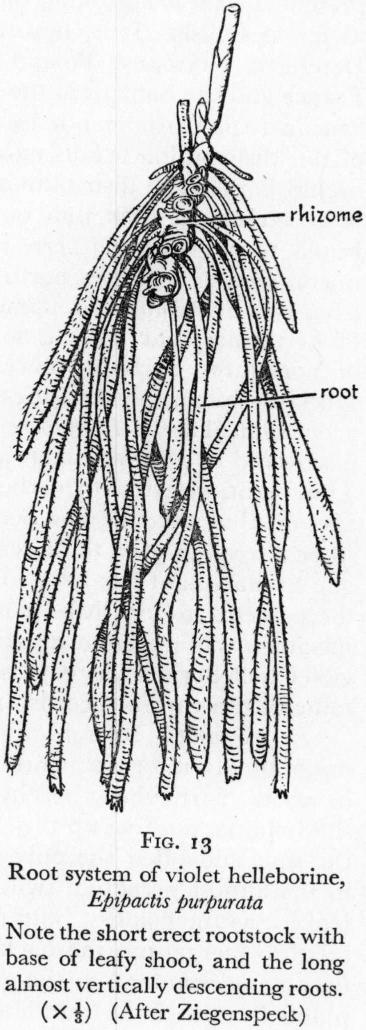

It should be noted that the violet
helleborine, like the dark red helleborine, has also been given several
different scientific names, of which
Epipactis violacea has commonly been
used. Here again the rules governing botanical nomenclature make
it clear that the correct scientific name for the species is the one used
here, namely *E. purpurata*.

Unlike the marsh, broad-leaved and dark red helleborines, the

FIG. 13

Root system of violet helleborine,
Epipactis purpurata

Note the short erect rootstock with
base of leafy shoot, and the long
almost vertically descending roots.
($\times \frac{1}{3}$) (After Ziegenspeck)

present species is not found outside Europe, except for western Siberia as far as Omsk. It is, however, widely distributed in Europe, from Denmark, Germany, Poland and Russia in the north, to Portugal, France and the Balkans in the south, but does not occur in the Mediterranean region proper nor in extreme northern Europe. On account of this distribution it falls naturally into the European element of our orchid flora. The distribution of the violet helleborine in this country is in agreement with that outside, the species being generally distributed throughout southern England, but gradually becoming more uncommon as one goes north (Map 6, p. 347). It has been recorded from two Scottish areas, namely, West Lothian and the northern part of Perthshire, but there is some doubt about all records from north of Yorkshire. Perhaps, however, it may be able to maintain itself in specially favourable localities some distance to the north of its main geographical area. *E. purpurata* was first described in 1828 from a plant discovered in 1807 at Leigh in Worcestershire by the Rev. Dr. Abbot. This plant, referred to earlier on, was entirely of a red-lilac colour, and on that account has been considered by some authorities either to be a freak or even to be really a form of some other species. At least one similar plant has been found since, and on the evidence available there seems to be little reason for doubting the view that Abbot's specimen was merely a marked colour variation. For a long time the violet helleborine was confused with other kinds of helleborines, and some of the earlier records are therefore doubtful.

E. purpurata, though apparently not restricted to limy soils, is undoubtedly most frequently found on them. It nearly always grows in woods, particularly beechwoods, where it may be found in the most shady parts, pushing up through the deep layer of dead leaves covering the soil, and often the only plant to be seen. Indeed when growing in the almost perpetual twilight of such places, it may easily be overlooked, as the colours, both of the vegetative parts and of the flowers, seem to merge into the background. It is only when one's eyes have become accustomed to the gloom that it is at all easy to pick out the plants from their surroundings. It may sometimes be accompanied in very shady places by the green-leaved helleborine (*E. leptochila*), bird's nest orchid (*Neottia*), and by scattered individuals of other species such as dog's mercury (*Mercurialis perennis*), dwarf brambles (*Rubus* spp.), ivy (*Hedera helix*) and ferns (*Dryopteris filix-mas*, etc.). The violet helleborine may, however, be found also in small openings or at the edges of woods, and here, of course, the accompanying herbaceous vegetation is more abundant and varied. Rarely the species may occur in the open, but this is usually following partial clearing of the wood, and it is doubtful if it persists in such places. It is also less frequently found in oakwoods on clay or sandy soil, and then may be seen poking up through the bracken rather in the same manner as the broad-leaved helleborine.

One characteristic habitat is in woods on clay-with-flints and similar soils lying on the flatter tops or gentle dip slopes of the chalk downs. Here it often grows under tall coppice of hazel or other shrubs, usually in rather heavy shade. A feature which seems common to nearly all the habitats is the considerable depth of the soil, not a surprising fact when one bears in mind the deeply penetrating root system of the species. Shallow soils, such as those beloved by *E. leptochila*, seem to be quite unsuitable for the violet helleborine. It is clearly a lowland species in this country, being replaced in woods at higher levels, for instance, in the West Riding of Yorkshire, by *E. helleborine*.

There is still a lively controversy in progress between various authorities as to the chief way in which the violet helleborine obtains its food. One school of thought looks upon the species as intermediate in its nutrition between the ordinary green plant and saprophytes such as the coral-roots and the bird's nest orchid, which are unable to manufacture sugars, etc., but obtain them from the soil humus through the agency of their associated fungus. This view is supported by the frequent occurrence of the species in soil very rich in humus, where it is often associated with true saprophytes such as the bird's nest orchid itself and the bird's nest (*Monotropa hypopitys*). The comparatively small purplish or pinkish violet leaves, which are sometimes much the same colour as those of other saprophytes, for example the toothwort (*Lathraea squamaria*), or even of parasites such as Alpine bartsia (*Bartsia alpina*), are considered by supporters of this view to be totally inadequate to manufacture sufficient food to nourish a large robust plant. As the largest plants often grow in very shady woods, where the amount of light available for food manufacture must be on the low side, it would appear that there is some weight in this contention. It is further pointed out that individuals observed in Europe growing in open spots are usually much greener than those in the shade, and bear larger leaves. The conclusion reached on all these lines of evidence is that the violet helleborine is usually almost entirely dependent on its associated fungus for its energy-producing food, but that it still retains the power of manufacturing a certain amount of its own food, especially when there is more light available.

There are, however, a number of other facts which are scarcely in accordance with the above conclusion. For instance, the roots of most saprophytes are either short or very superficial in position, thus being placed in the upper layers of the soil where the food they require is to be found. On the other hand, the roots of *Epipactis purpurata* are long and descend vertically into the soil to a depth of two or three feet (Fig. 13, p. 153), the absorbing portion therefore being well down in the underlying mineral soil, where humus is comparatively scarce. These roots are quite efficient means of absorbing water (and mineral salts), a feature which is usually associated with orchids which manufacture their own food. A second important point is, that so far as they have been examined, the roots of this species have been found not to be infected by any fungus, at any rate after the seedling stage. This is also true of those orchids which have well-developed green leaves and make their own food. It remains to be proved that this absence of the fungus is the normal state of affairs in the violet helleborine, but at all events our present knowledge cannot easily be reconciled with the theory of saprophytism mentioned above. It has also been suggested that the reddish or purplish coloration is not associated with decreased food manufacture by the plant, but is, on the contrary, a device for making the maximum use of the light available. The general conclusion of those who follow these interpretations of the facts, is that the violet helleborine is entirely self-dependent, and is, moreover, specially adapted to life in shady woods. Be that as it may, it is clear that much more has yet to be discovered before we can accept in its entirety either of the views put forward. Here indeed is a fruitful field for further investigation.

The violet helleborine is one of the latest flowering of our orchids, plants being frequently still in flower in the middle of September. The species usually comes into flower at the beginning of August, but specimens may often be found flowering in July, or even in June. Godfery has suggested that such early flowering individuals may be those in which the saprophytic type of nutrition is most developed. It is an interesting point that in many localities, if not in all, the plants with the broadest leaves flower earliest, those with narrower leaves later. If we accept the view that the plant is dependent on the food manufactured by the leaves, it is clear that the time of flowering will be related to the speed at which the food necessary for the development of the flower-spike can be produced. The relationship between leaf size and time of flowering, mentioned above, is quite easily explicable on this view, but it is more difficult to reconcile with the views put forward by Godfery. Indeed the supposedly saprophytic reddish plants may well be able to manufacture food at an exceptional speed, which would explain their early flowering. It is obvious, however, that further observations are desirable in this connection.

The pollination and fertilisation of *E. purpurata* is carried out by wasps exactly as in the broad-leaved helleborine. Wasps may frequently be seen walking about on the stems or flowers ; one was seen in Surrey vainly trying to remove the numerous pollinia which were attached to it. Examination shows that the pollinia are removed from most flowers, while, on the other hand, most of the flowers will be seen to have set fruit by October. There are no records of any sort of multiplication by vegetative means, such as is known in the dark red helleborine and marsh helleborine, but this is not surprising in view of the upright rootstock and deeply descending roots.

Green-leaved or Narrow-lipped Helleborine (*Epipactis leptochila*)

This interesting helleborine has been recognised as a distinct species only during the last thirty years, having before that been confused with some of the variations of the very variable and widely spread broad-leaved helleborine. Further study has, however, shown that it is very different from *E. helleborine*, not only in the general shapes of the parts of the flower, but also in the fact that the flowers are almost always self-pollinated. In this respect it agrees with the dune helleborine, but there is otherwise very little in common between the two species. The green-leaved helleborine is usually a woodland plant (Pl. 13a, p. 142), and can frequently be found growing with either the broad-leaved or violet helleborines ; little difficulty, however, need be experienced in distinguishing it from either species once the salient features of *E. leptochila* have been grasped. As the name indicates, the whole plant, leaves and flowers alike, is practically devoid of any red or purplish colouring, thus contrasting with the three commoner species already described.

The rootstock in the green-leaved helleborine is somewhat similar to that in the violet helleborine, situated rather deeply in the soil and often more or less thickened in old plants. Numerous roots arise from it, but although these permeate a rather large volume of soil, they do not usually penetrate so deeply as in *E. purpurata*. It is not known to what extent they are infected by the usual fungus, but judging from the habitat and root system, it is probable that there is a certain amount of infection. The rootstock frequently bears only one aerial leafy stem, but in older plants, and also in certain localities, there may be as many as five or six stems ; this helps to distinguish the species from the broad-leaved helleborine, in which there are rarely more than one stem in woodland plants. The stems are from six inches to over two feet in height, bearing numerous rather broad green or yellow-green leaves in two rows, in which respect the species differs from *E. helle-borine*, where the leaves are in three rows and often look to be placed all round the stem. The stem terminates in a slender rather loose flower-spike about three to nine inches in length, containing up to 25 flowers. The flowers are rather larger than in the broad-leaved helleborine, and are mostly pale yellowish green in colour with a whitish or rarely very pale pinkish lip epichile. The cup-shaped hypochile may be various shades of pink or purplish pink, but this scarcely affects the general appearance of the flower. The sepals and petals are all spreading, relatively longer and much more pointed than in *E. helleborine*, and pale green, or in the case of the petals whitish, in colour. The lip is also whitish, but its most striking feature is the long narrow and very pointed front part or epichile, which is very rarely curved underneath as is generally the case in the broad-leaved helleborine. This distinct lip shape gives the plant its alternative name of narrow- or slender-lipped helleborine. The column differs from that in both *E. helleborine* and *E. purpurata* in that it is so con-structed that when viewed from the side a gap appears between the front part and the stalked anther at the back (Pl. VIII, p. 95). In the other two species the column is more solidly built, so no space can be seen between it and the anther, which in these species has no obvious stalk. The large pear-shaped hanging fruits, which are devel-oped from practically every flower, give the plants a rather charac-teristic appearance after flowering is over.

For some time *Epipactis leptochila* was thought to be numbered among the endemic species of our islands, that is, those not occurring elsewhere. The species has, however, been recorded from several

PLATE 15

Robert Atkinson

Common Twayblade (*Listera ovata*). Hampshire; June

PLATE 16

Robert Atkinson

b. Autumn Ladies' Tresses (*Spiranthes spiralis*).

Robert Atkinson

a. Lesser Twayblades (*Listera cordata*). Angus; June

places in western (Westphalia) and central Germany (Brunswick) and in Denmark, while it seems probable that it occurs elsewhere in western Europe. It has apparently remained unrecognised in much the same way that it did for so long in this country. The green-leaved helleborine therefore falls into the small group comprising the Western European element of the British orchid flora. It is only fair to point out, however, that the various forms of *Epipactis*, whether they be really species or varieties, which are allied to *E. leptochila*, are still so poorly understood by botanists that our views about their distribution are still very tentative, and may have to be modified as more knowledge is obtained. The reader may gain a clearer insight into these difficulties when he reads the accounts dealing with the pendulous-flowered and Isle of Wight helleborines which follow this.

So far as distribution in this country is concerned (Map 10, p. 348), the green-leaved helleborine lies between species like the broad-leaved and marsh helleborines, which occur throughout the greater part of the British Isles, and the two species just mentioned (as well as the dune helleborine), which are known from a few localities only. *E. leptochila* is, however, definitely southern in distribution in this country, occurring in many of our southern counties from Kent westward to Devonshire and South Wales, and as far north as Gloucestershire and Shropshire. It has also been recorded from Durham, but there is some doubt about this. For reasons already mentioned it is probable that it will prove to be more widespread than present records would suggest. In some respects there is a great similarity between its distribution and that of the violet helleborine, but the latter species is more widely spread.

Like so many other helleborines, the green-leaved helleborine is predominantly, if not invariably, a woodland plant, only flourishing where there is considerable shade. It is known only from calcareous soils, especially the chalk, another respect in which it resembles many other species of *Epipactis*. It is most frequently found in beechwoods or in woods with an admixture of beeches, but has also been recorded growing under oaks. Generally the plants may be found where the tree canopy is complete, and the shade heaviest, so that the ground is devoid of other vegetation, except for a few scattered plants such as small brambles, ivy and wood violets (*Viola riviniana*). There may sometimes be a thick layer of leaves or, alternatively, the surface may be almost bare of leaves, but covered with a layer of mosses. In slightly lighter parts, for instance, towards the edges of the wood, other plants may accompany the green-leaved helleborine, but such places are clearly not its normal habitat. *E. leptochila* may be accompanied by either the broad-leaved helleborine or the violet helleborine, but the conditions which determine these occurrences are not at present known. Other orchids which occur with the green-leaved helleborine are the bird's nest orchid (*Neottia*) and the very rare spurred coral-root (*Epipogium aphyllum*), both of which are saprophytes lacking the usual green colouring of ordinary plants.

Epipactis leptochila flowers a little earlier than *E. helleborine*, being in good flower during the second half of July and the first half of August. Occasional plants may still be found flowering towards the end of August when the violet helleborine is in full flower. The green-leaved helleborine differs from both these species in the way in which the flowers are fertilised. It will be remembered that in these species (as well as in the dark red helleborine) there is a well-developed rostellum (a small bag containing a very sticky liquid) on which the pollinia rest. When an insect (usually a wasp) visits the flowers the rostellum is broken, and the escaping liquid sticks the pollinia to the insect's body, on which they are carried away to another flower. In the present species, however, the rostellum, though present in the bud, usually dries up just as, or even before, the flowers open. Opened flowers may sometimes be found with a properly developed rostellum, and from these a visiting insect can remove the pollinia, as has been observed on rare occasions. Godfery records a wasp removing pollinia from a flower and afterwards visiting a plant of *E. helleborine* nearby. The mechanism is, however, not so perfect as in other helleborines, as the anther leans so far forward that in falling out the pollinia do not usually come into contact with the rostellum, but slide down on to the surface of the stigma. Here the pollen grains germinate, and self-pollination and fertilisation of the flowers result.

As Godfery points out, it is still a matter of doubt whether the rostellum is in process of development, but is not yet perfected, or whether the species once had a properly functioning rostellum, which is gradually losing its efficiency. The evidence obtained by careful consideration of the pendulous-flowered and Isle of Wight helleborines provides a great deal of support for the latter interpretation. This matter is discussed further in the account of the last-named species.

PENDULOUS-FLOWERED HELLEBORINE (*Epipactis pendula*)

The discovery of this species is an excellent example of the way in which new discoveries may be made in the course of investigations on quite other problems. The discoverer, Mr. Charles Thomas, was visiting the dunes near Southport in July 1941, in order to study more closely the dune helleborine which grows there, when he came across a helleborine differing from all others known to him. The striking feature of this species, indicated in both its scientific and English names, is provided by the hanging flowers, which are of a brownish green colour (Pl. 13b, p. 142). Further study showed that this is a distinct species allied to the green-leaved helleborine, on the one hand, and to the Isle of Wight helleborine (*E. vectensis*), on the other. It has since been found in several other widely separated localities, and is probably a widespread, though rare, plant which has been overlooked in the past. This is not at all surprising in view of the close superficial resemblances between many of the species of *Epipactis*. Here we have a further illustration of how much more study is yet needed of our native plants.

The rootstock is rather variable, being either long or short, bearing one or more bunches (depending on its length) of rather long fleshy roots, and also in some plants a number of shorter ones. The purpose of these two kinds of roots is not yet known. Each rootstock usually bears only one aerial stem, but in a small proportion of plants there may be two or more stems, this being in agreement with most other normally single-stemmed species of *Epipactis*. The stems may be as much as two feet in height, although nine to eighteen inches is a more general figure. At the base there are several funnel-shaped sheaths, very similar to those found in the dune helleborine. Each stem bears three to six rather small and wavy-edged leaves in two rows on opposite sides, the lower leaves being almost circular or egg-shaped, while the upper are usually narrower and more pointed. They are of a rich green colour, which distinguishes the plant readily from the dune helleborine with which it sometimes grows, but whose leaves are of a rather unhealthy yellow-green colour. In the leaf colour *E. pendula* resembles more closely *E. leptochila*. The flower-spike is rather long (about six inches) for the size of the stem, containing about 15–30 rather densely placed greenish flowers, which hang almost vertically downwards. The sepals and petals, which spread rather widely, are pointed, but not so much as in the green-leaved helleborine. The sepals are often brownish on the outside, while the petals are whitish green. The lip has the usual two divisions, a greenish cup-shaped hypochile, and a triangular pointed white sometimes faintly tinged pink epichile, with a greenish rarely slightly recurved tip. Unlike so many other helleborines, the inside of the hypochile is very little different in colour from the outside. The lip epichile is neither so narrow nor so pointed as in the green-leaved helleborine, but the coloration in the two species is very similar. The hanging flowers, however, distinguish *E. pendula* from the other species. Another feature is the early stage at which the lip and column wither away, this often occurring soon after the flowers open, so that one may frequently find on the spike numerous flowers in which the perianth members are still fresh, while the inner parts of the flower are shrivelled and black.

The pendulous-flowered helleborine (Map 11, p. 348) belongs to the small group, four in number, of endemic British orchids, that is, species which are not known to occur outside the British Isles. As already mentioned, it has now been discovered in a number of widely separated localities, mostly in England, viz. Lancashire, Flintshire, Gloucestershire, Bedfordshire and Sussex. It will be seen that these places, in the aggregate, suggest a southerly distribution in Britain, somewhat comparable with those of the violet and green-leaved helleborines, but not enough is known of the species to speak with confidence of its actual distribution.

Although, like most other helleborines, *Epipactis pendula* is an inhabitant of woodlands, it is already known to have relatively catholic tastes. It was first found growing in the Scots pine plantations on the Lancashire sandhills, but Mr. Thomas has since found it in the same neighbourhood growing in large numbers under silver birches, which habitat is likely to be more natural. In both of these places the plant does not appear to grow in very heavy shade, for among the pines it favours the more open spots, while, as is well known, birches cast a very moderate shade even when growing close together. Curiously enough, in the other places where the pendulous-flowered helleborine has been found, it occurs under beeches, which cast a very heavy shade. In at least two of these places the habitat of our species is very dark, with a minimum of other vegetation, which consists of

PLATE IX

R. Atkinson

Clump of flowering stems of Violet Helleborine, *Epipactis purpurata*, by roadside in Hampshire ($\times \frac{1}{4}$)

PLATE X

C. Thomas

Flower spikes of two forms of Violet Helleborine, *Epipactis purpurata* ($\times 1\frac{3}{4}$)

such shade-loving plants as ivy, wild arum, dog's mercury and the like. Indeed the habitat in these localities is very similar to that of both the green-leaved and Isle of Wight helleborines. It should, however, be pointed out that the species grows much taller and is more robust in the better lighted localities. All the stations known so far are on soils relatively rich in lime, for sea-sand often contains a high proportion of lime owing to the presence of numerous fragments of sea-shells.

The pendulous-flowered helleborine appears to have a rather shorter period of flowering than other helleborines, extending from about the middle of July to the same period of August, but not usually being in flower in any one locality for the whole of this period. It seems to flower later in its beechwood habitats than on the Lancashire sand dunes. The individual flowers do not remain in real activity for very long, this being connected with the type of pollination and fertilisation. Owing to the hanging position of the flowers they must be very difficult of access by insects, and indeed it is very doubtful if they ever are so visited. No insects have yet been observed visiting the species. In fact the rostellum and the rest of the column wither as the flowers open or very soon afterwards, and consequently there is little opportunity for any cross-pollination to take place. Indeed it is probable that self-pollination occurs either in the bud, or just after the flowers open, by the swelling of the pollinia, which thus come into contact with the receptive stigma. This process is evidently very efficient, in view of the formation of a large pear-shaped seed-pod by almost every flower in the spike. Here we have a species of helleborine in which, so far as we know, cross-pollination never takes place, the plant being entirely dependent on self-pollination for the production of seeds.

Whether *Epipactis pendula* is a species that has not yet developed an effective mechanism for cross-pollination, as is suggested by Godfery for other similar species, or whether it is, on the other hand, a degenerate form which in the course of time has lost this mechanism, is yet a matter for further research. It is worth noting, however, that all the self-pollinated species (*E. dunensis*, *E. leptochila* and *E. pendula*) are far less widely distributed than are the three cross-pollinated species (*E. helleborine*, *E. purpurata* and *E. atrorubens*), and it would certainly appear that the members of the latter group had an earlier origin. It will be remembered that in the genus *Cephalanthera*, which on other grounds may be looked upon as older and more primitive than *Epipactis*, cross-pollination is the usual method.

Isle of Wight Helleborine (*Epipactis vectensis*)

Whereas most British botanists are in agreement as regards the distinctness of all the species so far mentioned, there is still considerable difference of opinion with respect to the Isle of Wight helleborine. It is included here because what is known of the species sheds an interesting light on some of the features of the other species, notably the green-leaved and pendulous-flowered helleborines. Like the two species just mentioned, the Isle of Wight helleborine (Pl. 14, p. 143) has greenish flowers with practically no red or purplish coloration, while the hanging flowers are, so far as we are aware, always self-pollinated. It may be distinguished from both by the very shallow hypochile of the lip, which does not form such a clearly defined cup, and by the almost closed flowers, the sepals and petals scarcely spreading at all.

The rootstock is short with a number of thick spreading roots, usually producing a solitary leafy stem. This stem is from six inches to one foot (rarely sixteen inches) in height with several funnel-shaped sheaths at the base, very like those in *E. pendula*, and four to six rather stiff bright green leaves in two ranks. The flower-spike is only about two to four inches in length, and bears a few flowers (up to fourteen in specially large plants) which, as in *E. pendula*, hang almost parallel with the stem. The flowers never seem to open out properly, and sometimes do not open at all. The green or whitish-green perianth members are rather long, narrow and pointed, while the lip is similarly coloured to that in *E. pendula*, but has a very shallow hypochile which is yellowish or whitish. The lip withers very early in the development of the flower, and this is also true of the column. It can be seen that the Isle of Wight helleborine closely resembles the pendulous-flowered helleborine, differing in its scarcely opening flowers, the long narrow sepals and the shallow hypochile of the lip.

As both the English and scientific names indicate, the species was first discovered in the Isle of Wight, where the late Mr. Hunnybun found it in 1917 in a wood on the chalk near Ventnor. Only a few individuals were found, and unfortunately it has not been possible to rediscover the plant since. Two years later Colonel M. J. Godfery found a small colony of five plants, of what he thought was the same species, at Mold in Flintshire, but this colony apparently shared the fate of the other, for it could not be rediscovered in subsequent years. A third colony was discovered in 1927, this time in Kent, specimens from this locality agreeing, at least in vegetative characters, with the original ones from Ventnor. The species has since been found at Winchester in Hampshire, in Devonshire, and more recently in Berkshire and Suffolk. At most of these places only a few plants were recorded, though there are a fair number in the Kent and Berkshire localities. It is evident, therefore, that the species, if it be a distinct one, is widely distributed in the southern part of the country (Map 12, p. 348). There is some doubt about the Flintshire record, as *E. pendula* has recently been found in the same district. Possibly Godfery's colony belonged to that species, which was not known when he wrote about *E. vectensis*.

The species has been found in most cases in rather dense or shady woods, either of beech or of mixed beeches and other trees, usually on chalky or calcareous soil, and almost invariably associated with a thick growth of ivy (Pl. 14, p. 143). Indeed the usual habitat resembles closely that of the pendulous-flowered helleborine, although so far the two species have never been found growing together. In some places, indeed, the ivy was so luxuriant that the discoverers got the impression that it might be overrunning the orchids. In the Kent locality, however, where the ivy is quite thick, vigorous specimens of the large white helleborine (*Cephalanthera damasonium*) grow with our species, which has not diminished appreciably in numbers since first discovered. In Berkshire the plants occur very locally under very tall old birches on a brick-earth soil, in company with *E. helleborine*. Although the soil is clearly less acid where the helleborines grow than in the neighbouring heathy vegetation, it is obviously not so calcareous as in the other stations of the species.

As in the pendulous-flowered helleborine, self-pollination of the flowers is almost invariable ; indeed, the flowers open so little that cross-pollination would scarcely be possible even if the mechanism were in working order. As the rostellum withers in the bud, however, there is obviously no possibility of an insect withdrawing the pollinia. These are very friable, pieces breaking off as in the dune helleborine and fertilisation following. Most of the flowers seem to set seed, judging by the large proportion of well-swollen seed pods on the spike.

In most places the plants seen were small and not particularly vigorous, so Godfery put forward the view that they represented degenerate colonies of other species, which were gradually dying out. He supported this view by reference to the incomplete opening of the flowers, the quickly withering lip and column, and the complete absence of cross-pollination of the flowers. It should be remembered, however, that this theory was advanced before the discovery of the pendulous-flowered helleborine, which shares many of the apparently " degenerate " characters of *E. vectensis*, but is a very robust and vigorous plant, and certainly far from dying out in Lancashire ! Nevertheless, there seems to be some justification for Godfery's view. It is an interesting point that the discoverers of these various colonies seemed to be rather doubtful of the identity of their plant with the others already recorded, and usually indicate some differences between them. Now, of course, most species show some degree of variation, but the differences mentioned in these accounts seem rather important, for instance, the shape of the lip epichile, or the degree of distinctness of the cup-like hypochile. One rather gets the impression of a series of small colonies of plants each possessing their own proper qualities, but sharing with one another such features as vertically hanging flowers which do not open properly. The additional point, that many of these colonies seem to have a relatively transient existence, rather supports the view that they may be small groups of degenerate individuals. In this connection it is pertinent to mention that in several widely separated places specimens or colonies of the green-leaved helleborine have been found, in which the lip is improperly formed and somewhat resembles that in the Isle of Wight helleborine. Taking all the evidence together, it is clear that a good deal more research is required before definite answers can be given to the many questions which spring to mind in connection with this exceedingly interesting plant.

CHAPTER 8

TWAYBLADES

As THE name indicates, the two plants here dealt with (*Listera ovata* and *L. cordata*, Pl. 15, p. 158; 16a, p. 159) are characterised by the possession of two broad flat leaves placed in a pair on opposite sides of the stem some way above the base. The only other orchids among our native species which also possess a similar pair of leaves are the two kinds of butterfly orchids (*Platanthera bifolia* and *P. chlorantha*, Pl. 24, p. 203 ; 25, p. 210), but these may be distinguished by their much larger cream or whitish scented flowers whereas in the twayblades the flowers are small and green or reddish. Other distinguishing features of the twayblades are the relatively large lip, forked in a manner reminiscent of the tongue of a snake (Fig. 61, p. 31), and the short almost globular ovaries. The common twayblade is one of the commonest and most widely spread of all our orchids, but the lesser twayblade, though found in many places in the northern parts of the British Isles, is very insignificant and easily overlooked. A detailed account of the remarkable pollination mechanism found in these plants is given in Chapter 3 (pp. 44–46).

COMMON TWAYBLADE (*Listera ovata*)

The word common as applied to this plant is no mere relative term, for the common twayblade is probably commoner and more widely distributed in this country than any other kind of orchid. No doubt it owes this partly to its small green flowers and general unattractiveness, but this cannot be the whole explanation as many of the helleborines are quite as inconspicuous and yet none of them is as common as is *Listera ovata* (Pl. 15, p. 158).

The underground parts of the plant consist of a short thick creeping stem or rhizome bearing a large tuft of long sinuous roots which penetrate the ground in all directions. Each year the rhizome grows up to form the aerial flowering stem, the underground growth being continued by a lateral bud which grows out from the base of the flowering stem, in fact the same type of growth as in the lady's slipper. The plants go on growing for many years, as many as 24 old flower-spikes having been observed on an individual rhizome. Although the mycorhizal fungus is needed for germination of the seeds and the plant is infected during the first four years of its life, subsequently the roots are completely devoid of the fungus. From this period onwards the plant is therefore entirely dependent for energy on the food which it can manufacture in its leaves, in this respect forming a marked contrast with its relative, the lesser twayblade. Although a leafy shoot is produced during the fourth year after germination and in subsequent years, another ten years elapse before the plant flowers, the intervening years being spent in building up sufficient stocks of food. The aerial stem reaches a height of six inches to over two feet, depending on the situation in which the plant is growing, being usually taller in shady places and shorter and stockier when in the open. It bears at a varying distance below the middle the two leaves, which are broadly egg-shaped or elliptical, up to six inches long and five inches wide, and more or less horizontal in position. Sometimes there is a third smaller and more pointed leaf just above, or more rarely below, the normal pair ; occasionally one may encounter colonies in which a large proportion of the plants have this additional leaf. In shadier spots the leaves are of a rich deep green colour, but on dry banks or open downs they may be quite yellowish-green, giving the plant a somewhat unhealthy look. The slender erect flower-spike, which is usually from four inches to one foot in length, bears a large number (sometimes as many as a hundred) of small green rather inconspicuous flowers, the sepals and petals of which are dull green sometimes tinged brownish or reddish, while the much larger hanging lip is a bright rich yellow-green, the central groove and base glistening with nectar. Exceptionally plants may be found in which all the three petals have the shape and character of lips, or, on the other hand, the lip may be quite simple in structure and resemble the other petals. In yet other plants there may be two lips of more or less normal structure. I saw a colony in Kent a few years ago in which, owing apparently to attacks by some insect, the spikes had hardly lengthened at all and the flowers remained so close together that they were unable to reverse in the normal manner (see also Pl. IIIb, p. 26). The lips in most cases were therefore pointing upwards or in a horizontal position.

The common twayblade has a very wide distribution outside the British Isles and on that account belongs to the Eurasian Element proper of the British orchid flora. It is found throughout Europe from north of the Arctic Circle in northern Scandinavia and Russia southwards to the Mediterranean, though in this latter region it is comparatively rare, while eastwards it extends through Siberia to the region of Lake Baikal and through Asia Minor and Persia to the western end of the Himalayan Range.

The species is found throughout the British Isles with the exception of the Shetland Islands (Map 17, p. 350). It has been known from England for a long time, the earliest record being in Turner's *Names of Herbes* . . . published in 1548. Here it is stated that the " Martagon ", as it is called, is found " in many places of Englande in watery middowes and in woddes ". The very distinct appearance of the plant, of course, enables one to identify old records with greater certainty than would be the case with other less easily recognisable orchids. On the whole the common twayblade may be looked upon as a lowland plant, in this respect contrasting with the lesser twayblade, but it has been recorded, sometimes in abundance, from altitudes of as much as 1,500 feet in this country, while on the Alps it is found up to 7,000–8,000 feet above sea-level.

Not only does *Listera ovata* occur in practically all parts of these islands, but it occupies a great variety of habitats throughout its range. Like most other British orchids, it is rather more common on limy soils than on those devoid of lime, but on both types it may be found as well in shady places as in the open. On the whole it grows better and forms larger plants where there is some shade, as in woods, coppices, scrubby places or shady lanes. However, it may be seen in large numbers on open chalk downs or in grasslands on limestone soils, either in short turf or among coarse grasses, although it rather favours the latter. On acid mineral soils, whether in the south or north of the country, it may be found among mixed grass and bracken or in mixtures of grass and heather. For instance, it is found in the Orkney Islands in damp places of the latter type. Although less common on peaty soils it sometimes occurs on such, particularly in the damper places among rushes, tall grasses, etc., where it may be associated with marsh and spotted orchids of various kinds, with the fragrant orchid (*Gymnadenia conopsea*) or with one or both of the butterfly orchids (*Platanthera bifolia* and *P. chlorantha*). Finally, the common twayblade has been recorded from the extreme inland portions of sand-dune areas though it only rarely occurs on the sand-hills themselves.

As regards woodland habitats *Listera ovata* is one of the few orchid species to be found in comparatively young plantations of pines and other conifers or of broad-leaved trees, while it may often be seen under dense growths of seedling trees, ash, oak, birches or the like, in openings of woods or at their margins. In such places the orchid can evidently stand extremely heavy shade, a high proportion of the plants being sterile either on account of the shade or because they represent young individuals which have not flowered.

The species occurs in an equally wide range of habitats on the Continent, where it has been recorded from a great variety of woodlands, bushy places, grasslands of various kinds, on both dry and damp soils and even in marshes or flushes below springs.

Listera ovata has quite a long flowering period, the first flowers opening soon after the middle of May or rarely even earlier in the south, while plants still in flower can usually be found in July. In the north of England and in Scotland July is the usual flowering month, but here, as elsewhere, the earliness or lateness of the season governs the time of first flowering. Plants have been found in full flower as late as September but this is rather exceptional.

The pollination of the common twayblade, already described fully on pp. 44–46 (see Fig. 9, p. 45), is carried out by small insects, ichneumons, flies, small beetles and the like. Hive bees also visit the flowers for the plentiful nectar but are too large to effect pollination. The insects climb up the centre of the lip, following the nectar, until they come into contact with the delicately adjusted and projecting rostellum on the short column. This causes a miniature explosion liberating some sticky liquid which very rapidly cements the pollinia to the insect's head and simultaneously frightens the insect off to another flower-spike, thus ensuring cross-pollination. Darwin and Godfery have pointed out how delicately adjusted the mechanism is at every stage, from the first release of the pollinia on to the rostellum, to the final movements which leave the receptive stigma clear for the insect bearing the pollinia. All observers testify to the numerous and varied

PLATE XI

b. Flower spikes of Irish Ladies' Tresses,
S. romanzoffiana (×¾)

E. J. Bedford

a. Flower spikes of Summer Ladies' Tresses,
Spiranthes aestivalis (×2)

E. J. Bedford

PLATE XII

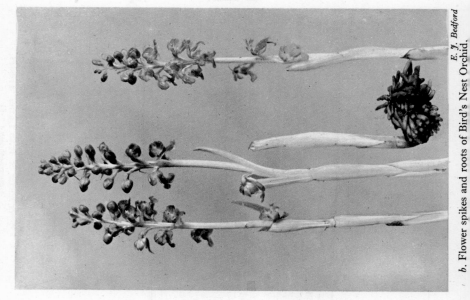

b. Flower spikes and roots of Bird's Nest Orchid.

a. Flower spike of Creeping Ladies' Tresses.

visitors to the flowers of the common twayblade, and their effectiveness in pollination is proved by the very high proportion of ripe seed pods which may be seen on most plants later in the season.

The species is, however, by no means entirely dependent on seeds for the production of new individuals and consequent multiplication of numbers. The long-lived roots store up food in swollen portions, this food being used in the production of buds at or near the tip of the root (see Fig. 3, p. 23). Such buds give rise to rhizomes producing aerial shoots, and following the eventual death of the root new individuals are formed which then carry on a separate existence. The advantage of this method of vegetative multiplication of individuals lies in the relatively rapid development of the plant in the early years when it can still draw food from the attached root. In the case of a plant so slow-growing as *Listera ovata*, this by-passing of the early seedling stages enables the species more quickly to take advantage of favourable circumstances. It also enables the plant to multiply in situations where the shade is so dense that even the common twayblade is unable to obtain effective pollination or indeed, perhaps, to produce flowers at all.

Lesser or Heart-leaved Twayblade (*Listera cordata*)

Although this species possesses all the essential features of its larger relative, yet it is so much smaller and the flowers so differently coloured that the inexperienced nature-lover might well be excused for not recognising the relationship. Indeed he might easily fail to see the plants at all, so inconspicuous are they in the great majority of habitats in which they occur. Nevertheless *Listera cordata* (Pl. 16a, p. 159) shows well the paired leaves somewhere near the middle of the stem, the relatively large forked lip (lower petal) (Fig. 6I, p. 31), and the almost globular ovaries which are the characteristic features of the twayblades. The whole plant, however, is only about a quarter to a third of the size of the common twayblade, the leaves are rarely more than an inch long and more or less heart-shaped, while the comparatively few reddish-tinged flowers are very much smaller than those of *Listera ovata*.

The rhizome in the lesser twayblade is slender and creeping, and bears a small number of rather thin roots which spread widely in the surface layers of the soil where there is plenty of humus, or in the upper parts of the moss-cushions in which the plant is often embedded. Contrary to the state of affairs in the common twayblade, the rhizome in the present species stores very little food and is comparatively short-lived. The roots are almost invariably heavily infected with the mycorhizal fungus, and there is no doubt that the plant is nourished to a great extent through the agency of its fungal associate. The aerial stem, which is produced in the same way as in *Listera ovata*, is slender and is usually from three to six inches in height, although it may occasionally surpass this height when growing under favourable conditions. The two more or less heart-shaped leaves are borne almost horizontally at about the middle of the stem ; they are usually rather deep green in colour but paler underneath. The short loose flower-spike contains about 6–12 very small reddish-green or reddish flowers, with a relatively large spreading or hanging lip which is darker coloured than the remainder. The whole plant is very inconspicuous and easily overlooked.

Listera cordata is one of the three species forming the Northern Montane Element of the British orchid flora. These are plants which are characteristic of the mountainous regions of northern Europe and Asia, but are less widely spread in the mountains farther south ; they are not found on lower ground in these latter regions. The lesser twayblade has a comparatively wide distribution, occurring throughout the northern part of Europe and extending eastwards across Siberia to Japan and Kamchatka. Southwards it occurs as far as the Pyrenees, northern Italy, Bosnia and Bulgaria, and has been recorded from the northern part of Asia Minor. It is also found in Greenland and throughout the northern parts of America from Newfoundland and Labrador in the east to Colorado and Alaska in the west. It will be seen that the species completely encircles the Arctic regions, though, like other orchids, it is not a member of the true Arctic Flora. Throughout this huge area it shows very little variation except such as may be more or less directly ascribed to differences in the habitat.

In the British Isles the general distribution of the lesser twayblade is in conformity with its distribution outside (Map 18, p. 350). That is to say, it is only really at home in northern districts, particularly in Scotland and the northern half of Ireland, but it extends southwards as far as Derbyshire, Shropshire and Cheshire in England, and into Wales north of Merioneth and Montgomery inclusive. South of the above limits our species has been recorded from several southern and south-western counties, but the plant is very local and rarely occurs in colonies of more than a dozen individuals. However, recent records indicate that it is still to be found in Devonshire, Somerset and Hampshire, though the inconspicuousness of the species and the short life of any given individual tend to make the re-discovery of plants in any one year rather difficult. *Listera cordata* is also found in a number of places in southern Ireland, but it is hardly so common there as farther north. It is possible that the lesser twayblade is more common in south-west England than is generally considered to be the case, as there are very extensive stretches of suitable country there. It is less likely to occur in south-east England, but even there the possibility of finding the species cannot be excluded. It would seem, however, that a fairly high rainfall is needed for it to maintain itself successfully.

Listera cordata is found in two well-marked habitats, in the open moorland or in wet bogs among heather and other Ericaceous shrubs, on the one hand, and in pine and other upland woods, on the other. In both places the soil is usually relatively acid, and since the plants usually grow in the shelter of comparatively tall heather on north-facing slopes, the two habitats may not be so different as might appear on first consideration. Indeed the plants grow frequently among heather or bell-heather (*Erica cinerea*) as much as two or three feet in height, so that they can only be seen when the bushes are separated. Usually the orchids are actually rooted in tufts of moss growing among the stems of the heather plants. As might be expected, the plants in the woods are usually larger and more vigorous-looking than those in the open, with larger and thinner leaves. It has been suggested that there are perhaps two races of the species, which are adapted to living in their own special set of conditions. The lesser twayblade is often to be found in comparatively damp spots or small bogs, growing in large sopping moss-cushions among the surrounding heather, etc., or on slopes where water tends to trickle down from above. In such places it may be associated with the bog orchid (*Hammarbya paludosa*), sundews (*Drosera* spp.), cranberry (*Oxycoccus quadripetala*) and similar plants. In woods it prefers rather open places, where it may be found among heather, bilberry and other heath plants, between bracken if not too thick, or sometimes in quite bare places in moss or pine-needles (Pl. 16a, p. 159). It is usually a plant of hilly districts, contrasting in this respect with the common twayblade, being found up to 2,500 feet and over in Scotland and Ireland. In northern and western Ireland, however, the species descends almost to sea-level, this no doubt being associated with the generally cool damp climate in these regions. In favourable localities the lesser twayblade may occur in large numbers forming quite extensive sheets, but more frequently the plants are scattered about rather sparsely or in small groups.

Listera cordata flowers a little later than its larger relative, that is, from about the middle of June to the middle of August, but it may be found as late as September. Pollination is carried out in the same way as in the common twayblade, the usual insect agents being small flies and ichneumons. As in *L. ovata* the pollinia may be partly distributed by small insects crawling over the flowers, or the pollen may fall on to the stigma and self-fertilisation follow. In any case the process of fertilisation is a very rapid one, as it is possible in the same flower-spike to find flowers open at the top while the seeds have ripened and are being shed from the lowermost capsules.

The lesser twayblade, however, is by no means dependent on seeds for the production of new plants, since vegetative multiplication by means of root buds is on an even larger scale than in the common twayblade. Such buds may be developed on the roots when the plant is quite young (Fig. 3 A, p. 23). The roots penetrate into the soil for considerable distances and, owing to the high degree of fungal infection, are able to live more or less independently of the plant. They store food, and buds develop from the swollen portions, these buds growing up and forming aerial shoots which eventually develop into separate individuals. These new plants flower in their third year, and at the same age are already producing further root-buds themselves. This rapid multiplication is probably the explanation of the great local abundance of the species in favourable localities, enabling it to take immediate advantage of a change in the habitat. There is thus a marked similarity between the lesser twayblade and the red helleborine in the important role which the fungal-infected roots and root-buds play in the life-history of the species.

PLATE 17

Photograph by E. J. Bedford.   Coloured by hand
Summer Ladies' Tresses (*Spiranthes aestivalis*).   Hampshire

PLATE 18

G. H. McLean

Irish Ladies' Tresses (*Spiranthes romanzoffiana*). Co. Antrim; August

CHAPTER 9

THE LADIES' TRESSES

THIS SMALL group consists of only four species, all of which may be distinguished from other British orchids on account of their flowers being arranged in an obvious spiral or spirals. Usually there is only a single row of flowers, but in the Irish ladies' tresses there are three. The degree to which the flower-spike is twisted varies in different individuals, but only rarely is there no perceptible twist ; in such cases the general appearance and structure of the flowers enable one to distinguish the plant from the few other similar orchids.

The four species fall into two distinct genera, *Spiranthes*, which contains the true ladies' tresses, and *Goodyera*, the creeping ladies' tresses or creeping goodyera. The former have erect stems with a basal tuft of leaves and divergent swollen tuberous roots often rather like those of a dahlia (Fig. 2 D, p. 12) ; in the latter, on the other hand, the lower part of the stem is weak and creeping, with the leaves in a rosette-like tuft at its tip, and relatively slender roots at intervals. A further difference is furnished by the geographical distributions, for whereas the true ladies' tresses are restricted to England and Ireland (with the exception of two places in the southern Hebrides), the creeping ladies' tresses is essentially a Scottish plant, being found otherwise only in a relatively few localities in northern England and Norfolk.

SPIRANTHES

There are three British members of this genus, which is represented by numerous species in North America, and another which is widely spread throughout southern and eastern Asia and Australia. Those occurring in these islands are the common or autumn ladies' tresses

(*S. spiralis*, Pl. 16b, p. 159), the summer ladies' tresses (*S. aestivalis*, Pl. 17, p. 174) and the Irish ladies' tresses (*S. romanzoffiana*, Pl. 18, p. 175). Apart from the spiral flowers and general habit, already referred to, *Spiranthes* may be distinguished from *Goodyera* by the pollinia, each of which consists of two thin leaves of pollen grains, these " leaves " being attached to a sticky disc or viscidium. The viscidium is a special part of the rostellum, which may be detached and carried away together with the pollinia. We have here, therefore, a mechanism comparable with that in *Orchis* and other highly developed genera, a much more elaborate arrangement than that in the helleborines, or even in the twayblades. The more or less horizontally placed flowers are somewhat tubular in structure (Pl. XI, p. 170), the upper sepal and two petals being joined together to form the upper side of the tube, while the long trough-shaped lip constitutes the lower half. The lip is wrapped closely round the column in its lower part, while near the base are two small glands which secrete the nectar for which insects visit the flower. The stamen rests on the upper side of the column, while the rostellum projects forward below it bearing the long narrow strap-shaped viscidium along the middle with the sticky surface downwards ; on the column behind the rostellum is the receptive stigma. When the flowers first open the rostellum is situated very close to the under-lying lip, leaving a very narrow aperture, which is just large enough to admit the relatively long slender proboscis of the humble-bees and other bees (*Halictus*, etc.,) which visit the flowers. The insects alight on the broad spreading front part of the lip, inserting their proboscis into the narrow opening in order to reach the nectar collected in the hollowed-out base. The proboscis, of necessity, touches and exposes the long sticky viscidium, which adheres to it, the pollinia being withdrawn as the insect leaves the flower, while the cement sets hard in a short period so that the whole pollen apparatus is firmly fixed. In the course of a day or so the opening is widened by the moving apart of the column and lip. If the flower is visited now by an insect bearing the pollinia from another flower, there is room for them to be inserted with the proboscis. The brittle pollinia are pushed against the sticky stigma, and portions are broken off, pollination thereby resulting. It will be observed that it is not possible for the pollinia from a flower to be deposited on the stigma of the same flower, except during two distinct visits, and even then only in the later stage of development of the flower. Self-pollination has not been observed and must be exceedingly rare ; indeed observations show that the flowers are usually visited soon after opening.

Common or Autumn Ladies' Tresses (*Spiranthes spiralis*)

This is much the most frequently met of the three British species of *Spiranthes* for, although not in any way a common plant, it is widely distributed over the greater part of England and Wales, and in southern Ireland (Pl. 16b, p. 159). It may even be found very abundantly, though like many other orchids, the number to be seen in any given place fluctuates much from year to year. It is the smallest of our ladies' tresses, and indeed is among the smallest of all our British orchids, only the bog orchid (*Hammarbya*) being consistently smaller. In addition, it has the distinction of flowering later than any other orchid, often being still in flower in late September or early October.

The autumn ladies' tresses is very different in appearance from all the orchids previously described, having a bunch or rosette of leaves at the very base of the stem and thick fleshy tuberous roots. In these respects it resembles much more closely the genus *Orchis* and many other well-known British orchids. There is no persistent underground rootstock or rhizome, as in the helleborines, the seedling rootstock dying when the plant is about eight years old before the first leaves appear. Instead the food is stored in two or three (rarely as many as five) finger- or carrot-shaped fleshy roots about half an inch to an inch in length. The food in these is used to produce the flower-spike and fresh leaf-rosette, after which they are replaced by new ones, the old ones shrivelling up and dying away when the food is exhausted. There are usually four or five leaves in the rosette, each short and broad, rather stiff, deep or bluish green in colour, about one or two inches in length, and a quarter to half an inch broad. These leaves are produced during the autumn, last through the winter, and die away about late May or June, the flower-spike developing from their centre. By the time it is fully developed, however, the old leaves have withered away and a new rosette has appeared next to, but separate from, the flowers. In the possession of this curious mode of growth the common ladies' tresses is unique among our orchids. During the first year after its appearance each root is free from fungal infection, but this takes place during the next autumn, and it is evident that the plant depends considerably on the food obtained through the activity of the fungus.

This is not surprising in view of the small volume of soil which the roots penetrate and from which they can absorb food and water for the plant. Lateral buds on the leafy stem of any year may develop separate root tubers, the small plant produced forming eventually a distinct individual when the connecting stem dies away. This process, repeated several times, gives rise to a group of plants growing close together, a very characteristic feature in *Spiranthes spiralis*. The erect flower-spike reaches a total height of from three to six inches in this country, but it may be as much as a foot in height elsewhere. The closely placed whitish flowers, about ten to twenty in number, usually form a single spiral row about one to five inches in length, though this spiral may sometimes not be very evident. They are sweet-scented during the daytime, in this respect contrasting with the summer ladies' tresses (*S. aestivalis*) in which the flowers are more powerfully scented at night. As mentioned previously, the upper sepal, the two petals and the lip form a horizontal or sloping tube which encloses the column, the two lateral sepals being curled back one on each side.

The common ladies' tresses belongs to the Southern Eurasian Element of the British orchid flora, as its distribution in Europe and Asia is distinctly southern. In the north it extends only as far as Denmark, northern Germany and then through Poland and central Russia to the Ural Mountains, while southwards it occurs throughout central Europe. It is, however, abundant in the Mediterranean region from Spain to Greece, occurring also in Algeria in North Africa and through Asia Minor and Syria to the Caucasus district. The species appears to be restricted to regions in which the rainfall is mostly during autumn and spring when the fungus is most active, but owing to its summer resting period, when there are no properly developed leaves, the plant can stand considerable summer drought. The late flowering no doubt restricts its distribution, both northwards and also above moderate altitudes, as the early snow in these regions would prevent setting of seed in most years. As a result *S. spiralis* is usually a lowland plant, although it may be found on the European mainland to nearly 3,000 feet above sea-level.

The distribution in the British Isles is in conformity with that elsewhere (Map 13, p. 349). The species is most abundant in the south of England and Ireland, becoming less frequent as one goes north. In England it reaches its northern limit in northern Yorkshire and the extreme south of Westmorland, while in Ireland it is not found north of a line running diagonally from Wexford through Tipperary and Galway to Mayo, except for Co. Dublin, where it occupies what might be termed an outlier some distance beyond the line mentioned. The common ladies' tresses has been known for a long time, the first reference to its occurrence in this country dating from 1548. William Turner mentions in his little book entitled *The Names of Herbes . . .* that " Satyrion is very commune in Germany, and a certeyne ryghte kynde of the same groweth besyde Syon, it bryngeth furth whyte floures in the end of harueste and it is called Lady traces ". The Syon referred to is Syon House between Brentford and Isleworth on the opposite side of the Thames from Kew Gardens. In those days, and for many years afterwards, the autumn ladies' tresses grew in quite a number of localities in Middlesex, some of them, such as Islington and Highgate, now well within the built-up area of London.

As might be guessed from the low stature of the plant, *S. spiralis* usually grows in short turf or other low vegetation. It is most characteristic of sunny slopes, but may be found in a variety of localities, either on chalk downs, on the more stable and overgrown parts of sandhills, on roadside verges or in dry pastures. It is found especially in the neighbourhood of the sea, and seems on the whole to prefer a certain amount of lime in the soil. However, the species has also been recorded from sandy heathy places, even in company with heather or other heath plants. It would seem that a well-drained soil is usually preferred, but the plant occurs rarely in wetter places. In western Ireland the ladies' tresses is a common constituent of the flora growing in the cracks in the extensive areas of limestone " pavement " which extend through Clare, Galway and Mayo. Judging from the usual localities where it occurs, *S. spiralis* is unable to stand very much shade, but it may sometimes be found at the edges of woods, and has been recorded from open scrubby woods in Europe. It is one of the earliest orchids to re-occupy grassy downs or pastures which have formerly been under the plough. Owing to the position of the leaf rosette practically at ground level, the species is able to exist even if the flower-spikes are regularly removed by cutting. Indeed there are many records of the ladies' tresses appearing in large numbers on lawns which for some reason or another have not been cut. At one locality in Somerset the species used to flower regularly on a tennis court immediately underneath the net, where the mowing was not quite so vigorous as elsewhere. From what we know of the life-history, the plants must have been growing in such places for a number of years before being seen in flower, even assuming that they were able to flower successfully immediately on reaching maturity. The autumn ladies' tresses shares with many other orchids the habit of fluctuating greatly in numbers from year to year, so that at a locality where hundreds of flower-spikes are to be found in one year, a careful search in the following year may reveal no more than a dozen flowering plants. This is probably due to varying activity on the part of the fungus, which contributes very largely to the nourishment and consequent vigour of the plants. There is no evidence that more than a small proportion of the plants die after flowering, as in the case of the bee orchid (*Ophrys apifera*), which also exhibits these striking fluctuations.

Pollination is carried out in the manner described in the account of the genus *Spiranthes* (p. 176). The flowers are scented in the daytime, and are normally visited and pollinated by humble-bees, which carry off the pollinia adhering by their long narrow sticky viscidium to the flat proboscis of the insect. The bee usually starts at the bottom of the spike, where the flowers are in the right state to receive the pollen on their stigmas. As the pollinia are very brittle a single insect may pollinate a number of flowers with pieces from the same pollinium, a comparatively small number of grains being sufficient to fertilise all the ovules in a seedpod. The insect then climbs to the upper flowers, where the pollinia are all ready for removal, and the procedure is then repeated on another spike. The process is evidently very effective in the autumn ladies' tresses, as observations show that the pollinia are removed from most of the flowers, while seed is set by practically every flower in a spike. This regular and copious seed production no doubt contributes towards the ability of the species to colonise suitable newly available habitats such as ploughed land which has reverted to grass. The only method of vegetative multiplication is that described above, arising from the development of more than one lateral bud on the leafy stem and the subsequent separation of the new plants thus formed. But clearly these young plants are very near the parent, and this method cannot enable the plant to spread at any appreciable speed.

SUMMER LADIES' TRESSES (*Spiranthes aestivalis*)

Unlike the last species, the summer ladies' tresses is one of the rarest of British orchids. For many years it has been known from only two very limited localities in the New Forest in Hampshire, and it is to be feared that the species may now be extinct in both of these places. It differs from the autumn ladies' tresses in the time of flowering, which is during July and August, and by possessing long narrow leaves and a longer, more slender flower-spike (Pl. 17, p. 174).

The rootstock in *S. aestivalis* is very similar to that in *S. spiralis*, consisting of a small crown to which are attached several (two to six) fleshy tuberous roots, which taper gradually downwards and may be as much as four inches in length. These roots are more numerous, longer and narrower than those in the autumn ladies' tresses. Two new roots are formed each year after the plant has reached the flowering stage. There may also be a few short slender roots, but it is evident that quite a small volume of soil is penetrated by the roots, which are strongly infected by the mycorhizal fungus on reaching a certain age. The plant clearly obtains a good deal of its food as a result of the activity of this fungus. The stem, which is usually from four to eight inches in height, may in favourable conditions be as much as fifteen inches. It bears several erect leaves, which are about two to four inches long and between $\frac{1}{4}$ and $\frac{1}{2}$ inch broad ; most of these form a kind of tuft near the base, but there are usually one or two smaller ones well up the stem. The leaves are yellowish green in colour, containing little chlorophyll, and thus provide another indication of the degree to which the plant is dependent on its associated fungus. These leaves are still only quite small in the autumn, and do not develop to full size until the spring, being in this respect quite different from those in the autumn ladies' tresses. The rather slender flower-spike is usually about three inches long, containing from five to twenty flowers which, as in the common ladies' tresses, are arranged in a single spirally twisted row (Pl. XIa, p. 170). The small white flowers are very similar in appearance and structure to those of *S. spiralis*, but are longer and relatively narrower.

The summer ladies' tresses also falls into the Southern Eurasian group of British orchids, but is even more southerly in distribution than is the preceding species. It is much commoner in France and the Mediterranean region than elsewhere, extending north and east from this area, in a rather irregular manner, as far north as Holland, southern Germany, Austria and the western Carpathians. The species occurs in Algeria in the south, and locally in Asia Minor. In all the warmer regions it is found in the damper more mountainous parts, being absent from the hot and parched districts. In Switzerland and the Tirol the summer ladies' tresses may be found at altitudes of over 4,000 feet, a good deal higher than the autumn ladies' tresses. This is probably because its earlier flowering enables fruit to be set before the earliest autumn snow falls.

In the British Isles (Map 14, p. 349) the summer ladies' tresses is a very rare plant, which has evidently been decreasing in numbers for many years, and is now almost, if not entirely, extinct. Apart from Jersey and Guernsey in the Channel Islands, where the species may still be found in small numbers, it is known only from the New Forest in Hampshire. The species was thought to have been discovered in a bog in the Forest of Wyre in Worcestershire as long ago as 1854. A single specimen only was said to have been found, subsequent search both in the same and following years failing to yield any further plants. Luckily the solitary specimen was preserved with full details of its discovery, though it has remained overlooked for many years. Examination shows that the specimen is not a *Spiranthes* at all, but an abnormal individual of the fragrant orchid (*Gymnadenia conopsea*), normal plants of which were recorded as occurring in the bog at the time of the discovery of the supposed ladies' tresses.

In the New Forest, where the species was first discovered in 1840, it appears to have been found in three or four localities altogether. In one of these as many as two hundred flower-spikes could be seen annually for some years after 1900, but in the course of thirty years the number had dwindled to about a score. At one time the surface of the bog in another place where the plant grew was described as being " white " with the flower-spikes. Plants have been seen in only two localities within recent years, and no flowers could be found in either during more recent visits. It is well known that the number of spikes fluctuates considerably from year to year, so it is to be hoped that there has merely been a succession of bad years, and that the species may be discovered again. Unfortunately the localities have been interfered with by draining and in other ways, so possibly the habitat may have been altered materially. In any case it is evident that the species has decreased much in the New Forest since the turn of the century.

Both in this country and elsewhere the summer ladies' tresses almost invariably occurs in boggy or marshy ground, usually associated with springs or streams. The vegetation of such places consists mainly of grass-like plants such as purple moor grass (*Molinia caerulea*), sedges (*Carex* spp.) or bog rush (*Schoenus*), but this though thick is not usually very tall, the orchid being killed off if the vegetation becomes too luxuriant. The soil in these bogs may be slightly acid or more frequently neutral, but the species is never found in true moors. Other plants which may occur are bog moss (*Sphagnum*) and the shrubby sweet gale (*Myrica gale*). In Europe the summer ladies' tresses is accompanied by the early marsh orchid, marsh helleborine and fragrant orchid, all of which are quite general in marshy places in this country. The restriction of the species to quite wet habitats distinguishes it clearly from the autumn ladies' tresses, which shows a definite preference for dry banks and slopes.

As the name indicates, *Spiranthes aestivalis* flowers in the summer months, from the middle of July to the middle of August, the beginning of August being the best time to see it in flower. In more southern latitudes it flowers earlier, in June and early July. The pollination mechanism is clearly the same as in *S. spiralis*, but from the fact that the flowers become fragrant in the evening, it is thought that they may be pollinated by night-flying insects, perhaps by moths. However, this is only a surmise, as we do not know what insects visit the species. Multiplication of the plants vegetatively takes place, as in the autumn ladies' tresses, by the development at the base of the leafy stem of additional lateral buds, which form their own tuberous roots ; the small plants thus formed become separate when the connecting part of the rootstock dies away.

Irish Ladies' Tresses (*Spiranthes romanzoffiana*)

This species is in some ways the most remarkable of British orchids, for although it occurs in several localities in Ireland, and also in the southern Hebrides, it is not found elsewhere in Europe. On the other hand, it is widely spread in North America from Alaska and Canada in the north to California, Colorado, Illinois and Pennsylvania in the south. The North Atlantic Ocean therefore separates the two areas in which this species is found. Apart from its remarkable geographical distribution, the Irish ladies' tresses differs from the other two British species of *Spiranthes* by having the flowers in three spirally twisted rows instead of in a single row, this resulting in a thicker and denser flower-spike (Pl. 18, p. 175).

The main stem of the plant, as in the other two species already described, arises from a lateral bud at the base of the preceding year's stem, and in its turn grows out to form the flowering stem for the current year. The underground part of the stem bears a variable number of fleshy but relatively slender tuberous roots, not so thick as in the summer ladies' tresses but usually considerably longer (Fig. 2 D, p. 12). In drier habitats the roots tend to be thicker and to grow down more or less vertically ; in wet boggy places, where the plant usually grows, they spread more or less horizontally. A plant generally has from three to five tuberous roots, but in America there may be as many as twelve. The tubers appear first in autumn, usually two in each season, but do not attain their full size or number until the next summer ; they are strongly infected with the mycorhizal fungus associated with the species. The fully developed stem is usually between four inches and a foot in height in British plants, but in America may be nearly two feet in really fine specimens, with an average height of between nine inches and a foot. Plants from southern Ireland are, on the whole, smaller than those growing farther north. The leaves, which are about five or six in number, are more or less erect and narrow, about the same width as in the summer ladies' tresses. In the southern plants they are nearly flat, but in northern Ireland the edges fold or curl back so that the narrower leaves appear tubular and consequently even narrower still. The flower-spike is much thicker than in the species already described, consisting of three rows of flowers, more or less spirally twisted, but it is also usually shorter than in the summer ladies' tresses (Pl. XIb, p. 170). The closely placed flowers are either white or creamy white in colour and strongly scented, recalling either hawthorn or vanilla according to different observers. They are distinctly larger than in either the summer or autumn ladies' tresses. All the sepals and petals, and also the seedpod, are covered with hairs ending in a knob-like gland, which secretes a slightly sticky liquid.

Spiranthes romanzoffiana is not found anywhere in Europe outside the British Isles, but occurs throughout the northern parts of North America. In the more southern parts of its range in America it is a mountain plant, but extends northwards to Alaska and the Aleutian Islands. The occurrence of species such as the Irish ladies' tresses and the blue-eyed grass (*Sisyrinchium angustifolium*) on both sides of the Atlantic Ocean has raised interesting speculations as to how this could have come about. It is generally accepted that the area of distribution of the species must at one time have been continuous, while it is also agreed that the breaking up of this single continuous area into two, separated by thousands of miles of sea, must have been the result of the vast climatic changes associated with the last great Ice Age, which terminated about 10,000 years ago. There is not, however, the same amount of agreement with regard to the more detailed course of events which finally left *S. romanzoffiana* stranded in two parts of Ireland and in the Hebrides, but nowhere else in Europe. The question is still a matter for vigorous controversy, from which it appears that a good deal more information from various sources will have to be obtained and correlated before a solution can be offered which is likely to gain general acceptance.

Within the British Isles the species is known to occur in three distinct regions, separated from one another by distances of sixty miles or more (Map 15, p. 349). The first of these, in which the species was first discovered so long ago as 1810, lies in western Cork and southern Kerry. Here the Irish ladies' tresses has been recorded from about eight different localities scattered at intervals from Timoleague (a little east of Clonakilty), the most easterly locality, westwards to the West Cove and Waterville region north of the mouth of the Kenmare River. The second region, which is situated about 200 miles north of that just outlined, has Lough Neagh as its centre. *S. romanzoffiana* has been recorded in this area from all the counties bordering on the Lough, usually not far from its shores, but it also grows along some of the streams running into the lake, while it is found along the River Bann as far north as Coleraine in Co. Derry. The species is very much more abundant in this second region than in the first, more than a hundred plants having been seen on different occasions in each of several localities.

The third region, unlike the other two, lies not in Ireland, but in the southern islands of the Inner Hebrides in Scotland. So far the species has been found only in the islands of Colonsay and Coll, but it is quite likely to occur in other islands as well. The plant from Coll was first recorded as *S. spiralis*, the autumn ladies' tresses, but in view of the general distribution of that species in Britain, it seems almost certain that it was the Irish ladies' tresses which was found. In 1939 and 1940 the species was found in numerous localities in Coll, growing in damp moorland. Dr. J. Heslop Harrison informs me that it was still flourishing in the island in 1947. Very few plants have been discovered so far in Colonsay.

It is interesting to note that there are quite marked differences between the plants growing in the first of the three areas mentioned above and those found in the latter two. The southern plants are on the whole shorter and stouter with broader flatter leaves, while the flowers are closer together and pure white in colour with a broad lip. In the northern Irish and Scottish plants the flowers are creamy-white in colour and the lip is narrower. On account of these differences some authorities have considered that there are two distinct species in the British Isles, the northern one being the same as the American species, whereas the southern form is an endemic species which does not occur anywhere else. However, all study of *S. romanzoffiana* in America makes it quite clear that, like most other species with extensive distributions, it is a very variable species. It seems more reasonable to regard the two Irish forms as only variants of a single species which, as a result of isolation from one another, have become more or less segregated in their two areas of distribution into two distinct populations. Admittedly, this is a way in which new species can and do arise, but separation of the two types has not yet reached that stage.

The Irish ladies' tresses resembles the summer ladies' tresses in preferring wet boggy places. On the whole, however, it grows in rather more acid situations than its English relative. Its favourite spots are wet peaty or spongy marshes apparently flooded in the winter. Here it is associated with sedges and rushes (Pl. 18, p. 175), and also marsh and bog plants such as meadow sweet (*Filipendula ulmaria*), sneezewort (*Achillea ptarmica*), marsh cinquefoil (*Comarum palustre*), marsh pennywort (*Hydrocotyle vulgaris*), bog pimpernel (*Anagallis tenella*), etc. Praeger, in recording the original discovery of the northern type in County Armagh in 1892, states that the species was growing in the old dug-out portion of a peat-bog, on hard wet peat intersected by drains and pools. Other habitats where it is found include wet stony lake shores and damp rushy or grassy meadows. The species grows in similar places in America, but in that country it is also found in rather drier spots.

The flowering period of *S. romanzoffiana* lies between those of the summer and autumn ladies' tresses, extending from the end of July throughout the month of August, the first two weeks of August being usually the best period for seeing the species. Like both the other ladies' tresses, the present species is very variable as regards flowering. For instance, at one locality near Portadown the bog was said to be " white " with flowers in 1930, while over 200 flower-spikes were counted in 1931, whereas in the following year an hour's search yielded only three.

There seems little doubt that the species is usually dependent on insect visitors for pollination and fertilisation, but the identity of the insects which carry out the process in the British Isles is not known. In Canada species of bees and of humble-bees have been recorded as removing the pollinia. The mechanism is clearly the same as already described, the flowers at first opening only far enough to allow removal of the pollinia, whereas later they open more so as to permit deposition of the pollinia on to the ripe stigma.

When the Irish ladies' tresses was first discovered in Co. Cork in 1810, it was called *S. gemmipara*. This was because it was thought to produce small buds which fell off and gave rise to separate plants, comparable to those in the bog orchid (*Hammarbya*) and in many cultivated *Kalanchoes* and *Crassulas*. It has been shown, however, that the buds referred to by Drummond in his original remarks are merely extra lateral buds, which form their own tuberous roots and leaves. On further development of the plant, and the death of the old tubers and stem, these small additional plants become separated from the parent and lead an independent existence. This procedure occurs to varying extents in most British orchids. Plants of Irish ladies' tresses in cultivation have by these means formed four or five separate leaf rosettes (and presumably later on flower-spikes) in the course of two or three years.

GOODYERA

It is easy to distinguish *Goodyera* from the three ladies' tresses already dealt with, because instead of a tuft of leaves at the base of an erect stem with several more or less swollen tuberous roots below, it has a slender stem creeping in the lower part and giving off numerous thin roots at intervals. In addition, the flowers are shorter and fatter, while the lip, instead of possessing a broad front part, terminates in a kind of narrow spout (Pl. XIIa, p. 171). Another technical difference lies in the pollinia, which are formed of numerous packets of pollen grains held together by slender elastic threads. There is only one species of *Goodyera* in the British Isles, but there are several more in North

America, and also quite a number in Japan, China and the mountains of India.

CREEPING LADIES' TRESSES (*Goodyera repens*)

This delightful little plant is not likely to be encountered unless a visit be made to Scotland, where it is a characteristic inhabitant of the ancient pine forests still surviving here and there in the Highlands and elsewhere (Pl. 1, p. 46 ; 19a, p. 190). It is often abundant where it does occur, when the delicate white flowers and prettily veined leaves render it very attractive. As in the other ladies' tresses, the flowers are usually arranged in a distinct spiral, although in some plants this may not be very evident.

The stems in *Goodyera* are more or less horizontal in the lower part, usually with a few leaves at or near their tips. The stems have many slender branches, which extend through the layer of moss and pine needles with which the ground is covered (Fig. 14, p. 189). For some years after it appears a new branch bears no green foliage leaves, only short sheathing scales, but each year it grows a little longer, leaves being produced in the fifth year ; these leaves are larger each subsequent year with the continued growth of the stem. In a mature stem there are about four or five leaves, about one to two inches long and half to one inch in breadth, with a rather long sheathing stalk, and a broadly spear-shaped blade which is frequently dark green with paler green marblings. In the early stages of development the stem bears a few very short roots, and in addition numerous tufts of hairs, which appear to the naked eye as small black spots dotted over the surface. In about the eighth year there is a change in the growth, the stem turning upwards and producing the flower-stalk ; in this and the preceding year several longer and thicker roots are produced, apparently to enable the plant to cope with the additional water and food which is required for flower production. The erect flower-spike is about three to four inches high, bearing a number of small white sweetly scented flowers in a single more or less twisted row. The flowers are shorter and fatter than in the other kinds of ladies' tresses (Pl. XIIa, p. 171), with rather blunt sepals and petals and a boat-shaped lip with a sort of spout-like tip. After flowering the main stem dies away, and as a result all the branches are left behind as separate individuals, which pass through the same stages of development, and in their turn flower and die. In fact the general type of growth is much the same as in the perennial sunflowers and artichokes of our gardens (*Helianthus* spp.) and in the pernicious weed known as enchanter's nightshade (*Circaea lutetiana*), except that in these plants the new stems flower and die in the year following their appearance instead of taking eight years to reach maturity.

In its general distribution the creeping ladies' tresses resembles in

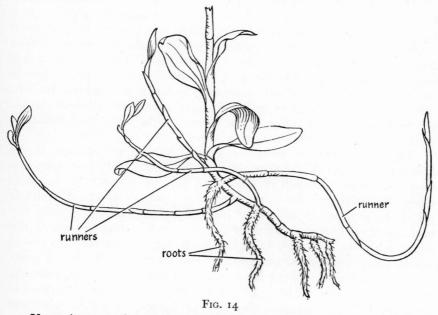

FIG. 14

Vegetative parts of plant of creeping ladies' tresses, *Goodyera repens*, showing development of characteristic runners at base of upright stem. (× ⅔)

many respects the lesser twayblade (*Listera cordata*), being placed in the small group of Northern Montane species of our orchid flora. In Europe the species is distinctly northern, occurring as far north as the 70th parallel in Scandinavia, and being commoner in the north than elsewhere. However, it is also found as far south as the Pyrenees, northern Italy, Bosnia and the mountains of Bulgaria. Eastwards it occurs in Asia Minor and the Caucasus, and right across Siberia and Turkestan to Kamchatka and Sachalin on the shores of the Pacific Ocean, and in the Japanese Islands. It also occurs in temperate China and in the western Himalaya Mountains. Like *Listera cordata, Good-yera* is also widely distributed in North America, occurring throughout Canada and the northern United States as far south as North Carolina, and extending in the west to Alaska. In most southerly regions the creeping ladies' tresses is a mountain plant, being found at nearly 7,000 feet above sea-level in the Bavarian Alps.

Its distribution in the British Isles is in conformity with that already outlined, for it is a distinctly northern species here also (Map 16, p. 349). Apart from two stations in Norfolk, where it is thought to have been introduced, and a record for eastern Yorkshire where it seems to have been extinct for many years, the creeping ladies' tresses is not found south of Durham and Cumberland. North of these counties it occurs almost throughout Scotland, extending as far as the Orkney Islands, but it is most abundant in the central and eastern Highlands. It has not been recorded from any of the islands on the west coast, probably because no suitable habitats occur there.

The creeping ladies' tresses, in spite of its wide distribution, is not found in a great variety of localities or habitats. In this country it is nearly confined to woods of pine or of pine mixed with birch. It is especially characteristic of the ancient pinewoods of the Highlands (Pl. 1, p. 46), woods which are generally considered to be only the remains of much more extensive forests which covered much of the country a long time ago. The species is usually restricted to places where the pines are present, but plants have been found in some localities among heather or other heathy shrubs, in such cases usually near the sea-shore. The lesser twayblade is a frequent associate of *Goodyera*. On the Continent *Goodyera* also occurs normally in pine and other coniferous woods, or in mixtures of these and broad-leaved trees, but practically never in pure deciduous woods. The species has also been recorded from pine plantations both in Scotland and elsewhere. The best-known example of this is in Norfolk, where the orchid is now very abundant in certain pine plantations, having been introduced, it is thought, with the soil on the roots of the young trees.

The ladies' tresses plants grow in the thin layer of moss and pine needles which is almost always found covering the ground in these woods. The numerous slender often leafless stems penetrate this moss layer in all directions, only the leaves and flower-stalks emerging. For the maintenance of the moss layer a certain amount of light is required, and in dense woods of broad-leaved trees, such as beech,

PLATE 19

Robert Atkinson

b. Common Coral Root (*Corallorhiza trifida*). Forfarshire; June

Robert Atkinson

a. Creeping Ladies' Tresses (*Goodyera repens*). Strath Spey; August

PLATE 20

Robert Atkinson

Bird's Nest Orchid (*Neottia nidus-avis*). Chiltern Hills, Oxfordshire; May

the light is not sufficient. Most pinewoods are rather broken, with open heathy spots, such circumstances providing suitable conditions for the growth of the orchid, though it rarely grows right in the open. It will be remembered that the stems of the young runners or branches are set with bunches of dark hairs. These absorb water and food in conjunction with the mycorhizal fungus with which the stems are heavily infected, this food being eventually passed on to the host plant. However, the distance to which these hairs, and the few short undeveloped roots, penetrate into the surrounding soil is very short. For the proper functioning of such a circumscribed means of absorption, a constantly damp surrounding layer is necessary, this being provided by the moss and pine needles.

The creeping ladies' tresses is one of our later flowering orchids, being in bloom throughout July and August, though the latter part of July is probably the best time. This, however, as in other species, depends a good deal on the season. Nectar is secreted into the cup-like lower part of the lip, while the flowers are sweetly scented, no doubt to attract the few insects likely to be flying in a pinewood. Humble-bees are the visiting insects, several kinds of these having been seen carrying pollinia from the flowers. The mechanism is practically the same as in *Spiranthes*, the flower tube being at first only wide enough to allow the pollinia to be removed on the insect's proboscis. Later the aperture is widened by the downward movement of the lip, and pollinia may then be introduced so as to make contact with the receptive stigma. This is so very sticky that some of the small packets of pollen are broken off and left behind, this process being repeated in many flowers before all the pollen has been removed. There seems no doubt that pollination is quite effective as many ripe seedpods may be seen on wild plants.

It is doubtful, however, if seed production is very important for the maintenance of the species in any given locality, this being probably more efficiently done by the extensive method of vegetative multiplication already described. Seeds probably serve mainly to enable additional suitable localities, such as plantations or young pinewoods, to be occupied by the species.

CHAPTER 10

SAPROPHYTIC ORCHIDS

THE THREE plants which are the subject of the present chapter are not grouped together because they are considered to be close relatives botanically, as in the preceding chapters, but because they all obtain their food in the same manner. They are all plants which, because they possess none or extremely little of the green colouring matter chlorophyll, cannot make the sugars, proteins and other energy- and body-producing substances required by them by their own efforts like ordinary green plants. Instead they have to obtain such food already manufactured. A ready source of this type of food is the humus of the soil, which consists of numerous more or less decayed parts of plants and also animals. Plants which make such use of *dead* vegetable or animal matter are termed saprophytes, the three orchids here dealt with falling into this category. Other plants, for instance, toadstools, broomrapes (*Orobanche* spp.), dodders (*Cuscuta* spp.), obtain their sugars, etc., directly from other *living* plants, and are therefore termed parasites, but no orchids are known which belong to this group.

Our three British saprophytic orchids are the bird's nest orchid (*Neottia nidus-avis*, Pl. 20, p. 191), spurred coral-root (*Epipogium aphyllum*, Pl. 21, p. 194) and coral-root (*Corallorhiza trifida*, Pl. 19b, p. 190). These plants have no foliage leaves and are all brownish, yellowish or pinkish-brown in colour, the first two usually completely devoid of chlorophyll, the third developing the pigment only to a small extent in the flower-spike and fruits. They are all most generally found in situations where the soil is rich in the humus which is necessary for their nutrition, for instance, in shady woods where the fallen leaves form a thick layer covering the soil.

In spite of their similar nature the student should have no difficulty in distinguishing the three species in view of their very different flowers, and it is only when they are flowering that they are visible at all. The spurred coral-root has a small number of large pinkish flowers about half an inch in diameter. The bird's nest orchid, on the other hand, possesses a tall dense spike of pale brown flowers similar in structure to those in the common twayblade, while the coral-root is much smaller with a slender few-flowered greenish spike of tiny yellowish or whitish flowers.

The three species are by no means abundant, though the bird's nest orchid is generally distributed throughout the greater part of the British Isles. The coral-root, however, is found only in the extreme north of England and in Scotland, while the spurred coral-root is among the rarest of our native orchids, its discovery being always an event of considerable interest to botanists.

BIRD'S NEST ORCHID (*Neottia nidus-avis*)

The pale brown erect flowering spikes of this interesting orchid, sticking up out of almost bare ground like a number of small pokers (Pl. 20, p. 191), are often a striking sight in June in the shady beech-woods of southern England, and less frequently in other parts of the British Isles. Later on the dark brown fruiting spikes are often the only objects projecting above the monotonous carpet of dead leaves and twigs. There are a number of other species of *Neottia*, all occurring in the Himalaya Mountains, in the mountains of western China, or in Japan, and all share the saprophytic nature of their British relative. The name, both English and scientific, is given in allusion to the roots, which form a large more or less solid clump (Pl. XIIb, p. 171; Fig. 15, p. 194), with individual roots sticking out in all directions, and bearing a fanciful resemblance to the rather untidy nests of birds such as rooks, pigeons and the like. This ball, or irregular mass, of roots is buried in the thick layer of fallen leaves and other decaying humus matter. It consists actually of a short thick central stem or rhizome, from which the numerous short fleshy blunt roots arise so closely together as almost completely to hide it. These roots and rhizome are strongly infected with the mycorhizal fungus, and through them the plant obtains all the food it needs from the surrounding humus. The whole of the plant is underground with the exception of the flower-spike, which in a seedling plant is not developed until the ninth year, by which time sufficient food has been stored up. There are no ordinary leaves, these being represented by small scale-like structures on the rhizome. Small amounts of chlorophyll are some-times developed in the flower stems of plants exposed to the light, but never to the same extent as in the coral-root (*Corallorhiza*). The flowering stem consists of an erect rather stiff shaft, six to eighteen inches in height, cov-ered with numerous brown sheaths and ter-minating in a dense many-flowered spike up to six inches in length. The lower flowers are usually spaced out more than the upper ones, while there are often one or two individual flowers quite a long way below the rest of the spike. These flowers may be abnormal in structure, with the lip or other parts of the

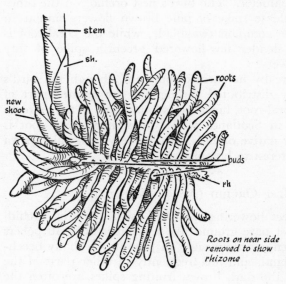

FIG. 15

Underground parts of bird's nest orchid, *Neottia nidus-avis*

Note the slender more or less horizontal rhizome producing an erect aerial stem, and enveloped in short blunt roots. rh. rhizome; sh. leaf sheath. (×⅔)

flower lacking or reduced in size. The flowers are yellowish brown, or more rarely whitish or sulphur coloured, these being merely colour forms. In structure they resemble in most respects those of the common twayblade (*Listera ovata*), the sepals and petals forming an open hood at the back, and the large two-lobed lip hanging down in front below the rest of the flower. The bright yellow pollinia provide a sharp contrast with the brown perianth and column.

Usually each plant produces a single inflorescence, but some-times an exceptionally robust plant will have more than one aerial

PLATE 21

Photograph by Robert Atkinson. Coloured by hand. By kind permission of the Reading Museum and Art Gallery
Spurred Coral Root (*Epipogium aphyllum*). Oxfordshire

PLATE 22

Musk Orchids (*Herminium monorchis*). Kent; July

stem. Where several flowering stems occur quite close together it is generally found that they arise from several distinct, but more or less entangled, plants. Whether these have arisen by division or vegetative propagation of one original plant, or from seed, is not easy to say in any given case. Often the plant exhausts itself in the production of flowers and fruit and dies away, but the same stem may develop a flower-spike in three successive years, if not during a longer period. Examples are on record of flower-spikes being developed underground, usually owing to some obstacle, such as a stone, preventing the stem from growing erect. Such inflorescences develop their flowers and also subsequently set seed, which germinates in the seedpod.

Neottia is one of the eight species comprising the Central Eurasian group of our orchids. As this group title indicates, the bird's nest orchid is commonest in the more central parts of Europe, becoming less frequent in the extreme north, and in the Mediterranean region. In the latter area it is, like many other similar species, always a mountain plant. Eastwards it extends through Siberia to Sachalin off the Pacific coast, and is also said, but doubtfully, to occur in Korea and Japan. More to the south the species is found in the Caucasus and in north-western Asia Minor, but is entirely lacking from the eastern part of the Mediterranean basin. The bird's nest orchid, though characteristically a lowland plant, is found in the central mountain massif of the Austrian Tirol and Switzerland at altitudes of as much as 5,500 feet.

In the British Isles (Map 21, p. 351) *Neottia* is found very generally throughout the greater part of the country, with the exception of the northern mainland of Scotland beyond Inverness-shire, and the islands off the west coast of that country. It is, however, much more common in the southern half of England than elsewhere. In Ireland the distribution is rather patchy, but there is no extensive part of the country in which the species is more common than anywhere else. Over the greater part of its range in these islands the bird's nest orchid is by no means a common plant, occurring in small numbers, and rather uncertain in its appearance.

Owing to its special mode of nutrition, the species is restricted to places where a sufficiency of humus is present in the soil, and where this is damp enough continually, as well as suitable in other respects, to permit the fungus to carry on its work of feeding the plant. Such conditions can normally only be found in relatively dense woods where the drying power of the sun only rarely penetrates, and consequently it is only occasionally that the bird's nest orchid may be found growing away from such places. Indeed it is almost always a characteristic feature of the darkest and gloomiest parts of our beechwoods, often being the only living plant among the layer of dead and decaying leaves covering the ground, with the exception of the similarly saprophytic bird's nest (*Monotropa hypopithys*). It may also be found under well-grown hazel coppice, or beneath a mixed growth of hazels, oaks and other trees, provided that the conditions mentioned above are fulfilled. In Ireland the bird's nest orchid is a characteristic member of the flora of the aboriginal oak or mixed oak and birch woods which are scattered throughout the country. These woods are generally considered to be survivals from a much more extensive forest region which once covered much of the land surface, and presumably at that period *Neottia* occurred throughout these forests.

The species also occurs in more open woods, and here it is accompanied by occasional plants of other shade-loving species, such as ivy, wild strawberries (*Fragaria vesca*), wood dog violet (*Viola riviniana*), sweet woodruff (*Asperula odorata*), wood sanicle (*Sanicula europaea*), wild arum (*Arum maculatum*), dwarf brambles (*Rubus* spp.), etc. Other orchids which are often associated with the bird's nest orchid are the common twayblade, large white helleborine (*Cephalanthera damasonium*), broad-leaved helleborine (*Epipactis helleborine*) and less frequently the fly orchid (*Ophrys muscifera*) and green-leaved helleborine (*Epipactis leptochila*). However, *Neottia* is practically never found where the amount of light allows a luxuriant growth of other plants. The species, like many other of our orchids, seems to thrive best on chalk, limestone and other soils rich in lime, but this does not appear absolutely essential for its growth. On the other hand, acid humus soils are apparently unsuitable, presumably because the mycorhizal fungus cannot live in these. Although it is essential for the humus to remain damp, water-logged or even very wet soils are avoided by the bird's nest orchid, which requires a well-drained substratum for its successful growth.

Neottia is usually in full flower in June, but early flowering individuals may be found in May, while the flowering season is often extended into the early part of July. Pollination is usually carried out by insect visitors, the mechanism being identical with that found in the common twayblade. Nectar is secreted into the cup-like lower part of the lip, and the flowers are said to have a pleasant honey-like scent. On the other hand, the lower abnormal flowers have been reported to emit a rather unpleasant smell, but observations by the author have so far not confirmed this. Flies have been recorded visiting the flowers, from some of which they removed the pollinia, but we still know little about the active agents of pollination, or the means by which they are attracted to the very inconspicuous flowers in the depths of woods. There are two stages in the development of the flower, as in the ladies' tresses, firstly a stage in which it is only possible to remove the pollinia, and secondly a stage when, as a result of the rising of the rostellum, the aperture of the flower becomes enlarged sufficiently to allow insects to deposit pollinia on to the exposed stigma.

If the flowers are not cross-pollinated by insects it is easy for self-pollination to take place. The pollinia, which are very powdery and friable, after a few days swell up and slide off the rostellum on to the stigma below, or are carried there by the numerous minute insects like thrips which appear to frequent the flowers. In addition, examples are known in which self-fertilisation has taken place before the flowers opened, while self-fertilisation clearly takes place in the underground flower-spikes already mentioned. The production of seeds by all these means is usually very effective, most flowers on the spike developing ripe seed-capsules. An example in which 72 flowers out of 78 had set seed has been recorded, while other similar examples may readily be found. Flowers which are self-pollinated frequently produce fewer seeds than those in which cross-pollination has taken place, but the exact cause of this is unknown.

The bird's nest orchid is not, however, dependent upon seed-production, good though it may be, to maintain the population or even to increase in numbers. The roots—which, like those in other plants heavily infected by fungus, are capable of independent existence—may under suitable conditions produce new shoots from their tips. Such buds are produced especially as a result of injury to the plant, or separation of the roots from the rhizome. The young plants formed from the roots are very similar to those produced by germination of the seeds, reaching the flowering stage about the eighth year. This method of multiplication is possibly favoured by the exhaustion of the soil in the immediate neighbourhood of the rhizome. Consequently development of additional plants from lateral buds on the rhizome is usually not a practicable proposition. On the other hand, the young plants arising from the tips of the roots are able immediately to exploit the almost untouched soil beyond the limits of the parent root system.

SPURRED CORAL-ROOT (*Epipogium aphyllum*)

The history of this remarkable orchid in the British Isles provides one of the most interesting chapters in British botany. Always one of the rarest members of the British flora, its sudden appearances and disappearances, separated by long periods during which it has seemed to be extinct, have made it one of our most mysterious species. These peculiarities are bound up with its life-history and saprophytic mode of nutrition. In *Epipogium* this has been carried farther than in the other two species, the plant having lost the power of producing chlorophyll. The species may be recognised by the few large pinkish flowers with a large blunt spur pointing upwards, the lip being at the top of the flower (Pl. 21, p. 194).

The underground stem or rhizome, which in this plant for years is often all that can be found, consists of a much lobed flattened whitish or brownish coral-like structure (Fig. 16, p. 199), which grows slowly in the soil, adding fresh lobes or branches from year to year. There are no roots, nor is there anything at all like leaves, but the rhizome is sparsely covered with long hairs through which it is infected by the usual mycorhizal fungus. By means of the activities of this fungus food is absorbed from the dead and decaying plant remains in which the rhizome is buried. At an early stage in the development of a new individual the runners, which are a unique feature of this remarkable plant, are formed. These are long thread-like stems which grow out from the edge of the rhizome, bearing scale-like sheathing leaves at intervals. At each scale-leaf a bud is formed which develops into a new young plant, either while still attached to the parent rhizome, or on becoming detached. The runners otherwise soon die away, and fresh ones are produced from other parts of the rhizome in successive years. The young plants formed in this way continue their development along the same lines as the parent. After the plant has continued this extraordinary subterranean existence for about ten years, the bud of a future flower-spike may be produced in the autumn. It does not follow, however, that any flowers will be formed in the succeeding year, this probably depending on the weather during the early part of the year.

Observations seem to indicate that flowering usually follows a damp spring during which the soil is continually wet, allowing enough water to be stored up preparatory to the growth of the flower-spike. The latter is up to eight or nine inches high, but in this country is usually much shorter, with a large swelling just above the bottom, which acts as a reservoir for water (see Fig. 16, below). The stem is pinkish in colour with darker dashes or broken lines, somewhat wavy, bearing in the upper part from one to five flowers, or more rarely as many as seven. These flowers, which hang on rather slender short stalks, have yellowish sepals and petals, a large much bent pink lip with darker pink markings inside, and a small globular seedpod or ovary.

Although the spurred coral-root appears so infrequently, even in countries where it is commoner than here, it has a wide distribution in Europe and Asia, being placed in the Northern Eurasian Element of our orchid flora. The only other species of the genus *Epipogium* (*E. roseum*) has an even wider distribution throughout the tropics of the Old World. *E. aphyllum* is commoner in the northern part of Europe than farther south, extending in the latter direction only as far as the Pyrenees, central Italy and the northern parts of the Balkan Peninsula.

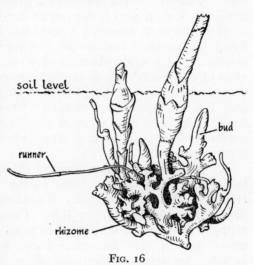

FIG. 16

Underground parts of spurred coral-root, *Epipogium aphyllum*, showing the flattened branched coral-like rhizome, the long slender runners and the lower part of the erect flowering shoot with its swollen base. ($\times \frac{2}{3}$) (After Ziegenspeck)

Northwards, on the other hand, it may be found almost to the Arctic Circle in Scandinavia and Russia, while eastwards the species occurs right across northern Asia to Japan. Farther south it extends from the Caucasus through central Asia to Kashmir, and along the Himalayan Range as far east as Sikkim, directly north of Calcutta.

The spurred coral-root is a very rare species in this country (Map 23, p. 351), having been found on only ten occasions altogether, usually singly and only on three occasions as many as two specimens. So far the species has been found in two distinct regions, the wooded districts of Herefordshire and Shropshire, on the one hand, and the country west of Henley-on-Thames in Oxfordshire, on the other. The species was first discovered in August 1854 by Mrs. W. Anderton Smith near Tedstone Delamere, by the Safey Brook which here forms the boundary between Herefordshire and Worcestershire. Unfortunately the plant was moved to a garden where, as might have been expected, it soon died ; the species has never been seen again in this locality. In 1876, however, a plant was found by Miss Lloyd at Ringwood Chase near Ludlow in Shropshire, a further specimen was collected at the same place in 1878, while a third was discovered in 1892 in a different spot in the same wood. Finally a single plant was discovered by Mr. C. C. Mountfort in July 1910 in the Wye Valley near Ross-on-Wye, Herefordshire. Since then no further plants have come to light in this centre of distribution, but in view of the very irregular flowering, there is no reason for thinking that the species is extinct.

In June 1923 two specimens of the spurred coral-root were found by a local girl in quite a new district, in Oxfordshire not far from Henley-on-Thames, and after a prolonged search Dr. G. C. Druce discovered a further one in July. Two more plants were discovered at the same place in the following year, this time in late May. Some years later (in 1931) two more plants were found, purely by chance, at a locality several miles west of the first, but in the same general district. It is almost certain that the species will turn up again in due course in both districts mentioned, and probably in yet further new localities. Indeed, it is not improbable that it may appear in quite new districts, since its very irregular occurrence and its dark and gloomy habitat make discovery mainly a matter of chance.

As might be concluded from its saprophytic mode of nutrition, the spurred coral-root, like the bird's nest orchid, is restricted to places where there is sufficient humus in the soil. As the rhizome is unable to absorb water quickly, having no proper roots, the plant needs for successful growth a soil which is more or less continually moist. Such conditions can only be found in dense woods where the sun only penetrates occasionally, and indeed all the recorded localities are of this nature. On the Continent *Epipogium* occurs in both deciduous and coniferous woods, although it seems more at home in the former. Beechwoods are its favourite haunts, and this is also the case in its Oxfordshire stations. In the western British region the species has been found on every occasion under the dense shade of oaks, usually the sessile oak (*Quercus petraea*), which forms the oakwoods in this part of the country. In both regions the exact spots are recorded as being in deep shade with very little other vegetation, and the ground covered by a thick layer of rotten leaves and other decaying plant remains. In the Oxfordshire localities the bird's nest orchid (*Neottia*) and the green-leaved helleborine (*Epipactis leptochila*) occur in the near vicinity on almost identical ground.

Flowering takes place any time between late May and early September, and seems to vary much from year to year even in the same locality. Observations in Europe suggest that continuous wet weather in the spring is essential to enable the necessary water to be accumulated in the rhizome and developing inflorescence. The result is that on the Continent suitable conditions produce good flowering years when many plants flower together, but unfortunately the species is too rare in Britain for this to be observed. The flowers are said to have a pleasant smell reminiscent of bananas or of certain tropical orchids such as *Stanhopea*. Fertilisation is the result of cross-pollination, carried out by insects which visit the flowers for the sweet liquid which is secreted within the walls of the large spur. The insects which are responsible are humble-bees, which are just about the right size to operate the mechanism. The bee alights on the exposed part of the hanging lip and climbs inside towards the spur, guided by the lines of coloured projections. Eventually it reaches the mouth of the spur, where it can easily obtain the liquid inside the tender inner skin. As it backs out, however, it bumps against the column just below, its back breaking the very delicate rostellum. The adhesive liquid comes out and fixes the ends of the slender stalks of the pollinia firmly to the insect's back or forehead. Further withdrawal by the bee pushes the anther cap away and draws the pollinia clear from it. When the insect visits another flower, the pollinia, which stand forwards from its head like a pair of clubs, come into direct contact with the projecting receptive stigma. The sticky surface detaches some at least of the packets of pollen, and evidently this may be repeated on visits to other flowers. Owing to the structure and relative positions of the pollinia and stigma, self-pollination is practically impossible, so the plant must depend on insects for seed production.

In spite of the excellence of the mechanism, all the available evidence shows that seed is rarely produced. This probably explains why the distribution of the species is so irregular and illogical ; apparently not sufficient seed is provided to enable the plant to colonise all the suitable localities available. The runners produced from the rhizomes maintain the species, and even produce a number of new plants in the immediate vicinity of the parent plant. It has been shown that if the flower-spike fails to develop, the food available is used to produce additional and more robust runners. This method, however, is not a means of spreading into new separate areas, but only operates within continuous areas providing favourable conditions for vegetative growth.

CORAL-ROOT (*Corallorhiza trifida*)

This species lies between the two already treated, with respect to the degree in which it has been modified by its adoption of the saprophytic existence common to all three. Like *Epipogium* it does not produce any roots, whereas *Neottia* possesses numerous, if rather short ones. The coral-root, therefore, depends almost entirely on the activity of its associated fungus to obtain the food it requires from the soil. In conjunction with this absence of roots, the underground stem or rhizome develops into a much-branched coralloid structure similar in many respects to that in the spurred coral-root, but lacking the slender runners so characteristic of that plant. Although, like both *Neottia* and *Epipogium*, the coral-root has no true green foliage leaves, only brownish sheaths, the inflorescence stalk and ovaries develop quite a considerable amount of chlorophyll, which gives the plant a distinctly greenish colour (Pl. 19b, p. 190). This no doubt enables it to manufacture a certain amount of its food. In this respect it has not diverged so far from the ordinary green plant as the bird's nest orchid and spurred coral-root, which have respectively lost almost, or entirely, the power of producing chlorophyll.

It is a much smaller plant than our other two saprophytic orchids, being rarely more than six inches in height, with a rather loose spike of fewer than a dozen small whitish-yellow or greenish-yellow flowers. As in *Neottia* and *Epipogium*, the plant lives an entirely subterranean

PLATE 23

Robert Atkinson

b. Small White Orchids (*Gymnadenia albida*). Perthshire;
June

Robert Atkinson

a. Frog Orchids (*Coeloglossum viride*). Isle of Lewis;
July

PLATE 24

Greater Butterfly Orchid (*Platanthera chlorantha*). Oxfordshire; June

existence except for the production of the aerial flowering stems. The underground rhizome is coral-like, cream-coloured and much branched, most of the branches being short and knob-like, the whole structure being rounded instead of flattened as in the spurred coral-root. There are no roots, but tufts of hairs grow out at intervals either from the side branches or from smaller knobs on the main branches. The rhizome is heavily infected with the mycorhizal fungus, which absorbs food from the dead plant remains in the soil, and eventually passes it on to its host. This absorption of food is associated with the hair-tufts mentioned above, which also act as further centres of infection from the soil outside. When a sufficient amount of food has been accumulated, the main shoot of the rhizome comes above ground to form a flowering stem. In a vigorous much-branched plant as many as ten flowering stems may be produced in the same year, and this results in a tufted appearance. The aerial stems are usually three to six inches in height, but in robust specimens may reach a height of nine inches. The lower part is encased in several brownish sheaths, while at the top it bears a loose spike of four to nine, or rarely as many as twelve flowers. These are small and inconspicuous, more or less hanging, whitish or yellowish in colour with a white lip which is marked with small crimson spots or blotches. Both the main stalk of the spike and the seedpods are more or less green in colour, while sometimes the sepals are tinged green also.

The coral-root has a geographical distribution somewhat similar to that of the spurred coral-root, although it is rather more abundant in northern regions than is that species. It differs in one important particular, however, as it occurs also in North America, where there are over a dozen species of the genus *Corallorhiza*. In Europe it is found as far north as Iceland, the North Cape region of Scandinavia and northern Russia, but towards the south the species becomes less common and reaches only the Pyrenees, central Italy and the northern parts of the Balkan Peninsula. In these southern regions the coral-root is always found at considerable elevations, while it is quite absent from the hotter evergreen zones of the Mediterranean region. To the east the species extends to the Caucasus Mountains, and across Siberia to the Lake Baikal region and northern China.

This generally northern distribution of the species outside the British Isles is paralleled by its distribution within these islands (Map 22, p. 351), where it is not found south of northern Lancashire, Cumberland and Northumberland. It becomes more frequent as one goes north, being scattered in odd places in southern Scotland, and reaching its greatest abundance in the eastern half of the northern part of the country. So far the species has not been found in Caithness or in any of the Scottish islands. Even in Scotland, however, the coral-root is a very local plant, although it may occur quite abundantly in some of its scattered stations. As, however, the species is rather inconspicuous and, like other saprophytic orchids, uncertain in its appearance, it probably occurs in more places than have so far been recorded, especially as there is a good deal of suitable country for it in many parts of Scotland.

Although the coral-root requires ample humus in the soil for successful growth, it does not appear to be so dependent on woodland as *Neottia* and *Epipogium*. In Europe the species is characteristically found in either coniferous (pine or spruce) woods, especially in more northern latitudes, or, when it occurs farther south, in mountain beech forests. *Corallorhiza* is often found in pinewoods, or in mixed pine and birch woods, in this country also, usually in damp places among thick leaf-mould or moss cushions, and often in considerable shade, sometimes accompanied by the creeping ladies' tresses (*Goodyera repens*). It also occurs in quite thick scrub or low woods of willows or alder, sometimes among dense vegetation of herbs and mosses. On the other hand, the species in other localities occurs in quite open places, particularly in damp marshy places among sand dunes near the sea. Here it has been found with both species of twayblade (*Listera ovata* and *L. cordata*). It even grows among the rough marram grass (*Ammophila arenaria*) which covers the less stable dunes (Pl. 19b, p. 190), although here it only occurs where there is adequate water not far below the surface. No doubt it is the ability of the coral-root to manufacture some of its own food which enables it to tolerate conditions where the humus of the soil cannot be very abundant. On the whole, however, relatively damp situations are usually chosen, but it is clear that the amount of shade available is not so important as in our other saprophytic orchids. This may be due to some quality intrinsic to the species itself, or it may be that in northern latitudes, where the sun never has the same power as farther south and humidity remains high, the soil conditions are favourable to saprophytic growth even where the protection provided by trees is absent.

The coral-root usually flowers in June and July, but in exceptional seasons or in special habitats it may also be found in flower as early as May or as late as August. The structure of the flower is rather similar to that in the twayblades, especially in the shape and position of the lip. The back sepal and petals form a sort of hood at the back, while the lip is much curved, the lower part being parallel with the column while the upper part curves down to form a steeply sloping platform in front. There is a groove along the middle, though no nectar is secreted, and the whole arrangement suggests that small insects alight on the lip and climb up the groove until they come into contact with the column and remove the pollinia. Hover-flies and other small insects (*Hymenoptera*) do alight on the lip, but experiments show that the pollinia do not usually adhere, probably owing to the degeneration of the rostellum which is here always very small. Self-pollination is actually the rule, the pollinia falling from the stamen on to the stigma below. This seems quite an effective method of fertilisation judging by the fact that usually from 85 to 100 per cent of the flowers set seed. The ovary and also the sepals remain green and actively produce food for the maturing seeds. The excellent seed production enables the plant to colonise any new suitable habitats in the neighbourhood, the species contrasting markedly with the spurred coral-root in this respect. On the other hand, the means of vegetative multiplication are nothing like so effective as in our other two saprophytic orchids, consisting merely of the automatic separation of branches of the rhizome as the rear parts die away.

CHAPTER II

THE HABENARIA GROUP

A s THE TITLE indicates, the six species dealt with here have nearly all, at one time or another, been considered by botanists to belong to the large genus *Habenaria*, and may often be found in British Floras under that heading. Most botanists nowadays, however, restrict *Habenaria* to tropical and sub-tropical plants with a flower structure differing markedly from that of any British plant. In the *Habenaria* group, as in the plants included in the next four chapters, the stamen is firmly fixed to the column, usually standing upright with the stalks of the pollen masses and the sticky viscidia towards the lower end immediately above the lip. In this respect these plants differ from those dealt with previously, in which the stamen is loosely attached, and the viscidia, if present, are at the top of the column. On the whole, the organisation of the flower, particularly the mechanism for ensuring pollination, has reached a higher degree of complexity in this group than in those already described. The members of the group also show the development of the special kind of tubers characteristic of so many of our orchids. Instead of a rather indefinite number of irregular fleshy roots, there is a single new tuber formed at the base of the flowering or leafy stem each year ; with this is a bud which develops into the next year's flowering stem. The old tuber dies away and the process is repeated in the following year. In the musk orchid more than one tuber is produced each year, and it is therefore intermediate in this respect between such plants as the ladies' tresses and the other members of the *Habenaria* group.

The species concerned are the musk orchid (*Herminium monorchis*, Pl. 22, p. 195), frog orchid (*Coeloglossum viride*, Pl. 23a, p. 202), greater and lesser butterfly orchids (*Platanthera chlorantha* and *P. bifolia*, Pl. 24,

p. 203 ; 25, p. 210), small white orchid (*Gymnadenia albida*, Pl. 23b, p. 202) and fragrant orchid (*G. conopsea*, Pl. 26, p. 211). It will be seen that they belong to four different genera, which are distinguished botanically by floral differences. The various species, however, are also for the most part dissimilar in general appearance. The musk orchid and frog orchid are both small plants with small rather greenish flowers, while the small white orchid has similar, but white flowers. On the other hand, the butterfly orchids have much larger white or cream coloured flowers with long spurs, while in the fragrant orchid the smaller red-lilac or rose coloured flowers are also long spurred.

MUSK ORCHID (*Herminium monorchis*)

The name of this plant is not very suitable, as the flowers, though scented, do not smell of musk. It is one of the smallest of our native orchids (Pl. 22, p. 195), often reaching a height of only two to six inches, though in favourable localities it may grow taller. The spike of small yellow-green flowers distinguishes it from all other British orchids except the bog orchid (*Hammarbya*), which, however, grows in quite different habitats. The structure of the flowers is in most respects more simple than in the other members of the *Habenaria* group, but the rather interesting pollination mechanism is not found in any other species.

In the musk orchid seedlings have very rarely been observed, most plants being produced by vegetative means from another plant as described on page 21. Apart from the tubers there are also a few normal-looking thread-like roots, which may be either infected by the usual mycorhizal fungus or almost free from infection. The above-ground stem is rather short, though it may rarely be as much as eleven inches high, bearing two, rarely three or four, broad and blunt leaves, the upper ones being very small. The flower-spike varies from half an inch to two, or rarely four, inches in length, and consists of numerous yellowish-green or green sweetly scented flowers usually set rather closely together. As many as 73 flowers have been recorded in a spike, but in British plants the number is generally much smaller. The sepals and petals, which are narrow and blunt, do not spread out, so that the flower is more or less tubular. The petals usually have a little tooth or angle at each side in the lower half. The lip is about the same length, and dagger-shaped with a short spreading lobe on each side

W.O.B

P

just above the middle ; at the base it is hollowed out to form a shallow cup representing an extremely short spur. The pollinia, containing numerous almost spherical packets of pollen, are each attached to a relatively large rounded viscidium, which viscidia lie almost immediately above the two stigmas.

The musk orchid is included in the Northern Eurasian group of British orchids, having a wide distribution throughout the northern parts of these two continents. Apart from the present species, there are about fifteen to twenty other species in China, Tibet and the Himalayan Range, Central Asia being evidently the centre of distribution. *H. monorchis* occurs generally in central Europe, extending northwards about halfway up Scandinavia, and to Leningrad and north of Moscow in Russia. In the south it is found in northern and central Spain, central Italy, the northern Balkans and also in the Caucasus. In the west the musk orchid is not so common, apparently avoiding the Atlantic seaboard of Europe with its markedly oceanic climate. Eastwards the species is found throughout Siberia to the Altai Mountains, Manchuria, Korea, northern China and Japan, and in central Asia as far as Tibet and the Himalayan mountains. The musk orchid often occurs at high altitudes, having been recorded at heights of 7,000 feet or more, but it also occurs at sea-level, at least in the more northern parts of its range.

In the British Isles the species is restricted to the southern part of England (Map 25, p. 352), being commonest in the south-eastern part of the country, as in Surrey, Sussex and Kent, but extending westwards to Somerset and Dorset. North of the Thames the musk orchid is abundant in places along the Cotswold Hills in Gloucestershire on both sides of Stroud and Cheltenham ; it also occurs at various points along the Chiltern Hills from Oxfordshire to Bedfordshire, while there is a single record of its occurrence in Rutland. Finally the species is found along the chalk hills of East Anglia nearly as far north as Hunstanton in Norfolk. As in Europe, it avoids the extreme west with its very oceanic climate, while it is also absent from Ireland.

Like many other British orchids, *Herminium* is found almost always on calcareous soils, being most at home on the numerous chalk hills. It also occurs on Oolitic limestones, as in Gloucestershire and Somerset. On the European mainland, although it prefers chalky soils, it does sometimes occur on other soils, provided they are not acid in nature. Owing to its dwarf stature, the plant can naturally only grow successfully in short grass ; indeed its favourite habitat is short turf on downs or old pastures, particularly in or around old quarries. The musk orchid can apparently stand a considerable amount of drought, as some of its stations must be very dry during the summer months. Curiously enough, in Europe it often grows in much damper places, damp meadows, spring flushes and the like, and even in open woods. In Britain it is almost invariably found growing in the open, only the slightest amount of shade being tolerated. The number of plants to be seen in any given place fluctuates very much from year to year, no doubt depending on how favourable the previous season has been for the production of stolons. In good seasons the spikes may be so numerous as to give a distinct colour to the grassland, as, for instance, when I saw the species on the Cotswolds in 1931. Owing to the vegetative means of multiplication the species tends to occur in colonies, but it is rather local in distribution, and small numbers of plants are easily overlooked.

The musk orchid flowers during the months of June and July, being at its best during the last two weeks of June and the first two weeks of July. The flowers emit a rather strong honey-like scent, not at all like musk, and are visited by numerous very small insects such as flies, beetles and various hymenopterous insects resembling ichneumons. On entering the flower these insects make their way to the cup at the base of the lip, the projecting bend of their fore-leg coming into contact with the hollowed-out viscidium just above. This is removed together with its attached pollinium, becoming attached to the rounded joint of the insect's leg. On entering another flower the projecting pollinium makes contact with one of the two stigmas just above the cup of the lip, and some at least of the pollen packets are removed. As the ovary is quite small a few packets provide enough pollen grains to fertilise all the ovules.

Although the very frequent visits of insects must result in fertilisation of the flowers, the plant is not entirely dependent on these visits. It has been shown that seeds are set by most flowers even if no access by insects is possible. Apparently as the anthers wither the pollinia fall out on to the stigmas just below, thus causing self-pollination. Taken in conjunction with the vegetative multiplication already mentioned, it would appear that the species is well equipped to maintain itself and even to spread. An explanation of its very local distribution is therefore probably to be sought on climatic grounds, particularly in view of the fact that it is right at the edge of its geographical range.

FROG ORCHID (*Coeloglossum viride*)

The frog orchid is one of the most inconspicuous of our orchids, for not only is the plant often very small—only a few inches tall—but the flowers frequently are practically the same colour as the leaves (Pl. 23a, p. 202). In fact it is easy to step on a plant without seeing it, so perfectly does it blend with the grassy turf in which it usually grows. The common name is not very suitable, since there is no very marked resemblance to a frog except, perhaps, in the colour of the flowers.

There are usually two tubers, each forked into three or four parts, which are continued downwards as slender thread-like roots. A new tuber is formed each year, the next year's aerial stem growing up from it, and the old tuber and stem dying away. Although the seedling is infected with fungus in the early stages, after the plant reaches maturity infection is restricted to the ordinary roots, the tubers being free from fungus. The flowering stem varies considerably in height, depending upon the habitat in which the plant is growing. In short turf the stem may be only two or three inches high, but in taller grass or in bushy places plants up to a foot or more tall may be found. There are three to five rather broad blunt dark green leaves along the lower part of the stem, the upper leaves being shorter and narrower than the others. The flower-spike, which is usually short, but in large specimens may be as much as four inches long, contains a varying number of green, brownish-green or reddish-tinged flowers. Plants bearing these differently coloured flowers usually occur mixed with one another. Sometimes the red coloration is quite dark, extending to the leaves and stems. The short and broad sepals and petals form an almost globular helmet, below which hangs the much longer strap-shaped lip, divided into three short teeth at the end. The spur of the lip is very short and blunt. The bracts occurring at the base of each flower may sometimes be very long, projecting beyond the flowers and giving the spike a very different appearance from that of plants where the bracts are shorter. Such long bracteate plants have sometimes been considered to constitute a separate variety, but as they almost always occur intermingled with plants bearing short

PLATE 25

a. Lesser Butterfly Orchid (*Platanthera bifolia*). Beechwood form, Oxfordshire; June

b. Lesser Butterfly Orchid (*Platanthera bifolia*). Moorland form, Ross and Cromarty; June

PLATE 26

Robert Atkinson

Fragrant Orchid (*Gymnadenia conopsea*). Buckinghamshire; June

or medium sized bracts, there seems little justification for any separation.

The frog orchid occurs throughout the greater part of Europe, but it is not especially commoner in either the north or the south ; it consequently falls into the Central Eurasian Group of British Orchids. Northwards, indeed, it extends as far as Iceland and the Faroe Islands, as well as northern Scandinavia and Russia, whereas it is not found in the southernmost parts of Europe, such as southern Spain and Italy and in Greece. In the Mediterranean region it is usually a mountain plant. Eastwards the frog orchid occurs in Asia Minor and western Siberia as far as Turkestan and Kashmir. It also grows in Alaska and Newfoundland in North America. Throughout the remainder of North America and in the Far East (China and Japan) it is replaced by the closely allied *Coeloglossum bracteatum*, a larger plant with constantly long bracts. The frog orchid occurs at considerable altitudes in mountain districts, reaching 8,500 feet in the Alps, and over 13,000 feet on the high mountains around the Turkestan plateau.

In agreement with this wide distribution outside the British Isles, *Coeloglossum viride* is found practically throughout these islands wherever suitable habitats exist (Map 24, p. 352). On the whole it appears to be more common in northern districts than in the south. Although so widespread it can scarcely be termed a common plant, tending to occur rather locally, sometimes in large numbers, and being absent from many other apparently quite suitable neighbouring localities. Like so many of our native orchids, it is rather uncertain in its appearance, and may disappear from a spot for several years. Whether the adult plants can remain dormant during this interval, nourished by the activity of the fungus in their roots, as has been stated by some authorities, has yet to be proved. In view of the efficient seed production, it seems more likely that the " blank " period represents the two or three years immediately following germination, while the seedlings are still in the leafless subterranean stage of their existence.

So far as habitats are concerned the species has a fairly wide tolerance on the Continent, occurring on various types of soil, in damp or dry localities, in open places or sometimes even in open woods. In this country it is rather more restricted, preferring on the whole chalky or limestone soils, and being commoner in drier places. Its favourite haunts are old pastures, downs, hill and mountain slopes, and the damper parts of sandhills near the shore. It may also be found on rock ledges in mountain districts, or more rarely in damp fields. A feature common to most of its habitats is the comparatively short turf in which the plant is usually to be found. No doubt its short stature makes continued existence difficult among taller vegetation, though sometimes quite tall plants may be found in such places. In this country the species rarely occurs in shady places, being usually well in the open. It occurs at quite high altitudes, reaching 3,300 feet in the Grampian Mountains in Aberdeenshire.

The flowering period of the frog orchid lasts from June until August, but July is the most likely month in which to find it in full flower. The flowers are inconspicuous, but they emit a faint honey-like scent, while there is free nectar in the short swollen spur at the base of the lip. Quite a variety of small insects have been observed visiting the flowers, including beetles and ichneumons. These alight on the lip, and walk along it towards the nectar-bearing spur. As there is a low ridge running along the centre of the lip, the insects are constrained to keep to one side or the other. As they approach the spur mouth their head comes into contact with one of the viscidia, which lie immediately above the stigma just behind the spur. The pollinium adheres to the insect, is removed and sinks slowly forward in the manner described earlier on for the early purple orchid (p. 48.) In the frog orchid, however, this movement is so slow (it takes about 20 minutes) that there is ample time for the insect to visit all the other flowers on the spike, and to fly to another spike, before the pollinium is low enough to make contact with the stigma of another flower. Packets of pollen grains are easily removed by the sticky surface of the stigmas, and thus several flowers may be fertilised by the same pollinium. It is evident from observations that pollination and fertilisation are very efficient processes in this species. Fruits are set very rapidly and may be ripe as early as July.

In sharp contrast with the musk orchid, there is no means of vegetative multiplication in the frog orchid, except the possibility of two separate buds and tubers being formed from the base of the old leafy stem, and the subsequent separation of these to form two plants. The species must therefore in most cases rely on seed production to maintain it over a period of years.

A number of naturally occurring hybrids have been reported between the frog orchid and species belonging to quite different genera. It should be understood that the evidence for the nature of these is purely circumstantial, no actually breeding experiments having been carried out, but there seems little doubt of the correctness of the views expressed. There are two main types of these, firstly, hybrids between the frog orchid and the fragrant orchid (*Gymnadenia conopsea*), and secondly, crosses with various members of the genus *Orchis*. In nearly all the observed cases the flowers and other parts of the plant were intermediate in structure and colour, while the two supposed parents were seen in the vicinity of the hybrid.

Hybrids with *Gymnadenia* (Pl. Vb, p. 78) have been discovered on several occasions and, as is usually the case with such hybrids, they differ markedly from one another, some more closely resembling one species and others being very similar to the other species. Some plants may, indeed, agree so closely with one or other of the possible parents that very careful examination is needed to discover the features pointing to hybridity. Usually, however, there is a mixture of the green and pink colourings of the two parents, while the lip and spur are intermediate in size and shape. The habit of the plant may also show intermediate features, especially between the long narrow leaves of the fragrant orchid and the shorter and broader leaves of *Coeloglossum*. Finally the characteristic and powerful scent of *Gymnadenia* may or may not be present.

Hybrids have also been recorded between the frog orchid and several species of *Orchis*, notably the common spotted orchid (*Orchis fuchsii*). These are usually very clearly intermediate, having more or less spotted leaves, and flowers curiously mottled with green and pink. The lip is often intermediate in shape and lobing, the characteristic line markings of the spotted orchid being replaced by irregular pink blotches or bands. An important point is the presence or absence of a covering to the viscidia, since these are naked in *Coeloglossum* whereas in *Orchis* they are embedded in a little pouch (bursicle). Although quite a rare hybrid, individuals have been found over a period of years in certain localities, and have been known to flower in several successive years. In 1948 I was shown in Wiltshire a plant which was clearly a hybrid between the frog orchid and the common spotted orchid. It was growing on a steep chalky bank with specimens of the latter species only a few feet away ; I did not see any frog orchids just here, but they occurred not far off. The flowers were of a very curious greenish-pink colour, making the plant easily distinguishable from any other orchids in the district. This plant had flowered two years earlier, when the spike was cut, but had recovered sufficiently to produce a further flower-spike. It will be interesting to see what is the future history of this plant.

LESSER BUTTERFLY ORCHID (*Platanthera bifolia*)

The two butterfly orchids form a marked contrast to the two species just dealt with, for they are in many respects among the most attractive and charming of our native orchids. Both have comparatively large cream or whitish coloured sweetly scented flowers in many-flowered conspicuous spikes, and a pair of elliptical or broadly strap-shaped leaves near the base of the stem. The lip is drawn out to form a long slender spur filled with nectar, on account of which the flowers are visited by butterflies and/or moths. Formerly botanists looked upon the greater and lesser butterfly orchids as being merely forms of one species, but they are now accepted as distinct and well-marked species, differing not only in flowers, etc., but also in their habitat preferences.

The lesser butterfly orchid (Pl. 25, p. 210) may be recognised by its smaller size, smaller and more delicately formed flowers, and narrower spike (Pl. XIIIb, p. 222), but particularly by the shape of the column. In *P. bifolia* this is comparatively narrow, so that the two halves (loculi) of the stamen are closely placed and parallel to one another, while the two viscidia lie side by side. The column differences between this species and the greater butterfly orchid may be seen in Fig. 17, p. 218, and in Plate XIIIa, p. 222.

The normal method of growth of the lesser butterfly orchid is much the same as that found in the frog orchid and in the genus *Orchis*. The aerial stem develops from food stored in the tuber formed the previous year, while a new tuber, with its associated bud for next year, is formed during the latter part of the growing season ; this is often well-developed by the time the flowers open. Although not forked, the more or less turnip-shaped tubers often terminate in a long narrow root, which penetrates downwards into the soil. There are also a number of other ordinary thin roots, which run more or less horizontally, or may even grow upwards into the surface humus layers of the soil. These roots, and also the narrow ends of the tubers, are infected with fungus, obtaining food from this source during the spring and autumn. The stem, which reaches a height of from six to fifteen inches, depending on the habitat, food available, etc., bears a pair of leaves in the lower part, and terminates in a flower-spike as much as four inches long, but usually much shorter. The leaves are broad and blunt, usually wider in the upper part, and deep green in colour ; occasionally there is an additional smaller one on the stem above them. The flower-spike, which is much narrower than in the greater butterfly orchid, contains from five to fifteen flowers. The flowers vary from white to cream coloured, or are even tinged greenish, the spur being often greener than the rest of the flower. A powerful and very sweet scent is emitted both by day and by night, but usually more strongly at night. The back sepal and the two petals form a sort of hood over the column, the lateral sepals spread out sideways, while the strap-shaped lip (Fig. 6 C, p. 31) is extended at the base into a slender spur nearly an inch in length.

The lesser butterfly orchid belongs to the Eurasian Element proper of our orchid flora. It occurs throughout Europe, with the exception of southern Spain and Greece, but is found also in North Africa. Eastwards it extends across Siberia to the region of Lake Baikal, while farther south it is found in Asia Minor, the Caucasus Mountains, Turkestan and the Himalayan Range. On the whole the species is commoner in northern regions than is *P. chlorantha*, while conversely it is not so widely spread nor so common as its relative in the Mediterranean district.

As might be expected from the above distribution, *P. bifolia* is found almost throughout the British Isles (Map 29, p. 353), with the exception of the Orkney and Shetland Islands. On the other hand, the species becomes decidedly more common as one goes northwards, being a relatively local and uncommon plant in the south. It is found on a great variety of soils, and in many different kinds of habitats. Compared with the greater butterfly orchid it is found on more acid soils, being a common plant on heaths and moorlands, where it grows among heather (*Calluna*), cross-leaved heath (*Erica tetralix*), mat grass (*Nardus stricta*), and other characteristic moorland plants. On the other hand, the species may be found on chalk downs and other calcareous soils, though admittedly it occurs in such places much more infrequently. It seems to be able to stand a considerable amount of shade, as it grows also in woodlands, but here it tends to favour the more open parts, while after a wood is felled numerous plants may sometimes spring up. In southern England it is sometimes found in beechwoods, where it is associated with twayblade, broad-leaved helleborine, and other orchids. In Europe it is a characteristic member of the beechwood flora. The lesser butterfly orchid also seems to be able to tolerate considerable differences in the dampness of the soil, being equally at home on dry slopes and in quite boggy places. For instance, in Somerset it is locally abundant in wet peaty fields with many sedges (*Carex* spp.), sweet gale (*Myrica gale*), common marsh orchid (*Orchis praetermissa*) and other plants usually found in damp or boggy places. It is particularly characteristic of grassy meadows or pastures in hilly districts, where it often occurs with the greater butterfly orchid, fragrant orchid (*Gymnadenia*), spotted orchids (*Orchis fuchsii* and *O. ericetorum*) and, where the turf is short enough, the frog orchid. It ascends to altitudes of 1,200 feet and over in northern England, Scotland and Ireland, but it may also be found almost at sea-level in many parts of the country. There is often a marked difference in size between plants growing in more open moorland or hilly situations on acid soils (Pl. 25a, p. 210) and those growing in woods on basic soils (Pl. 25b), the former being short, with the flower-spike rather dense, whereas the latter are taller with the flowers spaced out in the spike. In addition the leaves in the former are shorter and egg-shaped, while those of the latter are longer and relatively narrower. It is possible that these two forms are really distinct varieties or even sub-species. In the absence of *P. chlorantha* the woodland plants may at first sight be mistaken for that species, but when the two species occur together, as they do not infrequently, there is no difficulty in distinguishing them.

The lesser butterfly orchid is in flower during the months of June and July, usually opening in the former month in the southern part of the country, though in the north it may be rather later. In early seasons it may even come into flower late in May, but this is not common. From the general structure of the flower it is clear that long-tongued insects are necessary to effect pollination, as only such insects can reach the nectar in the long spur. The white flowers visible in the dark and the powerful scent, stronger at night, indicate that night-flying moths are the chief insect visitors. In this species the viscidia are relatively close together just above the mouth of the spur (Fig. 17B, p. 218). As the insect inserts its proboscis into the latter the base comes into contact with one or other of the viscidia, which adhere to it, so that the pollinium is removed as the insect leaves the flower. After removal the pollinium swivels forward (much as in *Orchis*) on the slender attachment to the viscidium, in such a way that it comes into contact with the stigma of another flower visited, some of the pollen packets being removed and causing fertilisation. Several kinds of moths have been recorded as removing pollinia, and clearly the process is effective, since usually from sixty to eighty per cent of the flowers produce seeds, though this figure may sometimes be considerably lower.

GREATER BUTTERFLY ORCHID (*Platanthera chlorantha*)

As the name indicates, this species is larger than the lesser butterfly orchid, not only in the size of the plant itself, but also as regards the width of the flower-spike (Pl. XIIIb, p. 222) and the individual flowers. Apart from the size, however, which is not an absolute criterion, since robust specimens of one species might possibly be confused with undersized specimens of the other, there are distinctive differences in the column (Fig. 17, p. 218 ; Pl. XIIIa). The two halves (loculi) of the stamens in *P. bifolia* are close together and parallel to one another, the viscidia being only a short distance apart. In *P. chlorantha*, however, the loculi are farther apart even at the top, while they diverge downwards so as to be far apart at the bottom where the viscidia are to be found. Although the degree of divergence of the two halves of the stamen varies a little from plant to plant, the general appearance is quite distinctive (see Fig. 17). Indeed the flower is relatively wider as seen from the front, while the upper central sepal is correspondingly broader.

In general growth (Pl. 24, p. 203) and life-history the greater butterfly orchid is closely similar to the lesser, the tubers and roots presenting no very marked differences. The paired leaves are usually longer, reaching a length of from three to seven inches, and often possessing quite long stalks. The stem varies from eight inches to two feet in height, with a flower-spike sometimes as much as nine inches long, containing ten to twenty-five flowers. The spike is always wider than in *P. bifolia*, as the flowers have longer stalks and therefore stand out farther ; this difference, which is recognisable even at a distance of several yards, is especially noticeable when the two species occur together. The flowers are very similar to those in the lesser butterfly orchid, but are more heavily built, and often tinged greenish, especially in plants growing in shady places, the end of the lip always being green. The spur in this species is an inch or more long, white or greenish, and filled with nectar at the tip for about a fifth or quarter of an inch.

As *Platanthera chlorantha* has much the same general distribution as *P. bifolia*, it also comes within the Eurasian Element of British

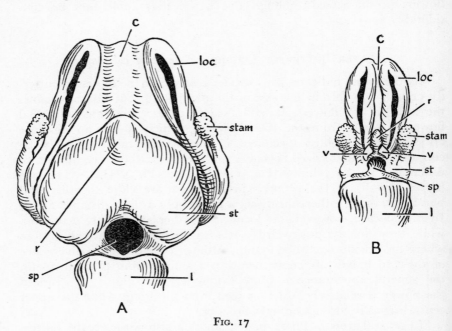

FIG. 17

Columns of A, greater butterfly orchid, *Platanthera chlorantha*, and B, lesser butterfly orchid, *P. bifolia*, to show the differences in size and structure. Note especially the divergent anther loculi in the former and the parallel ones in the latter. c. anther connective ; l. lip ; loc. anther loculus ; r. rostellum ; sp. mouth of spur ; st. stigma ; stam. staminode ; v. visci-dium. (both × 10)

orchids. It is, however, relatively more abundant in the southern parts of this common area of distribution, the lesser butterfly orchid, on the contrary, predominating in the more northern districts. The present species extends rather farther east than its ally, reaching Manchuria and Korea and also western China, while to the south it occurs in Asia Minor and northern Persia. The plants found in

PLATE 27

Robert Atkinson

Marsh Fragrant Orchid (*Gymnadenia conopsea* var. *densiflora*). Anglesey; July

PLATE 28

G. H. McLean

Dense-flowered Orchids (*Neotinea intacta*). Co. Clare; May

Japan and Sachalin, and formerly referred to this species, are now considered to belong to a closely allied species, *P. metabifolia*. The greater butterfly orchid is also more lowland in distribution than its British relative, rarely reaching altitudes of 6,000 feet and usually occurring below 4,000 feet. Although the two species have approximately the same requirements so far as climate is concerned, the greater butterfly orchid is clearly more at home in slightly drier and warmer regions, whereas the lesser is better suited by damper and cooler conditions. It is interesting to note that the majority of other species of *Platanthera* (there are some thirty or forty species in all, mostly in North America and eastern Asia) are natives of cooler temperate regions. Two species are found in Europe only in Scandinavia, while a third occurs at 66 degrees N. on the west coast of Greenland, where conditions are even more severe than in northern Scandinavia. *P. chlorantha* is undoubtedly one of the most southerly members of the genus.

In the British Isles the species is very widely spread (Map 28, p. 353), being found generally in England, Wales and Ireland, but less commonly in Scotland. In the north of that country it becomes relatively uncommon, and is absent from the Orkney and Shetland Islands. It is clearly a more southern species than the lesser butterfly orchid, reaching its greatest abundance in the southern half of England.

Ecologically the species, like its ally, has a wide range of tolerance, but it is more abundant on chalky soils than is *P. bifolia*; it only rarely occurs in the acid heath-like habitats often favoured by that species. Also it prefers rather drier localities, taken on the average, than does the lesser butterfly orchid. In the south, *P. chlorantha* seems to grow equally well in open fields or grassy slopes as in comparatively dense woods. It is especially characteristic of the coppiced oakwoods of southern England, especially those on neutral or alkaline soils. Here it is usually found in flower in lighter spots and along paths, but when the coppice is cut vast numbers of previously sterile plants come into flower, producing sometimes a magnificent effect. The species persists for a long time in quite deep shade, merely producing the two large ribbon-like leaves. In doing this it is undoubtedly much indebted to the activities of the fungus in the heavily infected roots. This enables the plant to maintain itself in spite of the reduced manufacture of food following the reduction of light available. Plants in shady situations seem to have rather greener tinged flowers than those growing in the open, though there is considerable variation in this respect. With it in these woods are also the early purple orchid (*Orchis mascula*), common twayblade (*Listera ovata*) and spotted orchid (*Orchis fuchsii*).

P. chlorantha is also often an inhabitant of scrubby and bushy places, where it seems to thrive under the shade of quite tall bushes or small trees, accompanied on chalk soils by several of the species already mentioned, and by the large white helleborine (*Cephalanthera damasonium*) and the fly orchid (*Ophrys muscifera*). Farther north the species is more frequently found on open grassy slopes or banks, in heathy fields, in hill meadows or pastures, or even among heather and other heath plants. Where the soil is less calcareous it is often accompanied by *P. bifolia*, but on limestone soils that species is often absent. There can be few more charming sights than a grassy slope studded all over with the tall creamy or white spikes of the greater butterfly orchid, reminiscent of a number of hyacinths. With it can also be found the fragrant orchid (*Gymnadenia conopsea*), spotted orchids (*Orchis fuchsii* and *O. ericetorum*) and also, though usually by that time in fruit, the early purple orchid (*Orchis mascula*). The species may sometimes be found in damp meadows and marshy ground, but is by no means as common as *P. bifolia* in such places. Fluctuation in the number of flowering specimens from year to year appears to be chiefly the result of locally, or temporarily, favourable or unfavourable conditions, as the species is very persistent, and in almost any locality a great preponderance of sterile adult specimens can be found in most years.

The greater butterfly orchid flowers usually in the months of June and July, being at its best in the south during the former month and reaching its maximum flowering in July farther north. In early seasons, or in sheltered localities, the first flowers may open during the latter half of May. The large white flowers, which have a much stronger scent by night than in the daytime, are visited and pollinated by night-flying moths, which visit them for the nectar in the long spur. Quite a variety of moths have been caught with pollinia attached to them, while it is easy to find flowers in which one or both of the pollinia have been removed. In this species the two viscidia, one on each side of the broad stamen, face inwards at some distance from each other, and just above the entrance to the spur. As the moth thrusts his proboscis into the spur the side of his head, particularly the large prominent eyes, comes into contact with one or other of the viscidia. The disc adheres to the insect, which consequently carries away the pollinium as it leaves the flower. A swollen pad at the base of the stalk of the pollinium dries up as the insect flies away, and as a consequence the pollinium swivels forwards and inwards (towards the moth's head). By the time another flower is reached the pollinium is properly placed to contact the centrally placed stigma, which lies below the stamen, and to which at least some of the pollen packets adhere. The effectiveness of pollination and fertilisation is shown by the fact that between 70 and 90 per cent of the capsules produce seeds.

Apart from the fact that more than one lateral bud at the base of the aerial stem may form tubers, and in time separate plants, there is no method of vegetative multiplication, the species depending upon seed for increasing its numbers and for the colonisation of new habitats.

SMALL WHITE ORCHID (*Gymnadenia albida*)

This and the fragrant orchid (*G. conopsea*), though both placed in the genus *Gymnadenia* on account of agreement in the details of their floral structure, are very different in general appearance. *G. albida* is one of the smaller and less conspicuous species of our orchid flora (Pl. 23b, p. 202), reaching usually a height of only six inches, which, taken in conjunction with its small white flowers, makes it easily overlooked. *G. conopsea*, on the other hand, with its spike of red-lilac or pink strongly scented flowers (Pl. 26, p. 211), and its habit of growing together in large numbers, is a very conspicuous and attractive plant.

The two tubers constituting the underground portion of a plant of *G. albida* are in shape rather like two minute parsnips, tapering gradually downwards, and often split almost to the base into several parts. They are widely separated from one another towards the tips, where they have the nature of ordinary roots, which serve for the absorption of water from the soil. These narrow ends, like the ordinary slender roots, are heavily infected with fungus, which helps to feed the plant. The ordinary roots run horizontally in the surface layers of the soil, where there is the maximum of humus available for the fungus. The aerial stem, which is first produced in the fourth year after germination of the seed, reaches a height of from four to twelve inches, though plants of the latter size are uncommon. There may be four to six leaves in the lower part of the stem, the lower ones being broad and blunt, while the upper are quite small and narrow. There is a strong resemblance, so far as leaves are concerned, between this species and the frog orchid (*Coeloglossum viride*, Pl. 23a, p. 202), but the flowers in that plant are larger and completely green or reddish. The very dense flower-spike, which is about one or two inches (in robust specimens up to three inches) in length (Pl. XVIIIb, p. 255), contains a large number (up to 32) of small white or yellowish flowers, sometimes tinged with green. The very short blunt sepals and petals form a hood or tube, below which hangs the deeply three-lobed lip bearing a short rounded spur containing nectar.

This species constitutes, with the lesser twayblade and creeping ladies' tresses, the Northern Montane Group of British orchids. It occurs throughout Europe as far south as Catalonia, Corsica, central Italy and the centre of the Balkan Peninsula, but it is much commoner in the northern parts of the Continent, and occurs only at high altitudes in the south. Eastwards it is found across Siberia to Japan, Sachalin and Kamchatka, and farther south in Asia Minor and the Caucasus Mountains. The species is also widely spread in North America from Newfoundland to Alaska, extending northwards in Greenland to 69 degrees N. latitude.

This generally northern distribution is paralleled in the British Isles (Map 27, p. 352), where it is a rare and local species in the south. In fact the only reliable southern records are from Sussex, in which county it has been seen in various parts of the heathy ridge which runs through the centre of the Weald and reaches its greatest extent in Ashdown Forest on the borders of Sussex and Kent. The species reappears in south central Wales, (Breconshire and Carmarthenshire), Hereford, Cheshire, Derbyshire and West Yorkshire ; from here northwards it gradually becomes more frequent, reaching its greatest abundance in Scotland. In Ireland it is also commoner in the northern half of the country, though scattered over most of the area. In Scotland the species is found up to 2,000 feet above sea-level, while it occurs at almost equal altitudes in western Ireland.

The small white orchid is more restricted as regards its habitat than either the fragrant orchid or the two butterfly orchids just dealt with. It is usually found in rough meadows, pastures, or grassy slopes, especially in hilly districts, but it also occurs in heathy places with a certain amount of heather or other heath shrubs present. It seems indifferent to the presence of lime, occurring on both non-calcareous and limestone soils, but sometimes it appears as though it prefers poor soils. In Europe it is occasionally found in open woods, especially

PLATE XIII

R. Atkinson

b. Flowers of Lesser (above) and Greater Butterfly Orchids, *Platanthera bifolia* and *P. chlorantha*, on the same scale, to show differences in size, and shape of column (×1¾)

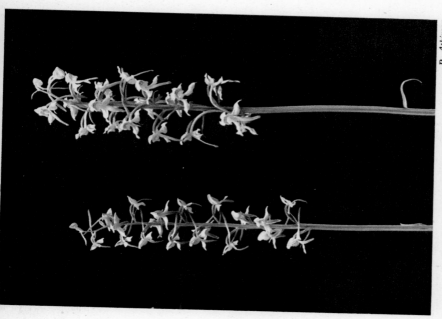

R. Atkinson

a. Flower spikes of Lesser and Greater Butterfly Orchids (×½)

PLATE XIV

E. J. Bedford

E. J. Bedford

pine and other coniferous woods, but it only rarely occurs in such places in the British Isles. It can, however, stand a certain amount of shade, as it is occasionally found in bushy places in the partial shade of the shrubs. Most of its habitats are rather dry, but it has sometimes been recorded from damp places, provided there is good drainage.

The flowering period of *G. albida* extends from about the middle of June to the middle of July, a relatively short period. Indeed the flowers will often be found over by the end of June, while well-developed fruits may be found by July 18th or so. The exact time of flowering depends on the locality and altitude, being on the whole a little earlier in the south. The sweet scent and free nectar in the spur attract a variety of insects, among them butterflies, solitary bees and other hymenopterous insects. Pollination and fertilisation seems an efficient process, as pollinia are removed from many flowers, but this is aided by self-pollination in some, at least, of the flowers. As the flowers fade the pollinia fall from the stamen on to the receptive stigma below. Fruit is recorded as being set in over 90 per cent of the flowers, by one means or another, and indeed most fruiting specimens appear to bear an almost solid mass of ripening seed capsules. Germination of the seeds and growth of the seedlings is often highly successful, resulting in a large number of plants occurring together. There is no special method of multiplication by vegetative means.

FRAGRANT ORCHID (*Gymnadenia conopsea*)

The fragrant or sweet-scented orchid is undoubtedly one of the most attractive of our native orchids (Pl. 26, p. 211 ; 27, p. 218), partly on account of its dense spikes of pink or red-lilac flowers, and partly because it often occurs in immense numbers. In fact *G. conopsea* provides one of the best illustrations of the way in which many of our orchids fluctuate in numbers from year to year. Sometimes you may find hundreds or even thousands of plants, but the next year you may be lucky if you can discover a dozen in flower. As regards the " fragrance " there is considerable diversity of opinion, some observers finding it pleasant, while others take the opposite view. There is, however, some evidence to support the view that there are several distinct varieties of the species in this country, each one of which has its own special scent. One of these, the variety *densiflora,* is dealt with more fully below.

W.O.B.

Q

The species is not likely to be confused with any other orchid except the pyramidal orchid (*Anacamptis pyramidalis*, Pl. 29, p. 226), which has flowers of much the same size and colour, and an equally long slender spur. The pyramidal orchid may, however, easily be distinguished by the two upright ridges on the lip, one on each side of the mouth of the spur; these are quite lacking in the fragrant orchid. In the pyramidal orchid also, the two pollinia are attached to one viscidium, and are always removed from the flower together, whereas in the fragrant orchid each pollinium has its own viscidium, and can be removed separately.

The underground parts of the fragrant orchid are very like those in the small white orchid, except that the tubers are larger and only divided into fingers for about half their length, not almost completely as in the latter species. There are a few ordinary roots, usually infected with fungus, which no doubt helps in the nourishment of the plant. The aerial stem first appears in the third year after the seed germinates; it varies in height from six to eighteen inches, depending on the nature of the habitat. In the normal form of the plant there are from three to five rather long and narrow, more or less erect leaves arising from the lower part of the stem, as well as several smaller ones farther up. The flower-spike is comparatively long and dense, from two to four inches in length, or in robust individuals even longer. It tends to become looser as the flowers open, especially in the lower part. The flowers are various shades of rosy or reddish pink, usually with a distinct lilac or bluish tinge. Bright magenta flowers have been recorded and also, as in many other British orchids, albinos with pure white flowers. In any large colony of plants a considerable range of colour can usually be found. The rather broad three-lobed lip bears a long slender spur which can readily be seen, especially in the lower flowers (Fig. 6B, p. 31). The flowers are strongly scented, this being an easy way of recognising the species.

The variety *densiflora* (marsh fragrant orchid, Pl. 27, p. 218) is on the whole a larger plant, usually with much broader leaves (up to nearly an inch broad) and a longer very dense spike of rather darker coloured flowers. In continental plants the spur is often shorter than in the usual form, but this is not a constant feature in British specimens of this variety. The rather pleasant scent is quite distinct from that of the ordinary variety, being said to resemble that of a clove carnation. In addition to these differences var. *densiflora* grows in different situations, being characteristic of marshes or bogs, as the common name suggests.

The fragrant orchid belongs to the Central Eurasian Element of our orchid flora, occurring throughout Europe, but less abundantly in the north and south than elsewhere. It extends across Siberia and Mongolia to northern China, Korea and the Japanese islands, while farther south it is found in Asia Minor, Caucasia and northern Persia. In the Mediterranean region it is a mountain plant, reaching altitudes of over 7,000 feet. The variety *densiflora* is also found throughout Europe, but is more abundant in the south-east, especially in the Balkans.

As might be expected from its general distribution, *G. conopsea* is found throughout the British Isles as far as the Shetland Islands (Map 26, p. 352). It is not a common plant, being rather local in its occurrence, but it may be very abundant in some places. In Ireland it is more common in the northern part of the country. Generally speaking it is a lowland plant, but it has been found at 2,000 ft. in Scotland.

Despite the local nature of its occurrence, the species may be found in a great variety of situations, varying greatly in the nature of the soil and also in the dampness of the habitat. It is found indifferently on soils rich or poor in lime, though it does on the whole seem more abundant on calcareous soils. In the south of England it is a characteristic plant of the chalk downs, sometimes in immense numbers so as literally to colour the hillside, on other occasions in small groups of a few plants. It may be found either in short turf with such plants as the bee orchid (*Ophrys apifera*), dwarf orchid (*Orchis ustulata*) and musk orchid (*Herminium*), or among tall grasses like erect brome (*Bromus erectus*) and false oats (*Arrhenatherum elatius*), where it may be associated with the spotted orchid (*Orchis fuchsii*) or the pyramidal orchid (*Anacamptis*). It is equally abundant on the steep limestone slopes of the Derbyshire dales and Mountain limestone of Yorkshire, where it is found with some of the species already mentioned as well as with the greater butterfly orchid (*Platanthera chlorantha*), the frog orchid (*Coeloglossum*) and the early purple orchid. In Ireland it is widely spread on the extensive limestone formations of Counties Clare and Galway. On the other hand, the fragrant orchid is a not uncommon plant in heathy places on rather acid soils, often growing among mixed heather, dwarf gorse and grasses, together with one or other of the two spotted orchids, particularly the heath spotted orchid (*Orchis ericetorum*).

Most of the habitats described are comparatively dry, but the species is also an inhabitant of wet boggy places, among rushes or coarse grasses like the purple moor grass (*Molinia*). Plants in such localities may be the ordinary variety or, in the wettest places, the marsh fragrant orchid (var. *densiflora*). This variety is found in very wet bogs or swamps among sedges (*Carex* spp.), cotton grasses (*Eriophorum* spp.) and other typical swamp plants, often with standing water even in the summer. In these places the accompanying orchids are usually marsh orchids (*Orchis praetermissa, O. latifolia*, etc.) or the marsh helleborine (*Epipactis palustris*). The variety *densiflora* also sometimes occurs in drier habitats, especially in Ireland.

In Europe *G. conopsea* not infrequently occurs among bushes, in open thickets, or even in light woods, but it seems to be a rare plant in such places in this country. Ordinarily it avoids shade, being most abundant in open grassland, commons, heaths and downs.

The fragrant orchid usually comes into flower in June, in the early part of the month in the south, nearer the end or early in July farther north. The time of flowering depends on the locality and latitude, plants growing in dry places usually flowering before those in the damper spots. The marsh fragrant orchid usually flowers about a fortnight or so later than the ordinary variety, that is, in July or even August.

The flowers, strongly fragrant both by day and night, are very attractive to moths, many kinds of which have been recorded on the flowers. Some species of butterflies have also been observed visiting this orchid. The long slender spur, containing a great deal of nectar, is clearly most suited to long-tongued insects. Some sorts of bees and also flies have been seen visiting the flowers, and the occurrence of frequent hybrids with species of *Orchis*, which possess shorter spurs, suggests that these insects (or perhaps other shorter-tongued insects) may remove the pollinia. Beetles have also been recorded, but it is not known if they take any part in pollination and fertilisation. The adhesive discs of the pollinia, long narrow strips in this orchid, are a part of the roof of the small chamber formed by the column just at the mouth of the spur ; as the insect's proboscis is inserted it almost of necessity comes into contact with these viscidia. As the pollinia are carried away they bend over forwards so as to lie parallel to the

PLATE 29

Robert Atkinson

Group of Pyramidal Orchids (*Anacamptis pyramidalis*). From Oxfordshire; July

PLATE 30

Robert Atkinson

Lizard Orchid (*Himantoglossum hircinum*). Bedfordshire; July

slender viscidia and facing forwards. On entering another flower they strike directly on to the sticky stigma, which drags away some of the loosely attached pollen packets. A single moth may carry away as many as seven pollinia in successive visits to different flowers. Fertilisation seems reasonably effective, as between 50 and 90 per cent of the flowers have been observed to produce seeds. It would appear that the remarkable fluctuations in the numbers of plants seen in different years is not due to poor seed production, but to difficulties in the establishment of the seedlings and young plants in many seasons.

Hybrids have been found very rarely between the fragrant orchid and small white orchid, notably in Inverness-shire, where they were growing with both of the supposed parents. The leaves and flowers were intermediate in character. Like most hybrids they are very variable, resembling one or other of the parents in the different examples found. Specimens found just before the War in Yorkshire resembled *G. albida* closely in general appearance, but the flowers were pink with a bluish tinge and the lip white.

Quite a number of hybrids have also been recorded between *G. conopsea* and various species of *Orchis*, particularly the two spotted orchids (*O. fuchsii* and *O. ericetorum*). These hybrids are usually intermediate in appearance and other respects (Pl. 3, p. 62), combining the long spur and sweet scent of the fragrant orchid with the spotted leaves and darker marked lip of the spotted orchid, but some individuals may more closely resemble one parent than the other. In some plants which I have seen the small pouches (bursicles) in which the viscidia rest, a characteristic feature of *Orchis* but absent in *Gymnadenia*, were present, absent, or imperfectly formed in different flowers on the same spike !

Hybrids have also been found between the fragrant orchid and common marsh orchid (*Orchis praetermissa*). These hybrids are usually more or less intermediate between the parents, possessing the robust habit and large bracts of the marsh orchid, with flowers intermediate in size and coloration, and a comparatively slender spur. Such hybrids are naturally restricted to the southern part of England where *O. praetermissa* is found ; in the west and north they are replaced by hybrids in which the marsh orchid parent is the dwarf purple orchid (*O. purpurella*), which is the most frequent species in those regions.

SHORT-SPURRED FRAGRANT ORCHID (*Gymnadenia odoratissima*)

This species has only once been found in this country, namely at Black Hall Rocks in Durham, in July 1912. There was only a single specimen, and although a careful watch has been kept since no further plants have been seen. The species resembles closely the common fragrant orchid, but the leaves are invariably narrower, while the flower-spike is usually much shorter with smaller flowers. These have a spur only about half as long as in *G. conopsea*. There are also other minor floral differences, particularly the shape of the lip, which is nothing like so deeply divided into lobes.

G. odoratissima usually occurs on limestone in its European localities, and it was on Magnesian limestone that it was found in Durham. It is not so widespread on the Continent as its ally, being more characteristically central European. It does occur in Scandinavia as well as in France and Germany, and seeds might easily have been carried casually by wind or other agency from any of these countries to give rise to the plant in Durham.

CHAPTER 12

ORCHIS RELATIVES

THE FOUR species included here, though differing enough among themselves to be placed in four different genera, all possess two features which link them with the common early purple and green-veined orchids. Firstly, they have egg-shaped or nearly globular tubers, while secondly, the sticky discs of the pollinia lie in a little bag or flap which keeps them moist until they are carried away by a visiting insect (see Fig. 10 B, p. 48). In other respects, however, they show certain resemblances to the *Habenaria* group just described, and may properly be looked upon as coming between these and the *Orchis* species which have globular tubers. The species concerned are the dense-flowered orchid (*Neotinea intacta*, Pl. 28, p. 219), pyramidal orchid (*Anacamptis pyramidalis*, Pl. 29, p. 226), lizard orchid (*Himantoglossum hircinum*, Pl. 30, p. 227) and man orchid (*Aceras anthropophorum*, Pl. 31, p. 234). Apart from the two features common to them all, these four plants show very few resemblances, either as regards general appearance, size and colour of flowers, or detailed floral structure. *Neotinea*, with small white or pinkish flowers in a dense spike, is very reminiscent of the small white orchid (*Gymnadenia albida*), the numerous small pink long-spurred flowers of *Anacamptis* may easily be mistaken by the beginner for the fragrant orchid (*Gymnadenia conopsea*, Pl. 26, p. 211), while *Aceras*, although its flowers are yellow or brownish, has many features in common with our rare military and monkey orchids (*Orchis militaris* and *O. simia*). The lizard orchid, on the other hand, though structurally not far removed from the man orchid, is a very distinct-looking species which could scarcely be confused with any other British orchid. The group contains two of our rarest orchids, the dense-flowered orchid being known only from parts of western

Ireland, while the lizard orchid, though more widely spread, occurs usually singly or in small numbers, and is very uncertain in its appearance.

DENSE-FLOWERED ORCHID (*Neotinea intacta*)

This plant is in certain respects one of the most interesting of our native orchids, owing to its remarkable geographical distribution. Indeed it is necessary to go to counties Clare, Galway or Mayo in the extreme west of Ireland in order to see the species in its natural haunts (Pl. 28, p. 219). However, the Burren limestone district, in which the plant is most abundant, is so interesting to any lover of the British flora that a holiday in this region is well worth the extra trouble and expense. Since the orchid enthusiast may also see the Irish marsh orchid (*Orchis occidentalis*, Pl. XX, p. 271) and, rather later in the year, the very striking sub-species of the common spotted orchid (*O. fuchsii*) first found by Dr. O'Kelly (Pl. 40, p. 267), as well as other orchids, he or she is strongly recommended to visit the town of Bally-vaughan or some other convenient spot nearby.

The underground parts at the time of flowering consist of the two egg-shaped tubers, one of which is produced each year, together with a few short fleshy roots. The leafy aerial shoot first appears in October, persisting throughout the winter, and developing the flowers comparatively early in the subsequent year. There are two or three broad leaves near the bottom of the stem and several smaller ones higher up (Pl. XIVa, p. 223). The leaves in Irish specimens are usually unspotted, but one not infrequently finds plants with bluish-green leaves bearing small reddish or purplish spots which may be in more or less parallel lines. Curiously enough, this spotted-leaved variety is the common one in the Mediterranean region, where the plant has its main centre of distribution. The flowering stem reaches a height of four to eight inches, or even a foot or more in robust specimens, including the one to three inches long flower-spike. This, as the name suggests, is very dense, containing quite a number of small whitish or pink flowers which often all face the same direction, and appear not to be properly open. Plants with whitish flowers invariably possess unspotted leaves, whereas the spotted-leaved plants bear pink flowers. The perianth members are short and broad, the sepals and petals forming a sort of hood. The lip is three-lobed, the middle lobe longer than the others and somewhat resembling a serpent's tongue, though the fork at the tip is not very pronounced. At the base is a short blunt spur which contains nectar. In general structure the column is like that in *Orchis*, except that the stalks (caudicles) of the pollinia are very short, while there are two separate stigmas, borne one on each side of the mouth of the spur.

As mentioned in Chapter 4, the dense-flowered orchid stands in a class by itself from the point of view of its present geographical distribution. In the British Isles it is restricted to three counties in western Ireland (Clare, Galway and Mayo, Map 32, p. 354), but outside of these islands it is known in Europe only from the Mediterranean region, extending from Portugal and Spain eastwards as far as Cyprus and Asia Minor. *Neotinea* is found also in Algeria and Morocco, as well as in Madeira and the Canary Islands. It is evidently adapted to life in countries with an oceanic climate, but this must also be of a relatively warm type. There is a large gap between its stations in Ireland, on the one hand, and those in northern Spain (Asturias) and Portugal, on the other. It is generally thought that the species reached western Ireland from farther south at a period when the climate was warmer than at present, and when there was more or less continuous land to the west of present-day France linking up Spain and Ireland. This very general view, the details of which are still the subject of active controversy, gains support by the presence in the same or other parts of western Ireland of other plants, such as the strawberry tree (*Arbutus unedo*) and various species of saxifrage, which are also otherwise natives of the Iberian Peninsula and the Mediterranean basin. It is known that such warmer periods occurred both during and after the last great Ice Age, but when the dense-flowered orchid arrived in Ireland, and when the plants there became separated by climatic changes from the populations farther south, is a more difficult question to decide. The latest evidence (see Jessen) suggests that *Neotinea* may either have survived throughout the entire Glacial Period, or have entered the country during one of the warm inter-glacial periods. It probably could have maintained itself during the subsequent glaciations either in what is present-day western Ireland or in land to the south or south-west of this. It is extremely likely that these regions, being in closer contact with the ameliorating conditions of the Atlantic Ocean, during and after the Ice Age, had a more favourable climate than that of other parts of the British Isles. This might well have allowed the species to persist there even when the vegetation of the remainder of Britain was of a much more northern type. When finally sea communication was established between the Atlantic and the North Sea via the Straits of Dover, the land communication between the Irish localities and the continent of Europe was finally broken. It does not seem that the dense-flowered orchid could have migrated from the south in the warm period following the Glacial Epoch (the so-called Atlantic Period), as otherwise one would expect to find it in Brittany, south-western England and counties Kerry and Cork. In any case there is evidence that the formation of the Straits of Dover preceded this warm period, and such a sea barrier would have made migration much more difficult. A vast literature, however, has grown up around the problems raised by the various species mentioned, and to this the reader is referred for further information, and, if he enjoys it, much sprightly controversy!

In Ireland *N. intacta* is characteristically an inhabitant of the bare or almost bare limestone country forming the Burren Hills and similar country to the south and west of these. In these regions the limestone forms extensive expanses or " pavements ", in which only the cracks and crevices between the blocks can support any vegetation. Elsewhere there is a shallow layer of soil in depressions of the rock. The dense-flowered orchid is generally distributed throughout this limestone area from Clare to Lough Mask in Mayo, and up to 1,000 feet above sea-level. Within the limestone area the species occurs almost universally, on rocky or grassy hillsides, in pastures, or on banks or grassy spots by the roadside. It appears to maintain itself even when the ground is heavily grazed, but flowering is difficult in such places. Other orchids associated with it, but not usually flowering at the same time, are the autumn ladies' tresses (*Spiranthes spiralis*), bee orchid (*Ophrys apifera*), pyramidal orchid (*Anacamptis*), and dark red helleborine (*Epipactis atrorubens*). Rarely *Neotinea* is found off the limestone, especially on calcareous sea sands, and also even in a few places on light semi-peaty soils overlying acid rocks. Little is known of the exact conditions in such places, and it is to be hoped that further observations may be made so as to explain the relation between these exceptional spots and the normal habitat on the limestone. It should be noted that in the Mediterranean region the dense-flowered orchid is by no means uncommon on non-calcareous rocks, as for instance in the French and Italian Riviera. Presumably we have here another example of southern plants, when at the extreme limit of their range, thriving best on the dry warm limestone soils which most closely resemble the conditions farther south. The other three species belonging to the present group all illustrate this general phenomenon.

Owing to the development of the leafy shoot during the preceding autumn, the dense-flowered orchid is able to produce its flowers early in the year, May being the usual month, though it may rarely still be found in flower in early June in late seasons. The presence of abundant nectar in the spur would suggest that the flowers are attractive to insects, and possibly small insects do visit the flowers and effect pollination. This has, however, never been observed, according to Godfery. The absence of insects appears to be of little consequence, since the pollen packets easily become detached, and fall on to the stigmas below, thus ensuring self-pollination of the flower. It is difficult to find an opened flower in which this has not happened, possibly merely as a result of wind action ; that it is effective is vouched for by the abundant fruit and seed set. Indeed it is often easier to detect the species by the dense spikes of swollen seedpods later in the year, than by the rather inconspicuous flowers at the time of flowering. These pods are often dead and dry even by the end of June, but in the absence of trampling may persist until August.

PYRAMIDAL ORCHID (*Anacamptis pyramidalis*)

There are probably few more charming sights than a chalk down or limestone hill in July dotted over with the bright pink spikes of this attractive plant. Superficially the species may be mistaken for the fragrant orchid (*Gymnadenia conopsea*), which often occurs in similar places, but is at its best a week or more earlier. *Anacamptis* (Pl. 29, p. 226) may, however, be distinguished by the purer pink colour— there is usually a distinct lilac tint in *Gymnadenia*—and by the pyramidal shape of the flower-spike, especially in the early stages. Technically it can also be recognised easily by the two tall upright converging walls (or guide plates) on the lip just in front of and leading to the mouth of the spur. The relatively long, very slender spur will distinguish the pyramidal orchid from any other British species at all similarly coloured.

The underground tubers are globose or more or less elongated, two in number at flowering time, and accompanied by a few slender, but fleshy, ordinary roots. For the first four years the young plant is fed by its mycorhizal fungus, no leaves being formed until the fifth year, and flowers not until several years later. The aerial stem develops in the autumn, the leaves remaining throughout the winter (winter-green species), but the stem does not grow out further until the following June. There are about three or four somewhat fleshy basal autumn leaves, which are rather long (4–6 inches) and narrow ; several more smaller leaves are borne on the flowering stem formed during the summer. Often by the time the flowers have opened the lower leaves are withered, the water they contained having been drawn upon to feed the rapidly growing flower stem. This stem varies considerably in height, often depending on the length of the grass in which the plants are growing, but is usually between 8 and 18 inches altogether, often rather slender and apt to fall over and so become bent.

The flower-spike is about one to two and a half inches in length, containing a large number of very closely placed flowers, which vary in colour from pale pink to deep pink-red, or rarely bright blood-red ; white flowered plants are occasionally found (Pl. XIVb, p. 223). In the early stages of development the spike tapers towards the pointed tip, producing a pyramidal shape, but this is less obvious as more and more flowers open. When the flowers are open the short upper sepals and petals form a hood, the almost evenly three-lobed lip sloping forwards on the lower side of each flower, and the slender curved spurs of the lower flowers projecting below the bottom of the spike. Some-times, due to unfavourable conditions, the flowers fail to twist into the normal position, so that the lip is uppermost (Pl. IIIb, p. 26). The two pollinia are in this species joined to a single narrow strap-like viscidium (Fig. 11 C and D, p. 50), which is covered by a flap-like pouch (bursicle) as in *Orchis*. There are two separate stigmas on the sides of the column above the spur mouth.

The pyramidal orchid belongs to the Southern Eurasian Group of British orchids. It has a wide distribution in Europe, but does not extend farther north than Denmark and south Sweden ; it is common in the Mediterranean region, including Morocco and Algeria. East-wards the species is found as far as Persia and Caucasia. This pre-dominantly southern distribution is paralleled in this country, for although the species is widespread in England, Wales and Ireland, it is found only in the southern part of Scotland, extending as far north as Fife along the east coast (Map 33, p. 354). In the west its most northerly stations on the mainland are in Dumfries and Kirkcud-

PLATE 31

Robert Atkinson

Man Orchids (*Aceras anthropophorum*). Oxfordshire; June

PLATE 32

Robert Atkinson

Monkey Orchid (*Orchis simia*). Oxfordshire; June

bright, but the species occurs in some of the islands as far north as Mull. This is apparently a continuation of its distribution in north Ireland. The species is most abundant in southern England, becoming less frequent the farther north one goes.

Like the other plants in this group, the pyramidal orchid is nearly always found in this country on soils rich in lime, though it may occasionally be found on other soils. It is a characteristic plant of the chalk downs of the south, but it is also common on limestones such as the Lias and Oolites. For instance, it is abundant on the Cotswold Hills in Gloucestershire and the Poldens in Somerset. Its usual habitat is among the taller grasslands of erect brome grass (*Bromus erectus*), false oats (*Arrhenatherum elatius*), oat grasses (*Helictotrichon pratensis* and *H. pubescens*) and the like (Pl. 29, p. 226), whereas it is less common in the short turf beloved by many other orchids. The species can evidently stand a fair amount of shade, as it frequently occurs among low scrub of hawthorn and blackthorn, and at the base of bushes of other species. It may also be found in open grassy woods of beech, oak and other trees, provided the canopy of the trees is not continuous. Dry soil seems to be a necessity, since the plant is rarely seen where the drainage is at all defective. Of other habitats, that of sand dunes is the most frequent, but as pointed out elsewhere sea-sand is often rich in marine shells, and therefore distinctly calcareous. The species is recorded from similar places in Holland and Belgium. Observations show that it is one of the first orchids to recolonise ground which has reverted to grass after cultivation.

The pyramidal orchid comes into flower rather later than most other chalk orchids, opening first about the middle of June and remaining in flower until the end of July. It is at its best at the end of June and during the first week of July. The species is often very abundant locally, exhibiting considerable variations in colour in quite a small area. The flowers emit a delicate scent, and are visited by day- and night-flying moths and butterflies for the liquid within the thick walls of the spur, there being no free-lying nectar. The remarkable pollination mechanism is described in detail in Chapter 3 (p. 50). It has been observed that abnormal flowers, in which the spur is short or lacking or the guiding plates not perfectly formed, are very rarely visited, and the pollinia are not removed. The upper flowers of the spike may not be fertilised, but as fruit is normally set in from 65 to 95 per cent of the flowers, it is clear that the pollination mechanism is very efficient. A single moth observed by Darwin bore no fewer than eleven pairs of pollinia on its proboscis, while Godfery records seeing an ordinary hive bee remove two pairs of pollinia from a plant at Guildford.

Hybrids have been reported between *Anacamptis* and the fragrant orchid (*Gymnadenia conopsea*), and also with the common spotted orchid (*Orchis fuchsii*), but such occurrences are very rare and not too well authenticated. The former hybrid seems not improbable in view of the very similar flower structure and insect visitors, but the flowering periods usually overlap so little that the opportunity of such a cross being effected is not very great. *Orchis fuchsii*, on the other hand, is usually in flower with the pyramidal orchid and often grows mixed with it, but in view of the short spur of the *Orchis* the only insect likely to visit both species is a hive bee. Even then the different flower structure in the two species, particularly the positions of the stigmas, would make effective pollination and fertilisation very difficult. I had a plant sent to me recently from Wiltshire which may have been this hybrid ; on visiting the locality in the following summer I was unable to rediscover the plant or any similar individual.

LIZARD ORCHID (*Himantoglossum hircinum*)

Probably this orchid is more frequently the subject of paragraphs in the press than any other British species. It is evidently one of the few orchids which has any " news " value, presumably because it is not only rare and sporadic in its occurrence, but also very striking looking (Pl. 30, p. 227). The flowers certainly do bear a quaint resemblance to a lizard, with the sepals and petals forming the head and body, the side lobes of the lip the hind legs, and the long twisted remainder of the lip a very plausible tail. There is very little likelihood of confusing the lizard orchid with any other British orchid in view of the colour of the flowers (which are of a very peculiar greyish purple-green colour), their remarkable shape, and the quite strong smell of goats. After being extremely rare and almost extinct in this country during the latter half of the nineteenth century, the plant has increased its area of distribution, and also in actual numbers, since 1900, though it is still quite a rare plant.

The two tubers in the lizard orchid are egg-shaped or more or less elongated, and larger than in most other British species. The lower foliage leaves are formed in the autumn, the species being thus wintergreen, the remainder of the aerial stem developing in the early summer of the succeeding year. The stem reaches a total height of nine to eighteen inches in this country, but it may be up to three feet high in Europe. There are usually eight to ten leaves, of which about a half are borne at the base, the remainder being smaller and scattered along the upper part. The lower leaves are from two to five inches in length, broad and blunt, rather fleshy, and deep green when young. By the time the flowers are expanding the leaves are often paler green, yellowish or even quite withered, the water they contained having been drawn upon to help produce the rapidly elongating flower-spike. This spike is four inches to nearly a foot in length, containing sometimes as many as eighty closely placed flowers, though in this country the number is usually much smaller. The flowers are of a purplish-green colour with a curious greyish tinge, the sepals and petals forming a darker coloured hood covering the column. The lip is very long (2 inches), narrow and ribbon-shaped, whitish towards the base with small red spots or blotches, the rest being dull green, more or less tinged with purple on the short curly side lobes. The main part of the lip (middle lobe) is rolled up to form a sort of coil when young, and remains spirally twisted several times when expanded; there is a short conical spur at the very base (Fig. 6 E, p. 31). The structure of the column, etc., is much as in *Orchis*, except that the two pollinia are attached, as in *Anacamptis*, to a single viscidium.

Himantoglossum, like *Anacamptis*, belongs to the Southern Eurasian Element of our orchid flora, but is distinctly more southern in its general distribution, extending northwards only as far as Belgium, Holland, south Germany, south-western Czechoslovakia, and from there to the mouth of the Danube. There is a definitely western bias in its occurrence, the species being especially abundant in western France, and becoming rarer in the Mediterranean district as one goes eastwards. It has been recorded from southern Asia Minor, but is not known farther east; in the eastern Mediterranean it is chiefly represented by the sub-species *calcaratum*, which by some authorities is considered to be a distinct species.

The history of the distribution of the lizard orchid in this country makes a fascinating story, which has been pieced together admirably by Good. According to his account three different phases or periods can be recognised since records were first made. During the first period, which lasted from some time before 1641, when the species was first recorded, until about 1850, the lizard orchid was known only from several localities in the neighbourhood of Dartford in Kent, in which district it seems therefore to have persisted for over 200 years. About the end of this period, however, the plant died out in the region, either through natural causes or perhaps through excessive gathering by collectors. During the next 50 years the species appeared merely to have occurred very sporadically in a number of different localities in the south-eastern part of England, especially in Kent, extending westwards to Hampshire and northwards to Suffolk. Throughout this time the lizard orchid was looked upon and recorded as very rare, probably dying out or even extinct. At the beginning of the present century, however, a remarkable change occurred, the species being found not only more frequently in south-eastern England, but turning up in new counties beyond the earlier limits of its distribution. This spread has been most striking since 1919, and the species is now known from most parts of the south-eastern half of the country, the most northern locality being in Yorkshire, and the most western in Devon (Map 34, p. 354). Apart from occurring in new localities, the lizard orchid in this last period has frequently been found in considerable numbers—as many as 200 individuals were seen at once in one locality in Kent—although the solitary specimen still provided the great majority of occurrences.

The question immediately arises " What is the explanation of this remarkable change in the behaviour of the lizard orchid ? " Since the spread seems to have been general throughout south-eastern England, it would appear that some change in climate is the only likely explanation. Examination of meteorological records shows that between 1900 and 1933 the climate of this part of England was slightly warmer and wetter in winter and spring with fewer severe frosts, while, on the other hand, there was a smaller decrease in temperature in summer and autumn, the latter period being drier. This means that the climate was slightly more equable, warmer in winter and cooler in summer, or of a more oceanic type, than in the period prior to 1900. It is interesting to note in this connection that the lizard orchid is said to be very abundant in western France, which has a marked oceanic climate. It therefore appears that the climate in England during the period concerned has more nearly approached that most favourable for the growth of the species, which has consequently been able to

PLATE XV

R. Atkinson

a. Flower spikes of Man Orchid,
Aceras anthropophorum (× 1)

R. Atkinson

b. Flowering stem of Monkey Orchid,
Orchis simia (× 1)

PLATE XVI

E. J. Bedford

a. Flower spikes of Lady Orchid. *Orchis purpurea* ($\times \frac{7}{10}$)

E. J. Bedford

b. Burnt or Dwarf Orchids, *Orchis ustulata* ($\times \frac{3}{4}$)

grow in a greater number and variety of localities than previously. It is too early to say if the spread of the lizard orchid is still going on ; no extensions in distribution have been recorded since 1939, and perhaps the series of cold winters during and since the War indicate another change in the climate.

Like *Anacamptis* and *Neotinea*, *Himantoglossum* occurs most frequently on calcareous soils, being especially characteristic of the chalk areas of England. Indeed the great majority of its stations are on the chalk, while several others are on limestone, as for instance, in Gloucestershire and Oxfordshire. There seems to be no record of the plant occurring on soils which are at all acid. The lizard orchid is usually found in bushy places among shrubs (Pl. 30, p. 227) or in rather tall grass, but it has been recorded from roadsides and railway cuttings, while Good mentions a Martello tower and the retaining wall of a river as exceptional habitats. In its more usual habitats on chalk downs the species is frequently associated with other orchids, such as the pyramidal orchid, common spotted orchid (*Orchis fuchsii*), and fragrant orchid (*Gymnadenia conopsea*). In some localities the species grows on sand dunes near the coast, a type of habitat in which it has been recorded also from Holland and France. Such sandy soils, being relatively warm and dry, resemble in these respects the chalk soils beloved of the plant ; moreover, they sometimes contain appreciable amounts of lime.

The lizard orchid flowers during the latter part of June and in July, being usually at its best in the early part of the latter month. The plant often looks rather shabby at flowering time owing to the withering of the leaves. There is doubt as to whether nectar is present in the fully opened flower, but it appears most probable, since hive bees have been seen visiting the species. The flowers emit a strong and unpleasant odour of goats, and this may attract certain flies which are recorded as visiting the flowers. These insects could easily obtain the nectar or other food from such a short and broad spur. Pollination is effected in much the same way as in *Orchis*, but, of course, the two pollinia are always transported together. Solitary plants usually ripen some seeds, presumably as a result of cross-pollination between different flowers on the spike. There is no real evidence of self-pollination in such cases. The seedpods contain about 1,200 seeds, and it is estimated that the average production of seeds per plant is just below 30,000. In such circumstances it is easy to see how the species can spread if the external conditions become at all suitable for establishment of the seedlings. It seems probable that some " wild " plants have arisen from seed originating from cultivated specimens, but there is no reason for thinking that this source of seed has been responsible to any appreciable extent for the rapid spread of the species.

Man Orchid (*Aceras anthropophorum*)

This delightful orchid, each flower strongly resembling a small human figure with head, arms and legs, is, unlike the lizard orchid, unfortunately on the whole decreasing in numbers, though it has recently been recorded from several new districts (Pl. 31, p. 234). The species is evidently more closely allied to the genus *Orchis* than either of the other three species in the present group. Indeed it has many features in common with the rare monkey and military orchids (*Orchis simia* and *O. militaris*, Pl. 32, p. 235; Pl. 33, p. 242), particularly the shape of the lip and the hood formed by the sepals and petals, and the presence of coumarin in the leaves, giving it a pleasant smell when dried. Indeed the only real difference between the two genera is the absence of a spur in *Aceras* (whence the name) and its presence in *Orchis*.

The underground parts of the man orchid are similar to those in its allies, consisting of two egg-shaped or globose tubers, and a few short thick roots. The aerial shoot sometimes develops in the autumn, the lower leaves remaining green throughout the winter, but this is not a constant feature ; in some regions the species behaves like the monkey orchid, carrying out its whole development in the spring. The flowering stem reaches a height of about 4 to 15 inches, depending a great deal on the nature of the surrounding vegetation ; when occurring in tall grass plants may be 18 inches or more in height and quite robust. The main leaves are from two to four inches long, nearly one inch broad and blunt, deep or greyish green in colour, but the upper leaves are smaller and more pointed, while the uppermost frequently clasps the stem like the similar leaves in the common early purple orchid (*Orchis mascula*). The flower-spike is long and narrow, containing as many as ninety closely placed flowers (Pl. XVa, p. 238), which, however, tend to become spaced out in the lower part as the spike develops. The flowers are greenish or yellowish in colour, often with the edges of the sepals and petals reddish and the lip more yellow than the rest. Sometimes the ends of the " arms " and " legs " are tinged reddish, but this often disappears as the flowers open properly, leaving the lip entirely yellow ; in other plants the lip may be entirely red, but this is much less frequent. The sepals and petals are partly joined together to form a short hood or helmet, which is the " head " of the " man ". The lip, which is considerably longer, hangs down (Fig. 6 D, p. 31). It has two narrow side lobes (" arms ") towards the base, and is divided into two similar lobes at its tip, these forming the " legs ", the main part forming the " body ". The photograph (Pl. XVa) shows this very distinctly, and gives a very good idea of the plant as a whole. There is no proper spur at the base of the lip, only a sort of shallow depression in which nectar occurs. The column and stamen are like those in the monkey orchid, but the two viscidia are very close together and sometimes more or less adherent to one another; they are both covered by a bursicle to prevent them from drying up.

The man orchid is a member of the European Element of the British orchid flora, having a distinctly southern and western distribution in the area. It occurs as far north as Belgium and Holland in the west, and is also found in southern Germany and Switzerland, but is absent from Austria and Hungary. In the Mediterranean region it extends as far east as Rhodes and Cyprus, but does not occur on the mainland of Asia ; the species is also recorded from Morocco and Algeria. It evidently has a distribution somewhat similar to, but less extensive than, the lizard orchid, with which it is allied.

In Britain the distribution is also clearly southern (Map 35, p. 354), the plant being commonest in the south-eastern counties, particularly Kent and Surrey, and becoming less frequent as one goes west and north. The present distribution shows a close parallel with that of *Himantoglossum*, the most northern locality being in south Lincolnshire, while it has been re-found recently in Somerset in the vicinity of Bath. A diagonal south-west to north-east line joining these two points indicates approximately the limits of distribution. At the present time the man orchid seems to be holding its own, for although it has become less common in Kent and elsewhere in recent years, mainly owing to a more intense agricultural exploitation of the countryside, it has been discovered during the last twenty years or so in a number of hitherto unknown localities in Lincolnshire, Somerset, Hampshire and Oxfordshire, all regions on the margins of its previous distribution. In Bedfordshire, where it was first recorded in 1926, it appears to be extending its distribution, and this also applies to at least one of the Hampshire localities. It is perhaps too early to determine if there is in progress a spreading of this species on the same lines as that already recorded for the lizard orchid. In this connection it should be noted that the man orchid is a rather inconspicuous species, which might easily remain undetected in an area for a relatively long time after arriving there. This feature, on the other hand, may equally well support the view that the supposedly " new " records are really old ones which had been overlooked. In view of the similarity in distribution outside the British Isles of the man and lizard orchids, it might be thought that the climatic change which has been suggested as responsible for the increase in distribution of the latter species would have a similar effect on the former. This possibility remains yet to be examined critically. On the whole, however, the general impression is that the species is extending slowly into suitable localities outside its previous area of distribution, whereas within this area the actual numbers and localities have decreased owing to more thorough agricultural development, particularly the increase of arable land during the two Wars. Orchids are always relatively slow in re-occupying ground once cultivated, and the adoption of ley-farming and similar practices makes much grassland and pasture unsuitable for their establishment and continued growth.

The man orchid is another of our orchids which is almost invariably found in England on soils rich in lime. In most parts of its range it is found on the chalk, being especially characteristic of the steep slopes of the downs in Surrey and Kent. However, it is found also on limestone (of Oolitic or Liassic types) in Northamptonshire, Lincolnshire and Somerset. On the European mainland the man orchid grows on a variety of soils provided they are not acid to any great degree. The species is usually a member of grassland communities, either the short turf characteristic of many of the flatter stretches (Pl. 31, p. 234), or more frequently in the taller grassland of erect brome grass (*Bromus erectus*), oat grasses (*Helictotrichon pratensis* and *H. pubescens*), quaking grass (*Briza media*), false brome grass (*Brachypodium pinnatum*), etc., which so often clothes the steep slopes of the main escarpment of the Downs or the sides of minor valleys. *Aceras* differs from many other orchids in being often found mainly or exclusively near the base of such slopes, though this is not always the case. There is as yet no explanation of this curious occurrence, which is presumably connected

PLATE 33

b. Soldier Orchid (*Orchis militaris*). Buckinghamshire; May

J. E. Lousley

a. Soldier Orchid (*Orchis militaris*). Buckinghamshire; May

J. E. Lousley

PLATE 34

Robert Atkinson

Lady Orchids (*Orchis purpurea*). Kent; May

in some way with the drainage. As, however, the species may be found only locally even in such situations, the problem is clearly an intricate one, and well worth solving. On the whole, the man orchid grows best in open situations, and does not appear to be tolerant of much shade. Sometimes plants may be found growing in the shelter of isolated bushes or among very open scrub.

Aceras flowers comparatively early in the year, its season lasting through May until the end of June, and rarely extending into July. It is usually at its best about the end of May and the beginning of June, the flowers sometimes being nearly over by the middle of the latter month. The species emits a smell which is described by most observers as rather unpleasant. This may attract some of the flies and other small insects which are known to visit the flowers, including ants and hover-flies. As the nectar is easily reached, visits of such insects are readily explained, but there are few actual observations on the removal of pollinia. Both of the kinds of insects mentioned have been seen to do so, and as seed is set in many flowers, pollination must be fairly effective. It has been suggested that self-fertilisation takes place, at least in some plants, or under certain conditions, but this is a matter which needs more exact investigation.

In Europe hybrids between *Aceras* and various species of *Orchis* (*O. militaris, O. simia, O. purpurea*) have been recorded, so obviously the same insects must visit all these species. Such hybrids have not been recorded from England, but this is not surprising in view of the great rarity of the monkey and soldier orchids. *O. purpurea* grows in Kent in the same districts as *Aceras*, but presumably the marked difference in the habitats of the two species—*O. purpurea* grows in woods and scrub—makes visits by the same insect species very improbable.

CHAPTER 13

ORCHIS PROPER

THE GENUS *Orchis*, which has given its name to the whole family to which it belongs, is the largest among British orchids, as it is among those of the European continent. Altogether it includes somewhere around seventy-five species, which extend over an area from western Europe, Morocco and Algeria to the Japanese Islands in the extreme east, and the Himalayan Mountains farther south in Asia.

Two clearly marked groups can easily be recognised, depending on the shape of the fleshy tuberous roots. There are in the first place those species in which the tubers are globular or egg-shaped, and not at all lobed ; these are the " true " *Orchis* species, which are dealt with in the present chapter. Secondly, there are the so-called palmate orchids (*dactylorchids*), in which the tubers are lobed or forked to form several finger-like parts, the whole tuber being flattened in one plane and somewhat resembling a hand. There are other differences associated with the differences in the tubers, so much so that some authorities have suggested that the two groups are really distinct genera.

The round-tubered *Orchis* species exhibit considerable differences among themselves, the six British representatives of this group falling into three distinct sub-divisions. Four of them, the monkey orchid (*O. simia*, Pl. 32, p. 235), soldier orchid (*O. militaris*, Pl. 33, p. 242), lady orchid (*O. purpurea*, Pl. 34, p. 243) and the dwarf or burnt orchid (*O. ustulata*, Pl. 35a, p. 250), have all the sepals and petals more or less cohering to form a hood, while the bracts at the base of each flower stalk are very small. In the green-winged or green-veined orchid (*O. morio*, Pl. 36, p. 251) there is also a hood, but the sepals do not cohere as in the previous group, while the bracts are comparatively long and coloured. Finally, in the early purple orchid (*O. mascula*,

Pl. 37, p. 258) the lateral sepals are spreading or bent right back so that their backs nearly touch, while the bracts are again large and conspicuous. It has been shown that the hood in the soldier orchid and its allies is very difficult to wet; this no doubt protects the column within, an important consideration as regards pollination and fertilisation in the species.

Quite apart from the floral differences between the species, the members of this group provide some striking contrasts in their abundance and distribution. The early purple orchid is one of the commonest of British orchids, occurring almost throughout these islands (Map 31, p. 353), whereas at the other extreme are the monkey and soldier orchids (Maps 36 and 37, p. 355), which are known only from one or two very restricted localities. Both the early purple and lady orchids are frequently found in woods, though the former is abundant also in the open, whereas the other four species in this group are characteristically inhabitants of open situations, particularly the green-veined and burnt orchids. All the species may be numbered among the most attractive and beautiful of our orchids, especially the lady orchid, for even the tiny burnt orchid on closer examination will be seen to be a little gem.

MONKEY ORCHID (*Orchis simia*)

On account of its being one of our rarest orchids, and the remarkable resemblance of each flower to a small monkey, this species has always had a special fascination for orchid lovers (Pl. 32, p. 235). Once a comparatively common plant in the valley of the river Thames between Marlow and Wallingford, it is now only to be found in one locality in Oxfordshire. The species has many features in common with the man orchid described in the last chapter, but the colour of the flowers is very different; white and red in the present species as against the pale ochre-yellow of the man orchid.

The two tubers are more or less egg-shaped, and are accompanied by a few short rather fleshy roots. The aerial part of the plant appears first in the fourth year after the seed germinates, a small leaf being produced for several years before flowers are formed. All the growth of the aerial shoot takes place in the spring, the plants not being at all wintergreen. The stem, which reaches a height of about 6–12 inches, bears usually two rather broad blunt dark green leaves at the base, and a further two or three higher up, these being narrower and more or less wrapped around the stem. The flower-spike is rather short and dense, about one or two inches long, and contains twenty or more flowers (Pl. XVb, p. 238). A remarkable feature of the monkey orchid, found in no other British species, is the order in which the flowers open, those at the *top* of the spike opening first and those at the bottom last, a complete reversal of the usual sequence. The hood formed by the sepals and petals is white, spotted or streaked with pink or violet, more rarely pale violet throughout. This hood, together with the column lying within it, forms the " head " of the monkey. The lip is much longer than the other floral parts and hangs downwards. It is relatively narrow, with two slender divergent arm-like lobes near the base, and divided into three slender lobes at the end. The side two form the " legs " of the monkey, and the central one, which is very narrow, the " tail ". The " body " varies in colour from white to deep crimson, while the lobes are either bright rose red, crimson or reddish violet, and usually darker than the remainder. When the " body " is white it is often studded with tufts of violet hairs forming small coloured spots ; similar spots are also to be found in the lady and dwarf orchids. There is a short rather blunt spur at the base of the lip. The British plant has been considered by some authorities to be a distinct variety or even species, but there seems to be little real basis for this distinction. Albino forms, with pure white flowers, have been recorded on the Continent.

The monkey orchid belongs to the Southern Eurasian Element of the British orchid flora, being widely spread in western and southern Europe and the Mediterranean region generally, including North Africa. Eastwards it extends through Asia Minor and Syria to the Caucasus mountains, Persia and Turkestan.

O. simia is now a very rare plant in this country. First recorded from Britain in 1660, the species was until about 1835 still widely distributed and locally plentiful on both sides of the Thames, where it cuts through the chalk hills of the Chilterns between Wallingford and Pangbourne, and as far east as the vicinity of Henley. Within a comparatively short time it had become rare, and it is now known from only one locality in this general region (Map 37, p. 355). It is difficult to account for this disappearance, but it was chiefly due, no doubt, to more intensive agricultural development of the meadows and slopes on which the plant grew. One observer records that in 1838 or 1839 the turf of the slopes near Whitchurch, where both this species and the soldier orchid were abundant, was pared off and burnt, the ashes being added to the soil, presumably to enrich it. In some places, as near Caversham, building has destroyed the plant. Rapacious collecting at one period probably contributed to its disappearance, and also the depredations of rabbits, which are very fond of the leaves and tender shoots.

Apart from the main centre of distribution in Oxfordshire and Berkshire, and possibly in the neighbouring parts of Buckinghamshire, the monkey orchid has been recorded on odd occasions from the counties of Surrey, Sussex and Kent. Most of these are old records, the most recent one being from Kent near Bishopsbourne. Four or five individuals were seen on an open grassy chalk slope at this locality most years between 1920 and 1923, one or two plants being in flower, but the species has not been seen there since. There seems to be evidence for thinking that these occurrences probably represent the germination of seeds blown over occasionally from the European mainland, where the species is not uncommon around and to the north of Paris.

Orchis simia is, like many other rare British orchids, almost invariably found on calcareous soils in this country. Observations in Europe indicate that the species almost always occurs on alkaline (often strongly alkaline) or neutral soils, never on those which are at all acid in nature. All the known British records seem to be from the chalk areas, which are the home of so many other rare orchids. It usually occurs on grassy slopes or borders of fields, especially among bushes or at the edges of woods, where there is a certain amount of shelter or perhaps partial shade. Like all its relatives it prefers rather dry localities, avoiding any spots where the drainage is poor. The number of plants flowering fluctuates considerably from year to year, as is common in many orchid species. In its Oxfordshire station the species was about holding its own, or perhaps its numbers were slowly decreasing until this summer, when the area concerned was ploughed up and nearly all the plants destroyed. It is hoped that a few may survive in an adjoining field.

The species flowers during the latter part of May and the first half of June, varying according to the season and the situation in which the individual plants are growing. The flowers do not emit a very powerful scent, but merely smell weakly of coumarin. There does not seem to be any nectar in the rather short spur, but it is suggested that, as in the man orchid, the two swellings near the mouth contain sugar which is extracted by the visiting insects. Hive bees have been seen carrying away pollinia ; Godfery records one bee with seven attached to it. No doubt the species is also visited by other insects with relatively short tongues, since the sugar is easily accessible.

When this species and the soldier orchid were both frequent around Goring and Streatley, hybrids between the two species occurred, and caused considerable confusion among the botanists of those days. Such hybrids have been recorded not infrequently in Europe. They are very variable in appearance, but are usually intermediate in some respects between the two parents, either as regards stature, the colour of the flowers or the shape of the lip.

Soldier or Military Orchid (*Orchis militaris*)

There is a striking parallelism between the history of this species and that of the monkey orchid, just dealt with. Both once grew frequently on the chalk hills of the Chiltern Range, and both are now among the rarest of British orchids. Indeed, until quite recently, the soldier orchid was thought to be extinct, as for many years the plant had been sought for fruitlessly. In 1947, however, a colony of this very attractive orchid was discovered in Buckinghamshire by Mr. J. E. Lousley, after an interval of about 25 years since the last record of its appearance (Pl. 33, p. 242). This interesting discovery gives hope that the species may also survive in other out of the way spots within its old area of distribution. In addition to its rarity the soldier orchid has claims to be considered one of the most beautiful of our orchids, the bright red or violet lip providing a pleasing contrast with the paler pink or whitish hood. Moreover, when well-grown the soldier orchid is one of the largest of British orchids, rivalling the lady orchid in size. It closely resembles the monkey orchid in flower structure, but the central and front part of the lip is much wider, particularly the front lobes. The lady orchid has a much broader and less cut-up lip (Pl. XVIa, p. 239), while the general colour is not red but purplish, especially the hood, which is very dark coloured.

So far as the underground parts are concerned the soldier orchid is similar to the monkey and lady orchids. The aerial stem is first formed in the fourth year, and a flower-spike several years later. In the mature plant the stem reaches a total height of from nine to sixteen inches, or even more in large specimens, with a group of four or five large broad blunt leaves two to five inches long near the base. There may be one or two smaller leaves farther up on the stem, which bears a many-flowered dense or loose spike usually one to four inches in length, but exceeding this in large continental specimens. The flowers in the spike open in the usual order, from below upwards, differing in this respect from *Orchis simia*. As in the latter, the hood or helm formed by the sepals and petals is relatively pale, usually whitish, but often tinged with rose, red or dull violet (Pl. 33b, p. 242). The large hanging lip, though four-lobed as in the monkey and man orchids, is not so much like a human figure. The two lobes in front are much broader and shorter than in the monkey orchid ; all the lobes are bright rose, red, or as in the specimens discovered recently, a sort of reddish violet, whereas the central part of the lip is paler, often white with reddish spots. The whole flower is larger and more sturdy than that in *O. simia*. The combination of red and white in the flower, and the vaguely human shape, are responsible for the name soldier orchid.

Orchis militaris is a member of the Central Eurasian Group among the British orchids. It is characteristically a central European species, but also occurs on mountains in the Mediterranean region. It is absent, however, from the hot dry parts in this area, while in western Europe it appears equally to avoid the most westerly districts with a marked oceanic climate. Northwards it extends as far as southern Scandinavia and Estonia, and then across Russia to the Caucasus mountains. Eastwards the species is found in western and central Siberia as far as Lake Baikal and the Altai Mountains. On the whole the soldier orchid grows best in regions with a warm spring and summer. It can stand cold winters, but clearly avoids areas where the climate, especially during the summer, is hot and dry.

The distribution (Map 36, p. 355), or rather the past distribution, of *O. militaris* in Britain is clearly in line with the general conditions mentioned above, since all the records are from the south-eastern part of England. At one time the species was distributed from just west of the Thames in the region of Streatley and Basildon, along the Chiltern Hills through Oxfordshire and Buckinghamshire, to the neighbourhood of Tring in Hertfordshire and to Harefield in Middle-sex. It seems to have been particularly abundant around High Wy-combe and between this town and Great Marlow on the Thames.

There are also several isolated records from the North Downs in Surrey and Kent (for instance, it was found on Box Hill in 1834), but all these records are very old and the species seemingly was never more than sporadic here.   In Buckinghamshire it was still to be found in the 1860's in several localities, but became much rarer after that period. Odd specimens were still known to exist in 1886, and isolated plants were discovered during the early part of the present century.   Searches for this very beautiful and rare orchid have long been a popular pastime among orchid enthusiasts, and most of the supposedly likely places have been visited in the hopes of rediscovering the plant. Ironically enough, the recent discovery of the species, in a locality from which it had not previously been reported, was made purely by chance by Mr. Lousley.   This very welcome event leads to the hope that the soldier orchid may still occur in other unsuspected localities.

As may appear from the distribution outlined above, *O. militaris* has always been found growing on chalk in this country.   In fact it seems to prefer calcareous soils over most of its range, and towards its northern limit it always occurs on limestone or similar soils as, for instance, in Sweden and Estonia.   Although in more southern districts the soldier orchid may be found on neutral soils, it avoids those which are at all acid and sour.   In Britain it has usually been recorded from the borders or more open parts of woods, in bushy places, on dry banks or in rough fields.   A certain amount of shelter or shade seems necessary, while north slopes provide more usual habitats than those facing southwards.   The recently discovered colony, containing a dozen or so plants, grew among scattered bramble and other bushes.   Usually only a proportion of the plants are to be found in flower, the remainder being in the vegetative condition only.   These probably represent individuals which have not yet reached the flowering stage, though they may also include plants which are recovering after flowering one or two years previously.   This feature is generally found also in the lady orchid.

The soldier orchid flowers during the latter part of May and the first week or so of June, much the same time as the monkey orchid. In Europe the species is visited, and presumably pollinated, by various sorts of bees and humble-bees ; these visit the flowers for the sugary liquid which occurs inside the walls of the spur. These walls are easily pierced by the insects' proboscis and the liquid extracted. Mr. Lousley informs me that the only insect visitors he has seen are Syrphid flies ;

PLATE 35

Robert Atkinson

b. Hebridean Orchid (*Orchis fuchsii* subsp. *hebridensis*).
Isle of Lewis; July

Robert Atkinson

a. Dwarf or Burnt Orchid (*Orchis ustulata*). Berkshire;
June

PLATE 36

Group of Green-veined Orchids (three colour varieties) (*Orchis morio*). Oxfordshire; May on the other hand, the pollinia had been removed from all the flowers, but whether by these or other insects is not known. The flowers have only a weak coumarin (woodruff) scent, but the red and white flower-spike must be very conspicuous to flying insects. Records seem to suggest, however, that the species does not set seed very effectively, counts showing only two to twenty-eight per cent of flowers with developing fruit. The seed production is very low in places in Germany where *O. purpurea* (lady orchid) is abundant ; it is thought that this is due to frequent cross-pollination which does not lead to fertilisation. Hybrids have been occasionally reported between *O. militaris* and *O. purpurea*, but they are decidedly less frequent than might have been expected. This rather lends support to the suggestion that there is marked incompatibility between the two species. The hybrids between the soldier and monkey orchids have already been mentioned under the latter species.

BROWN-WINGED OR LADY ORCHID (*Orchis purpurea*)

This beautiful species is one of the finest of our native orchids, not only as regards size, but also in the delightful contrast between the deep purple hood or helm and the delicate white or pink, crimson spotted lip (Pl. 34, p. 243). Although now almost restricted to the county of Kent, the species is still abundant in many places there, in spite of the depredations of rabbits and children, not to mention those of adults who ought to know better. Notwithstanding its similarity in growth to the soldier orchid, the lady orchid is very different in flower colouring, and could hardly be confused with any other British species. It is, however, in flower structure and colouring extremely like the dwarf or burnt orchid (*O. ustulata*), which is a sort of miniature replica of it (Pl. 35a, p. 250).

In vegetative characters the lady orchid agrees with the soldier orchid, both as regards the tubers and the leaves, though it is usually a larger plant. The flowering stem reaches a height of from nine inches to three feet, with a bunch of three to five broad blunt dark or bright shining green leaves near the base. These leaves may be spreading or more or less stiffly erect, four to nine inches in length, and usually between one and two inches broad. The flower-spike, two to five inches in length, or longer in large specimens, contains a large number of rather closely placed flowers (Pl. XVIa, p. 239). In this species the hood made up by the sepals and petals is shorter and blunter than in either of the monkey or soldier orchids, and is the darkest part of the flower, being usually of a deep dull purple or red-purple colour. The lip, on the other hand, is very pale coloured, the ground colour being white or, more frequently, variously suffused with pink or dull purple. Dotted over the central parts are numerous bunches of long violet or crimson hairs, which form spots of colour. The central part of the three-lobed lip is quite broad, and divided at the front into two short broad lobes, between which is a comparatively shallow indentation or sinus ; the long and narrow lateral lobes are similar in shape to those in *O. militaris*. The spur is short and curved, but longer than in the three other species of this group. The flowers show considerable variation in the depth of coloration and spotting of the lip, and also in the shape and breadth of the various lobes. Rarely the lip is quite white and the hood straw-coloured, an interesting case of albinism, which is not a common occurrence in this group of orchids.

Mr. Francis Rose has pointed out that there are two quite marked forms of this species in Kent, a western and an eastern form, the River Stour forming the approximate boundary between them. The former is not so tall as the eastern form (8–15 inches), the flower-spike is denser, the ovaries are shorter (only $\frac{1}{2}$ to $\frac{3}{4}$ inch in length), and the lip is more spotted with purple. In the eastern form, on the other hand, the stems are 1 to $2\frac{1}{2}$ feet in height, the flower-spike is longer and looser, the ovaries are $\frac{3}{4}$ to 1 inch long, the flowers are broader and the lip is not so heavily spotted. These distinctions are not entirely constant, but the features mentioned are possessed by the great pre-ponderance of the plants in the two areas concerned.

Like the monkey orchid, the lady orchid belongs to the Southern Eurasian Element of the British orchid flora. Its distribution is also very similar to that of the soldier orchid, but it extends northwards only as far as Denmark, whereas it occurs more frequently in the Mediterranean region than does that species. Eastwards it occurs in Asia Minor and Caucasia, but it is clearly not so southern in its distribution as *Orchis simia*.

In Britain it is similarly more restricted than either of its two relatives, though at present it is much more abundant than either of them. This is probably because it is normally an inhabitant of scrub and woodlands, which have not been much interfered with, whereas *O. simia* and *O. militaris* are both characteristic of more open ground, sometimes growing in open fields or grassy slopes. It is probable that the lady orchid was once distributed throughout south-eastern England, but it is now extremely rare outside Kent (Map 38, p. 355). It still occurs, however, in at least one station in Surrey (Coulsdon), and may also persist in other places in that county and in Sussex. Some of the more recent records in these counties may be new introductions, arising from seed blown from the Continent, or it may be that the plants remain dormant for many years without flowering. It is usually possible to see numerous sterile plants in the vicinity of those bearing flower-spikes. In Kent *O. purpurea* is very widely spread, occurring almost throughout the extensive area of the North Downs from the Surrey border in the west to just short of Dover in the east. Owing to the spread of London it has become much less common in the extreme west, but still occurs in considerable numbers in the Maidstone and Canterbury districts.

Like its relatives, the lady orchid is restricted in England to soils rich in lime, and this seems also to apply to the localities in which it occurs in Europe. In this country the species is now known only from chalk areas, particularly the North and South Downs. It is very definitely a scrub and woodland plant, though it does not flourish in the denser and darker parts of woods. Rather it prefers light coppice, hazel for instance, or open spots under bushes and scattered trees. It may often be found at the lower margins of beechwoods where there has been a certain amount of clearance, and is also common in chalk scrub. Rose suggests that it was originally a scrub plant which has since spread into woodland. Sometimes plants may be seen right out in the open, but even then it is rarely far from bushes or other shade. The plants can stand a considerable amount of shade, remaining, however, in the vegetative condition only until more light becomes available as a result of cutting or the death of some of the trees shading them, in this respect behaving like most other woodland orchids. In both scrub and beechwoods the species is most commonly associated with dog's mercury (*Mercurialis perennis*). Other characteristic associates are stinking hellebore (*Helleborus foetidus*), spurge-laurel (*Daphne laureola*), roast-beef plant (*Iris foetidissima*) and primrose (*Primula vulgaris*). Orchids occurring with the lady orchid are man orchid (*Aceras anthropophorum*), large white helleborine (*Cephalanthera damasonium*), twayblade (*Listera ovata*), fly orchid (*Ophrys muscifera*), early purple orchid (*Orchis mascula*), greater butterfly orchid (*Platanthera chlorantha*) and spotted orchid (*Orchis fuchsii*). Rabbits are a serious threat to the lady orchid. Often many, or even all, of the flower-spikes may be found bitten off, while the leaves are frequently nibbled.

The usual flowering time of the lady orchid is the latter half of May, though it may still be found in flower in the beginning of June ; it is thus a little earlier than either the monkey or soldier orchids, and more or less contemporaneous with the man orchid. The flowers are said to smell of coumarin and bitter almonds, and are visited, but apparently only rarely, by bees and certain sorts of flies. Observations show that few pollinia are removed, and only a few flowers in the spike produce fruit and seeds ; this is also true in Europe, at least in the more northern parts of the range of the species. It would seem that the species depends largely on the persistence of individual plants, rather than on abundant production of seed, to maintain itself in this country. Rose points out that the species is not necessarily monocarpic, the same plant sometimes flowering in successive years. I saw a plant in Mr. S. G. Jary's garden at Wye in Kent, which had flowered in three successive years. This repeated flowering may, however, be associated with the poor seed production. We do not know what happens if a plant produces a large number of ripe fruits. Since the seedlings develop rapidly compared with many other British orchids, this compensates, at least partially, for the poor production of seeds.

Hybrids are known between the lady orchid and either the monkey or soldier orchids, but these have not been recorded from this country, no doubt owing to the great rarity of the two latter species.

BURNT OR DWARF ORCHID (*Orchis ustulata*)

This delightful little plant, which in general flower structure and coloration is like a tiny edition of the lady orchid (Pl. 35a, p. 250), is often only a few inches in height, and very easily overlooked. The hood of the flower is very dark, almost blackish red, the unopened flowers at the top of the spike giving the appearance of having been burnt, hence the common and specific name. The lip, which is much larger than the rest of the perianth members, is white with small pink or violet spots formed of bunches of coloured hairs, as in *O. purpurea*.

The seedling development of this species (Fig. 1, p. 3), which is quite different from that of any other British orchid, is described in

PLATE XVII

D. Paton

Flower spike of Heath Spotted Orchid, *Orchis ericetorum* (×2⅔)

PLATE XVIII

R. Atkinson

R. Atkinson

a. Early Marsh Orchid, *Orchis latifolia*. Note especially the hooded tip to the lowest leaf and the distinct loops on the lip (× 1½)

b. Flower-spike of Small White Orchid, *Gymnadenia albida*; note the three-lobed lip and short fat spur (× 2)

detail in Chapter 1 (p. 9). The mycorhizome persists for ten to fifteen years before producing the first leafy aerial stem, the fungus providing the food during this long period. The stem reaches a height of from three to eight inches in this country, though in Europe specimens may be as much as a foot in height. There are usually three broad leaves, an inch or so in length, at the base of the stem, and several more smaller clasping ones on the stem itself. The very dense spike is conical at first, but lengthens and becomes cylindrical as the flowers open ; it is usually about $\frac{1}{2}$ to $1\frac{1}{2}$ inches long in England. The flowers are very small, the hood or helmet being dark red (almost black) at first, and becoming paler with age, whereas the lip is white with crimson or violet spots (Pl. XVIb, p. 239). The lip is shaped very much as in O. purpurea, except that the side lobes are relatively broader and the central lobe narrower, while there is usually no little tooth between the two front lobules. The spur is very short and conical, in this respect agreeing with the other three species of this group. There is little variation in the flower structure or coloration, but white flowered (albino) forms have been recorded very occasionally.

The burnt orchid belongs to the European Element among British orchids, occurring generally throughout central Europe as far north as the Faroe Islands, southern Sweden, and the Leningrad region of Russia, and southwards to the northern parts of the Mediterranean region. To the east it is found in the Caucasus Mountains and in the extreme west of Siberia as far as Tobolsk.

In Britain it has a decidedly southern and eastern distribution (Map 39, p. 355), for although it occurs very generally in England, it is not known from Wales, Scotland or Ireland. Even in England, however, it is most abundant in the south-east, becoming less common towards the north and west. Everywhere the species is very local and uncertain in its appearance, though it may sometimes be very abundant. Records suggest that it is slowly decreasing both as regards stations and numbers of individuals. This is probably due to more intense use of the land for agricultural purposes, particularly the ploughing and reseeding of old pastures and grasslands. In some counties at the extreme edge of its range, as in Northumberland, Durham and Shropshire, the burnt orchid has become almost or quite extinct during the last fifty years.

Like many other British orchids, O. ustulata shows a preference for limy soils, but it is by no means restricted to them, being sometimes found on sand or gravel. It is particularly frequent in the chalk districts of the south-east, while in the north, as in Yorkshire, Durham and Cumberland, most of the records are from the Magnesian limestone belts. It is also recorded from the Oolitic and other Jurassic limestones in the Midlands and southern England. It is usually an inhabitant of short grasslands, as on chalk downs, dry limestone slopes, old pastures and the like. This is, of course, not surprising in view of its low stature ; it is scarcely a plant which could grow successfully among tall grasses. The species is nearly always found in dry spots, and appears to avoid heavy or damp soils. Although a comparatively rare plant, the burnt orchid may occur in large numbers when it finds congenial conditions. There are few more delightful discoveries than of a group of plants with their deep red and white flower-spikes just peeping out of the short turf of grasses, salad burnet (*Poterium sanguisorba*), horseshoe vetch (*Hippocrepis comosa*), dwarf thistle (*Cirsium acaule*), mouse-ear hawkweed (*Hieracium pilosella*) and other lime-loving plants.

The burnt orchid is usually in flower from the latter part of May until the end of June, or perhaps later in northern districts. As the flowers open the hood becomes paler in colour until finally the whole flower is almost white. The flowers emit a very powerful sweet odour which no doubt is attractive to insects. The mouth to the spur is very narrow (rather like a keyhole in shape) with a deep groove in the lip leading directly to it. It has been suggested that the flowers are pollinated by day-flying moths or perhaps butterflies, but these have never been observed. Godfery, however, observed a large fly visit a flower-spike and remove the pollinia from four flowers. The insect, as large as a bluebottle, alighted on the unopened buds at the top and inserted his proboscis while in an upside-down position. The pollinia, after removal, in the course of the usual downward swivelling movement, diverge somewhat from one another, but not so much as in the pyramidal orchid (*Anacamptis*). This divergence is no doubt linked with the somewhat lateral position of the broad stigmas, proper contact between pollinia and stigmas being thus ensured.

GREEN-VEINED OR GREEN-WINGED ORCHID (*Orchis morio*)

Unlike most of the plants already dealt with in this chapter, the green-veined orchid is one of the commonest of British orchids, occurring throughout England and Wales, and in the central parts of Ireland, though it is not found anywhere in Scotland. Not only is the species widespread, but also it sometimes occurs in immense numbers —literally in thousands or tens of thousands—so that the ground is made purple by the innumerable flower-spikes. *Orchis morio* (Pl. 36, p. 251) is superficially very like the common early purple orchid (*O. mascula*, Pl. 37, p. 258), but it is on the whole a smaller plant with unspotted leaves and fewer deeper coloured flowers. Technically it may be distinguished by the green-veined lateral sepals, which lie forward and help to form a hood together with the petals and back sepal, instead of being widely spread or bent backwards as in *O. mascula*. Furthermore it is never a true woodland plant as the early purple orchid so frequently is.

The development of the green-winged orchid from the seed is exceptionally rapid, the first leaf appearing in the spring of the second year, and the first tuber in the same year. The leaves persist during the winter months, and no doubt provide food for the early development of the plant in the subsequent year. Flowering follows after a few years' vegetative growth, after which the plant usually dies. The mature plant develops a rosette of leaves at the base of the flowering stem, there being as many as seven rather narrow bluish or greyish-green leaves, with several more sheathing ones on the stem itself. This stem is usually rather short, often only an inch or so high, but in more favourable spots it may reach a foot in height. The flower-spike itself is comparatively short, only an inch or so long, usually containing up to twelve rather loosely placed flowers, but well-grown plants may bear considerably more. The flowers are rather large, varying in colour from deep red-purple to pale purple, lilac, pink or occasionally white. Most colonies of the species contain a great variety of colour forms (Pl. 36, p. 251), including pink ones, though the predominant tint may be paler or deeper purple in different places. The centre of the very broad lip is whitish or paler than the rest, usually with a number of much darker spots, though these may sometimes be entirely absent. The general shape and width of the lip varies a good deal from plant to plant, but it is usually broader than long, three-lobed, with the middle lobe very broad and a little longer than the side lobes. The relatively long spur is either horizontally placed or curved slightly upwards ; it is often thicker at the end, and more or less notched or shortly two-lobed. All the other perianth members form the short blunt hood or helmet covering the column, the sepals marked with several quite conspicuous green or bronze-purple parallel veins which give the species its English name. There is considerable variation in the size of the flowers, the plants in some places having flowers twice as large as those in other colonies. Some variants have been treated as distinct varieties, and given special names, but there is no justification for such discrimination.

Outside the British Isles the green-veined orchid has a very extensive distribution throughout Europe and in western Asia, and is therefore included in the Eurasian Element Proper of the British orchid flora. Northwards it extends to the Faroe Islands, southern Scandinavia and Estonia, across central Russia to western Siberia, and almost everywhere south of these areas as far as the Mediterranean region. Here it is represented by a southern form (the sub-species *picta*) with smaller paler flowers and a longer spur, which occurs throughout the Mediterranean region, North Africa and eastwards to Persia. Both the northern and southern forms occur together along the northern margin of the Mediterranean region.

In our islands *O. morio* occurs almost throughout England and Wales (Map 30, p. 353), though it is most abundant in the south, and becomes less frequent as one goes north. In the extreme north, as in Cumberland, Westmorland, Northumberland, etc., it is either restricted to the richer lowland areas, or is very rare and local. In Ireland it is not found either in the south-west or in the north, but is characteristic of the large central plain, its northern limits being in the counties of Louth, Meath, West Meath, Roscommon and Mayo. It has not yet been recorded from Scotland. Although so widespread, the species tends to be somewhat local in its occurrence, though it may be found sometimes in immense numbers. Like many other species of British orchids, the green-winged orchid exhibits great fluctuations in numbers, the appearance of vast numbers of plants in a locality being followed by long periods during which hardly a single individual can be discovered. It seems that most plants die after flowering, the species thus depending on new plants from seed to maintain itself. If the flower-spikes are cut off with the grass in which they are growing before seed is set the plants may produce inflorescences in several successive seasons, but very few accurate observations have been made in this connection.

The green-veined orchid is not quite so restricted to calcareous

PLATE 37

Robert Atkinson

Early Purple Orchids *(Orchis mascula)*. Oxfordshire; May

PLATE 38

Robert Atkinson
a. Common Spotted Orchid (*Orchis fuchsii*).
Oxfordshire; June

Robert Atkinson
b. Wicklow Marsh Orchid (*Orchis straunetinerioides*). Oxfordshire; June

soils as many others of our orchids, though it prefers such soils. It is
to be found especially on heavy marly or even clayey soils, provided
they are not too wet, and usually occurs in lowland areas though it is
found at 1,000 feet above sea-level in County Dublin. The species is
an inhabitant of short grasslands, such as old pastures, meadows,
limestone or chalk turf or on grassy railway cuttings and banks. It
usually avoids really dry slopes or hills such as are favoured by the
burnt orchid. In pastures and similar places it flourishes best in short
turf, and is especially characteristic of fields in which cowslips are
abundant ; where the vegetation is more rank the green-veined orchid
is absent. In very short turf the plants are often very dwarf, only an
inch or two tall, but in favourable spots quite robust plants may be
found. On the whole *O. morio* shuns shady spots, though it may sometimes occur in the partial shade of bushes or scrub ; it practically never
occurs in permanent woods.

The green-winged orchid flowers during May in the southern
part of the country, but in the north and in damper places it may still
be in flower in early June. The flowers emit quite a powerful odour,
which is especially noticeable in white-flowered individuals. There is
no free nectar in the rather long spur, the flowers being visited by insects for the sugar which is contained within the fleshy walls of the
spur. These insects consist of hive bees, various kinds of humble-bees,
and also some species of solitary bees. As many as sixteen pollinia
have been counted on a single hive bee, so it is evident that the flowers
are extremely attractive to these and other insects. This is supported
by the very good setting of seed, which may be produced by almost all
of the flowers in the spike. Salisbury has shown that the average number of seeds in a capsule is about 4,000, so that although there are few
flowers in the flower-spike, the total production of seeds is quite considerable.

Hybrids between the green-veined and early purple orchids have
been recorded in this country on several occasions. These are intermediate between the two parents, the spotted leaves of *O. mascula*
being sometimes combined with the green-veined sepals of *O. morio*.
When the leaves are unspotted, however, careful examination of the
shapes and positions of the floral parts is necessary to detect the hybrid
nature of the plants. It is extremely probable that owing to the similarity between the two species such hybrids are frequently overlooked,
but as the species are usually in flower at the same time, and are visited

by the same species of insects, the possibility of cross-pollination occurring is considerable.

EARLY PURPLE ORCHID (*Orchis mascula*)

There is probably no lover of wild flowers in this country who does not know this charming species, one of the most abundant and wide-spread of our native orchids (Pl. 37, p. 258). Its variously purple or rosy purple coloured flower-spikes are equally well known on the sea-cliffs of Ireland or Scotland, on the grassy slopes of the Derbyshire Dales, or in the shady oakwoods and hazel coppices of the Home Counties and southern England. The species has evidently been a well-known one for very many years, for in *Hamlet* we find the Queen saying, in reference to Ophelia,—

> " There with fantastic garlands did she come
> Of crow-flowers, nettles, daisies, and long purples:
> That liberal shepherds give a grosser name,
> But our cold maids do dead men's fingers call them."

The names " long purples " and " dead men's fingers " clearly refer respectively to the characteristic flower-spikes and to the curious bloated tubers. *Orchis mascula* probably has more local names than any other British species of orchid, these names including Cuckoo-flower (Devon), Gethsemane (Cheshire), Rams-horns (Sussex), Regals (Dorset), and Kettle-cases (Isle of Wight).

Normal coloured individuals are not likely to be confused with any other orchid except the green-veined orchid. That species (Pl. 36, p. 251), however, has forward pointing sepals with distinct green veins, and a broader lip with the central lobe only slightly, if at all, longer than the lateral lobes. Pinkish coloured forms have been confused with the spotted orchids (Pl. 38a, p. 259 ; 41, p. 274), which also have spotted leaves, but these, apart from the fingered tubers, have more numerous smaller flowers, and a short spur which hangs down instead of curving upwards as in *O. mascula*.

The development of the seedling of the early purple orchid is not so rapid as that of the green-winged orchid, but the first tuber is produced in the late summer of the second year after germination, while the aerial stem appears usually in the fourth year. Flowering follows several years afterwards in favourable conditions, the plant then often dying if ample seeds are produced. In the early stages only a single leaf is produced, which in subsequent years becomes larger and broader and is later replaced by several leaves in a rosette. The rather blunt leaves—about 4–8 altogether—may be either spotted or unspotted, the spotting varying considerably in intensity and degree. The spots are actually quite different from those in any of the spotted or marsh orchids, being usually rather irregularly shaped blotches, which are often elongated in the direction of the length of the leaf. Rarely the blotching is so heavy that practically all the leaf is blackish purple in colour with only the margins and narrow marblings green. Often groups of plants may be found with all the leaves spotted or blotched to the same extent. Whether these are the offspring of a single flower, or are the result of vegetative division of the plant, is not always clear. Often, however, the plants growing together show a complete admixture of unspotted and variously spotted forms.

The flowering stem is from four inches to a foot in height, though in robust plants it may be as much as eighteen inches or more. It bears several erect more or less sheathing leaves below the flower-spike, which may be as much as ten inches (usually two to four inches) in length, and is much more floriferous than that of *O. morio*. The flowers are rather loose, particularly in the lower part of the spike, and vary in colour from deep magenta or reddish violet, through various shades of rosy purple, to pale pink and sometimes pure white. White flowered plants most usually have unspotted leaves, but a few exceptions to this have been recorded. Otherwise there appears to be little relation between spotting and flower colour, except that very heavy spotting and deep colour are often associated. The back sepal and petals form the usual hood, but the lateral sepals are opened right back so that their backs almost touch. In the British Isles they vary from quite blunt to moderately acute, but the forms with very pointed sepals so characteristic of Central Europe do not occur here. Our forms are much more like those occurring in Spain, where the sepals are very blunt or even rounded at the tip (var. *obtusiflora*). The lip is three-lobed, as in *O. morio*, but here the length is greater than the breadth, and the central lobe is distinctly, and sometimes considerably, longer than the side ones. The centre of the lip is whitish or yellowish, usually with a few spots which are darker coloured than the remainder of the lip. The rather long and blunt spur is more or less curved upwards, or less frequently horizontal. The flowers have a rather unpleasant scent, which is said to resemble that of elder or of cats, and which becomes stronger after the flowers have been open for some time.

Like the green-veined orchid, the early purple orchid has a very wide distribution in Europe and Asia, thus belonging to the Eurasian Element Proper of our orchid flora. It is found throughout Europe, with the exception of northern Russia and Finland, in North Africa, and eastwards to Persia, the Caucasus and western Siberia. There are several recognisable sub-species in the Mediterranean region, and also in parts of central Europe, but none of these is really sharply defined from the normal forms. In the Alps the species occurs at altitudes of 6,500 to 7,500 feet, which is considerably higher than *O. morio*. This very wide distribution is repeated in the British Isles (Map 31, p. 353), the species having been recorded from all the recognised botanical divisions (vice-counties) except Wigtownshire and County Meath in Ireland. In the north the species extends into the Orkney and Shetland Islands. Not only does the plant occur over the whole area, but it is also abundant, if only locally, in all parts of our islands.

As might be expected from a species so widely distributed, the early purple orchid is found in a great variety of habitats, and on very many types of soil, except those that are acid or very wet. It certainly prefers calcareous or neutral soils, but also occurs on sand, provided there is no accumulation of acid raw-humus. In Ireland it is found widely in the crevices of the almost bare limestone of the Burren region in Counties Clare and Galway, while in Great Britain it may not infrequently be found on rock ledges or in similar places where the soil is very shallow. *O. mascula* is a constituent of a great variety of types of vegetation, from the short turf of chalk downs, sand dunes and sea- or mountain-cliffs, to the interiors of oak or other woods. It is a particularly beautiful sight, when occurring in vast numbers, on the open grassy slopes of the North or South Downs, or on the steeply sloping sides of the picturesque Derbyshire or Yorkshire Dales. In these places it often grows among comparatively tall grasses such as the erect brome (*Bromus erectus*), false brome grass (*Brachypodium pinnatum*) and others, but as the orchid develops early in the year it is in flower before the grasses reach their maximum growth. In southern England the early purple orchid is perhaps better known as a frequent inhabitant of the coppiced woods of oak, ash, beech, etc. It rarely grows in the dense shade of the standard trees where these are close together, but is usually to be found under the hazel, ash, maple and other coppice shrubs. A magnificent display may often be seen several years after the shrubs have had one of their periodical cuttings. The species is usually associated with the common bluebell or wild hyacinth (*Scilla non-scripta*), the two plants being normally in flower together. Where the shade exceeds a certain depth the orchid can no longer flower, but persists in the vegetative condition until the cutting of the shrubs again allows sufficient light to penetrate. On the whole, the plants occurring in open grasslands, etc., tend to have darker flowers than those in woodlands, but there are many exceptions to this. In south-west England, particularly in Cornwall, the species is extremely common on the built-up grass-covered walls which line the narrow lanes or even the main roads, while in Devon it is said to be increasing rapidly on moist railway embankments.

The early purple orchid is another striking example of the marked fluctuations in numbers from year to year so common in orchids. In one year the floor of a wood may be almost purple with the innumerable spikes of *O. mascula*, yet a visit in the following year may yield only a dozen or so after careful search. The explanation is undoubtedly that the species is normally monocarpic, most of the plants dying after flowering for the first time. A small proportion survive flowering and may be found again the following year ; occasionally last year's dried-up flower-spike may be found at the base of the current year's spike. If, however, the spike is cut or bitten off before seeds are formed, the plant does not die, but flowers again next year. This is well illustrated by an occurrence in Sussex during the recent war. About a thousand square yards of lawn were left unmown in 1941, and in this patch appeared 950 flower-spikes of *O. mascula*, a species which had not been noticed there previously at all ! In 1942, however, the number had dwindled to between 20 and 50. It is clear that the plants must have remained in a purely vegetative state for an unknown period until the cessation of mowing allowed them to come to flower. After this the great majority died, since the 50 which flowered in the following year almost certainly included some which had not been strong enough to produce flowers in 1941.

As the name indicates, the early purple orchid is one of the first of our native orchids to flower, appearing first in April or early May in the south according to the season. Farther north it is naturally later, but even there it has usually completed its flowering by the end of June. In the south of England it is usually about a fortnight earlier than *O. morio*. The flowers are visited by humble-bees (various species) for the sugar inside the fleshy walls of the spur. The mechanism by means of which pollination is achieved is described in detail in Chapter 3 (pp. 46–49), so need not be dealt with further here. Apparently the bees only visit a few flowers on each spike, and seed production varies considerably from place to place. Ziegenspeck gives figures of from 9 to 25 per cent of flowers producing ripe capsules, from different localities in Europe, but no doubt weather plays an important part in determining the number of insect visits. No special method of vegetative multiplication is known, but plants may sometimes produce two buds (and tubers), which give rise subsequently to two distinct aerial stems.

CHAPTER 14

THE SPOTTED ORCHIDS

THE GROUP known as the Palmate Orchids contains some of the most abundant as well as some of the most beautiful or our orchids. The species share with the members of the last group the characteristic features of the genus *Orchis*, namely, the two pollinia each with its separate viscidium, the latter immersed in a single pouch-like flap, the bursicle. The palmate orchids (sub-genus *Dactylorchis*), however, have the lobed finger-like tubers (Fig. 2 A and B, p. 12) found in genera like *Gymnadenia*, instead of the spherical or egg-shaped tubers characteristic of *Orchis* proper. As already suggested, they are perhaps better regarded as a separate genus, more closely related to *Gymnadenia* and its allies than to the other group of *Orchis*. The presence of the specially developed bursicle in the two groups of *Orchis* may therefore be merely an indication of parallel development in the course of adaptation to pollination by more highly developed insects. Be that as it may, the palmate orchids or dactylorchids, as they are often called, certainly form a well-defined and very " natural " group of species, easily distinguishable from the other species of *Orchis*, but often extremely difficult to distinguish from one another. Indeed this group of orchids is quite the most troublesome among British orchids, equally for the expert as for the beginner. We are still very far from a complete knowledge or understanding of the numerous forms observed, while as most of the species hybridise freely with one another the situation is rendered still more complicated. In examining a population of these species, therefore, it is always necessary to bear in mind two important points ; firstly, that two or more very similar species may be present, and secondly, that hybrids are extremely likely to occur or may even be in such numbers as to outnumber the original parent species ! A correct interpretation of what species are present can in such instances be made only by examining as nearly as possible the whole of the population ; merely to grab a single plant at random for more careful examination on some subsequent occasion is more likely to cause confusion than to help. Admittedly all this sounds rather laborious and time-consuming, but little progress is likely to be made in understanding and recognising the palmate orchids unless the student is prepared to take some trouble.

Two main groups of dactylorchids can be recognised, namely, the spotted orchids and the marsh orchids. The former are dealt with in this chapter, while an account of the marsh orchids follows in Chapter 15.

The spotted orchids can usually be recognised by their spotted leaves (though some species of marsh orchids also have spotted leaves), by the spreading lateral sepals, these being erect and back to back in the other group, and by the much more slender spur. By the older botanists they were all included in the single species *Orchis maculata*, which has a wide distribution in Europe, and this course is still followed by some modern authorities (e.g. Godfery). It is possible, however, to distinguish two species in the British Isles, the common spotted orchid (*O. fuchsii*, Pl. 38a, p. 259 ; Pl. I, p. 18) and the heath spotted orchid (*O. ericetorum*, Pl. 41, p. 274 ; Pl. XVII, p. 254), which are well marked, differing not only in vegetative and floral characters, but also in their ecological requirements. The common spotted orchid is highly polymorphic, showing great diversity throughout its geographical range. In certain areas, however, notably in the Hebridean Islands and in western Ireland, it is represented by distinct forms, which some authorities have treated as separate species, but which are best looked upon as sub-species or varieties. They will be referred to briefly at the appropriate places.

The two recognised species are probably the two most abundant orchids in the British Isles, occurring throughout almost the whole area, and often to be found in hundreds or even thousands, so that patches of vegetation are coloured pink by their flower-spikes. On the whole, however, they are more or less complementary in their distribution, *O. fuchsii* being predominantly southern and eastern, and being more abundant on calcareous soils, whereas *O. ericetorum* is chiefly western and northern, and is characteristic of acid non-calcareous soils.

PLATE 39

Robert Atkinson

Hebridean Orchids (*Orchis fuchsii* subsp. *hebridensis*). Isle of Lewis; July

PLATE 40

G. H. McLean

Irish subspecies of Common Spotted Orchid (*Orchis fuchsii*, subsp. *o'kellyii*).
Co. Clare; June

COMMON SPOTTED ORCHID (*Orchis fuchsii*)

The dense flower-spikes of this species, varying from pale to quite deep lilac pink in colour, are probably more frequently encountered than any other orchid, at any rate so far as England, Wales and many parts of Ireland are concerned (Pl. 38a, p. 259). Not only may they be found in a great variety of situations, such as dry downs, open woods, or marshes, for the spotted orchid is very catholic in its tastes, but vast numbers may often be seen in suitable localities.

Although the first foliage leaf is produced in the second year after germination of the seed, the plant takes some years to develop to full size vegetatively, the leaves increasing in size and number until flowering is possible. The tubers are flattened, thickened nearest the stem, but farther down divided into two to four tapering divergent lobes rather like the fingers of a hand (Fig. 2 A and B, p. 12). There are also a few thick rather fleshy roots. The aerial stem varies considerably in height, depending much on the habitat, plants in exposed or dry localities being only a few inches high, whereas in damp places or woods individuals may reach a height of two feet or more. The arrangement and shapes of the leaves are very characteristic, the leaf pattern thus produced providing one means of distinguishing the species from the allied heath spotted orchid. The lowest leaf, which is usually shorter than that immediately above, is always the broadest, with a very broad rounded tip. The leaves above this are progressively narrower and more acute, the next two or three being the longest. Above these are a variable number, sometimes as many as eight, which are even smaller and very pointed, the uppermost being indistinguishable from the lowermost bracts. In the heath spotted orchid the total number of leaves is smaller (usually from five to seven), and all the leaves, even the lowest, are acute.

In *O. fuchsii* the leaves are usually more or less spotted, but plants with unspotted leaves are not infrequent. The spotting may be scattered or quite dense, while the spots themselves may be very intense or so pale as to be almost invisible. Sometimes they may be so closely placed and so dark that the entire leaf seems to be of a blackish purple colour. The spots are almost invariably " solid ", that is, they are not ring-like nor with a paler centre, but of a uniform colour or intensity. They are usually not circular, but more or less transversely elliptical, with the long axis at right angles to the length of the leaf, whereas in

O. ericetorum the spots, which are on the average much smaller and less intensely coloured, are almost circular.

The flower-spike contains a considerable number of flowers rather closely arranged ; it varies from a half to five inches in length (Pl. I, p. 18). The flowers themselves exhibit great variation both in size and colour, from deep lilac-rose, through paler lilac or rose-lilac down to white ; the lip, and the lateral sepals to a lesser extent, bear deeper rose or red-violet markings. These vary very much in intensity, in some cases being extremely bright, whereas they may be very obscure or practically absent in other individuals. In albino forms the markings are quite absent.

The upper sepal and petals form a hood over the column as in other species of *Orchis*, but the lateral sepals spread widely rather like a pair of wings. The lip is very broad with a rounded base, and is divided into three more or less triangular lobes of about the same size (or the lateral ones rather larger than the central), the central one being always as long as, and most frequently distinctly longer than, the side ones (Fig. 18, p. 269). The lip markings usually take the form of double loops or concentric looped lines, but these are often much broken up into dashes of various lengths, or rarely into dots. In *O. fuchsii* the loops are on the whole much more complete and clearly defined than in *O. ericetorum*, in which the markings tend to take the form of numerous apparently irregularly arranged dashes or dots. The spur in the common spotted orchid is almost straight, cylindrical and rather slender, but distinctly thicker than in the heath spotted orchid.

O. fuchsii belongs to the European Element of the British orchid flora, being found in many parts of western and northern Europe, but not extending very far to the south-east. In Europe it is looked upon merely as a variety (var. *meyeri*) of the widespread *O. maculata*, but there is little doubt that the continental plant is the same as the British. Unfortunately the different varieties of *O. maculata* have not been clearly distinguished in all countries, so that we do not know exactly the European distribution of *O. fuchsii*.

As already mentioned, the common spotted orchid, though widely spread in the British Isles, is predominantly southern in distribution, the heath spotted orchid being the commoner species in the west and north, especially in the more mountainous districts. In England and Wales *O. fuchsii* is very generally distributed, and this applies also to

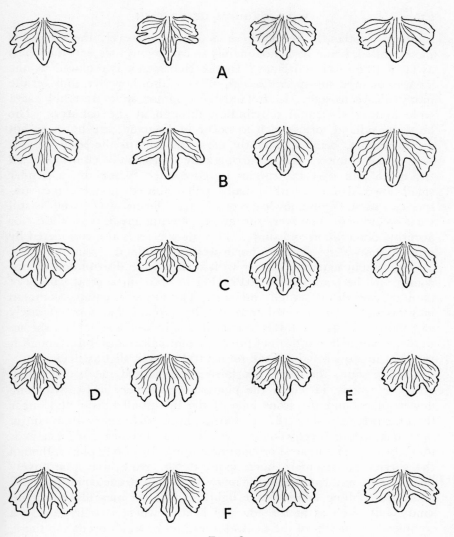

FIG. 18

Common spotted orchid, *Orchis fuchsii*

Lips of various forms and sub-species, drawn to the same scale. A. Northern meadow form, Westmorland. B. Southern woodland form. C. Chalk grassland form. D. Sub-species *hebridensis*, Barra. E. Sub-species *o'kellyi*, Fermanagh. F. Sub-species *o'kellyi*, Clare. (All ×2)

southern Scotland. In northern Scotland, however, the species is more limited, being restricted mainly to calcareous soils, but it extends as far as the Orkney Islands. In the Hebrides it is replaced by the darker coloured sub-species *hebridensis*, here also, however, only on the more calcareous soils. In Ireland the common spotted orchid has a wide and very general distribution throughout the country. The larger woodland forms, such as occur in England, are however not very common, being apparently most frequent in the south-eastern half of the country, and occurring only occasionally elsewhere. In the north and west the species is represented mainly by a slender small-flowered form with usually pale-coloured flowers, the sub-species *o'kellyi*. Our knowledge of the Irish forms of *O. fuchsii* is still very incomplete, however, the group offering great possibilities for accurate observation and study. This sub-species is also considered by some authorities to occur in north-western Scotland.

One might expect a species with such a wide distribution in this country as the common spotted orchid to occur in a great variety of habitats, and this is actually the case. The species is equally common in grasslands and in woodlands, on dry ground and in moderately wet places, though it rarely occurs in really wet bogs. The species shows, nevertheless, a distinct preference for calcareous soils, though it may not infrequently be found on neutral or even slightly acid soils.

In the south there are two fairly well marked races, one which grows in woods, in which the plants are tall, very leafy, with long flower-spikes, and the front lobe of the lip usually distinctly longer than the side ones (Fig. 18B, p. 269). This is particularly abundant in open oak, ash or beechwoods, especially on rather heavy soils, such as marls or clays of a neutral or alkaline nature. In woody places, though the species prefers more open spots, it can grow in comparatively dense shade, and can persist for many years in a sterile condition until clearing or felling admits more light. This form may also occur on sandy soils, such as at the edges of heaths, where it is frequently a common constituent of the neutral grassland or scrub occurring there, the heath spotted orchid being the characteristic species on the heath itself. Indeed the detailed distributions of these two species in such places is an almost certain indication of the nature of the soil reaction, which can usually be confirmed by the examination of the accompanying plants.

The other southern race or variety is characteristic of open chalk

PLATE XIX

R. Atkinson

Flower spikes of Common Marsh Orchid, *Orchis praetermissa*; important features are the saucer-like lip and its numerous small dot markings (×1)

PLATE XX

A. J. Wilmott

Upper part of plant of Irish Marsh Orchid, *Orchis occidentalis* (×1)

downs or limestone grassland. This is a smaller plant on the average than the woodland form, has fewer leaves on the stem, a shorter flower-spike, and the lobes of the lip about equal in length or the middle one a little longer than the others (Fig. 18 C, p. 269). There is, no doubt, crossing between these two races where the two habitats meet, and specimens of the woodland form may be found in the open.

Farther north these two types are not so clearly defined, no doubt due to the more limited areas available for the species. A short account of the two geographical " races " or sub-species is given to complete our present ideas of this common species, but it is probable that further study will lead to considerable alterations in our groupings and classi-fication.

The Hebridean orchid (*O. fuchsii*, sub-sp. *hebridensis*, Pl. 35b, p. 250) replaces normal *O. fuchsii* in most of the Hebridean Islands (e.g. Lewis, North and South Uist, Barra, Coll, Tiree, Rum, etc.). It is a smaller, stockier plant on the whole, usually about six to twelve inches in height, with fewer leaves than in *O. fuchsii* proper, these being usually rather heavily spotted, and has a short spike of deep lilac or almost magenta-pink flowers, though in individual plants the colour may be paler. In flower shape there is little difference between the two sub-species, though in the Hebridean orchid the middle lobe of the lip is nearly always distinctly longer than the laterals (Fig. 18 D, p. 269). The sub-species is characteristic of calcareous moist or rather dry places, but not of bogs, being especially abundant in the stable region immediately behind the coastal sand dunes (Pl. 39, p. 266). It is absent from the acid moorland or heath farther inland, where *O. ericetorum* is the sole spotted orchid.

The Irish " race " (the sub-species *o'kellyi*)* is not so well defined, nor has it been so accurately studied as has the Hebridean orchid. It is a rather slender plant (Pl. 40, p. 267) with a few relatively narrow lightly spotted or unspotted leaves, and a narrow spike of rather smaller flowers than in typical *O. fuchsii*. In particular the lower leaf is usually relatively long and narrow compared with that in *O. fuchsii* proper, though it is always rounded at the tip. The flowers are very

* Unfortunately this marked geographical race has been confused with the occasional albino specimens which turn up throughout the range of *O. fuchsii*, and consequently sub-species *o'kellyi* is stated by many authorities (e.g. Godfery) to occur in many parts of England. Although Druce based his variety *o'kellyi* in the first place on the western Irish plant, he later on included various albinos in his concept of the species, and this has led to the confusion mentioned above.

frequently almost white or very pale yellowish with very faint pink or lilac markings on the lip, but in some populations there may be quite a high proportion of plants with more heavily and brightly marked lips. In nearly all plants the three lobes of the lip are almost equal in length, rather as in the chalk-down form of *O. fuchsii* (Fig. 18 E and F, p. 269). Indeed sub-species *o'kellyi* appears to be the Irish version of this English grassland form, occurring in similar situations in Ireland. It is common in meadows and pastures in many parts of that country (counties Down, Fermanagh, Leitrim, etc.), usually on the lower ground. Sub-species *o'kellyi* is also a characteristic feature of many parts of the limestone hills of the Burren region in counties Clare and Galway. Here it grows in the cracks and crevices of the extensive bare limestone " pavements ", and especially abundantly in the larger grassy spots where there is a greater depth of soil. The Sutherland plant, if it really be the same as the Irish, is recorded from somewhat similar country on limestone. It is interesting to note that this distribution is paralleled by those of the Irish ladies' tresses (*Spiranthes romanzoffiana*) and the Irish marsh orchid (*Orchis occidentalis*). These plants may represent the remnants of a flora which at one time occupied a much wider area prior to some, or perhaps all, of the glacial maxima in the great Ice Age.

The common spotted orchid is one of our summer-flowering species, flowering in the south during the months of June and July, and rather later in the north. In favoured spots the species may come into flower in May, while in northern localities it often persists into August. In southern districts it is usually later than the heath spotted orchid, but in some northern districts (e.g. Hebrides) the position may be reversed. The species is visited by a great variety of insects, hive bees, solitary bees, humble-bees, syrphid and other flies, which seek the sugary liquid within the fleshy walls of the spur. The method of pollination is similar to that described for the early purple orchid. Many examples of insects carrying away pollinia have been recorded, as many as eight pollinia having been seen on a single insect. Judging from the abundant seed production, pollination and fertilisation are very effectively carried out.

Although the common spotted orchid produces seeds very abundantly, it appears to be a long-lived perennial. There are records of the same clump of plants persisting for a number of years, and steadily increasing in numbers as a result of vegetative duplication of the flowering shoots and tubers. We still do not know how long such plants can survive, and here is a possible field of investigation for someone interested.

HEATH SPOTTED ORCHID (*Orchis ericetorum*)

This species was for many years looked upon merely as a variety, or perhaps habitat-form, of the widespread *O. maculata*, and is treated as such in many standard British Floras. Indeed on the Continent there seem to be many more intermediate forms than in these islands, so there is still controversy with respect to the correct classification and nomenclature to be adopted. The present species is often identified with the continental *O. elodes*. In this country, however, the heath spotted orchid can usually be readily distinguished from the common spotted orchid, except where hybrids between the two are abundant (Pl. 41, p. 274). It is, in contrast to the other spotted orchid, and as the name indicates, an inhabitant of heaths and moorlands, and is commonest in the west and north where such country is more widespread.

In development it resembles the common spotted orchid, taking a number of years to reach the flowering stage, during which time the leaves each year gradually increase in numbers and size. The tubers are similar to those in the common spotted orchid, though when growing in wet ground, as the species frequently does, the lobes may taper very gradually to form quite long tail-like structures.

The leaf pattern, as in *O. fuchsii*, is very characteristic, enabling one usually to distinguish a specimen from that species even in the absence of flowers. The leaves are much more uniform in shape, and usually rather narrow, the lowest being the broadest, but all being acute at the tip. In very robust plants the lower leaves may be nearly an inch in width, but even in such cases they are never short and rounded as in *O. fuchsii*. On the average there are fewer leaves (about 4–8) on the stem, the small bract-like upper ones being much less evident. The spotting of the leaves is generally not so heavy, many plants having unspotted or faintly spotted leaves ; very heavily spotted leaves with the spots almost confluent are very rare. The spots are normally rather small, and more or less circular in outline, and are rarely widened transversely.

The flowering stems reach a total height of four to fifteen inches, rarely as much as two to three feet, but rather small slender specimens are quite frequent. The flower-spikes vary much in length, usually having fewer flowers than in *O. fuchsii*, but these are on the whole larger owing to the larger differently shaped lip (Pl. XVII, p. 254). The flowers vary much in colour, from almost white to deep lilac-rose, but the paler shades predominate, the average being distinctly paler than in *O. fuchsii*. The lateral sepals are very weak and spreading, not so erect as in the other species. The lip is very broad, and lobed only in the front half or third, the two side lobes being much broader and usually considerably longer than the small triangular middle lobe (Fig. 19, p. 276). The lip bears a complicated series of darker pink or lilac dash or dot markings, often covering more or less evenly almost the whole surface. These really form a series of paired concentric loops, as in *O. fuchsii*, but the broken-up portions are so small that the basic pattern is usually quite lost. The markings in any case are rarely so deep coloured or so heavy as in the common spotted orchid, while in many examples they may be very pale or almost invisible. There seems to be no direct relation between the depth of the colour and markings and the degree of spotting of the leaves. Some populations may contain a mixture of all shades and types of lip markings, whereas others may be composed almost entirely of pale-coloured individuals. The spur is about as long as the lip, but is very slender, in diameter only about half or two-thirds as wide as that in *O. fuchsii*.

The heath spotted orchid also belongs to the Western European Element of British orchids. As already mentioned under *O. fuchsii*, the exact distributions of the different spotted orchids have not been worked out everywhere in Europe. So far as our knowledge goes, *O. ericetorum* occurs generally in northern and western Europe, from western France through Holland, northern Germany, Scandinavia and Finland to northern Russia. It is also said to occur in northern Spain and in Switzerland, but is not recorded from anywhere in the south-eastern half of Europe.

In the British Isles the species is distributed in conformity with the European distribution, being more abundant in the north and west than in the south and east. It is a characteristic plant of the wilder and more hilly parts of the country, often ascending the hills to considerable altitudes. In many parts of Scotland it is the only spotted orchid, extending into the Orkney and Shetland Islands (and also to the Faroes and Iceland). In Ireland it is commoner in the

PLATE 41

Robert Atkinson

Heath Spotted Orchids (*Orchis ericetorum*). North Wales; July

PLATE 42

Robert Atkinson

Early Marsh Orchid (*Orchis latifolia*). Hampshire; June

northern half of the country, but occurs in most parts on the higher ground.

It is probable that the geographical distribution is determined to a great extent by the soil preferences of the species rather than by the different climates of the various parts of our islands. *O. ericetorum* is a very uncommon plant on calcareous soils, while it is only occasionally found where the soil is neutral, and is therefore excluded from large areas in the south-east where such soils occur. It is normally an inhabitant of heaths, moorlands, and other vegetation types occurring on acid soils, and can tolerate a considerable range of soil moisture from very dry heaths to comparatively damp marshy places, though it avoids deep peat bogs. It does, however, grow in bog-moss (*Sphagnum*) when this is not too wet. In boggy regions, however, it tends to grow on the drier grassy knolls which are usually to be found in such areas. In the south-east it is a common plant on the dry heaths of Kent, Surrey and Sussex, and also throughout the extensive heaths on Bagshot Sand and similar soils in the Thames valley and the New Forest region of Hampshire. In areas predominantly calcareous the presence of *O. ericetorum* is good evidence of the local occurrence of acid soils such as deposits of sand or gravel, or of patches in the chalk or limestone where the lime has been washed out of the surface layers so as to produce an acid soil secondarily. The species can stand a certain amount of shade, and may often be found in open woods of oak, birch or pine in the areas mentioned, or in bushy places at the edge of scrub. It is, however, not truly a woodland plant like *O. fuchsii*, and is never found in at all deep shade.

In many parts of Wales the heath spotted orchid is extremely common, especially at moderate altitudes (between 200 and 1,000 feet above sea-level). Here it may be found in almost any type of rough or uncultivated land, provided the soil is not calcareous, and the grazing is not too severe. It inhabits a wide range of situations from dry grassy or bushy places among rocks to swampy areas with cotton grass (*Eriophorum*), cross-leaved heath (*Erica tetralix*) and various kinds of sedges. In upland meadows it is often accompanied by other orchids, but in many habitats, especially the more acid ones, it is the sole orchid. This is also true of the extensive heather moors in parts of Scotland, including the Hebrides, in which it occurs scattered almost everywhere. When the soil is covered with a deep deposit of wet peat the species is either absent or only occurs locally. It is common, however, in the

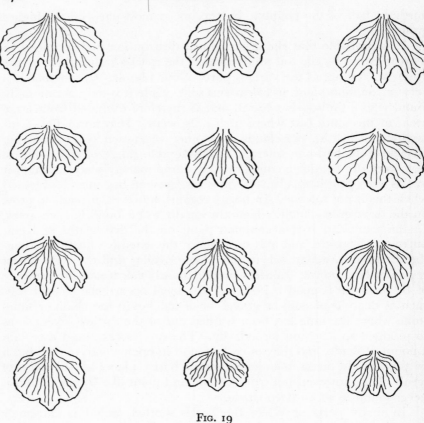

FIG. 19

Lips from plants of heath spotted orchid, *Orchis ericetorum*, from different
localities to show variation in size and shape. Note the large side lobes
and the rather small and short middle lobe. The average size should be
compared with that of *O. fuchsii* in Fig. 18. (All ×2)

grass moors composed mainly of such species as purple moor grass
(*Molinia caerulea*) and mat grass (*Nardus stricta*), or in marshy places
along drainage channels among either soft rush (*Juncus effusus*) or
jointed rush (*J. acutiflorus*). Where the drainage water in bogs or
marshes is calcareous, and so tends to neutralise the acid effect of the
peat, the two spotted orchids may be found growing together.

Over the greater part of the country the heath spotted orchid comes into flower earlier than the common spotted orchid, the flowers first opening in late May and early June even in the extreme north. In some regions, however, no doubt due to local conditions, it may flower much later, and may persist into August. Judging from the numerous hybrids which occur between this species and *O. fuchsii*, the two species must be visited by many of the same insects, this view being confirmed by the actual records of insect visitors. This is, however, not surprising when one considers the similarity in flower colour and size, and the equal spur lengths in the two species. It has been noticed also that *O. ericetorum* is often visited by species of flies which certainly carry off the pollinia, and presumably act as pollinating agents.

Hybrids between the two spotted orchids may often be seen, especially where the two species occur together in close proximity. They are usually intermediate in leaf and flower characters, but may often be recognised in the first place through the greater vigour of the plants. I have, in such mixed populations, sometimes seen hybrid individuals which were from six inches to a foot taller than any of the " pure " individuals around. Hybrids between each of the spotted orchids and the other palmate orchids are also very abundant ; these will be mentioned under the marsh orchids concerned.

CHAPTER 15

THE MARSH ORCHIDS

THE MARSH ORCHIDS are far and away the most difficult group of British orchids both for the serious student and for the ordinary nature-lover. Not only are the species very similar in general appearance, but they are extremely variable both within a single population and as between one population and another. The variability in different species often shows parallelism, as, for instance, in the spotting of the leaves or the shape of the lip, thus adding to the difficulty. Finally, frequent crossing between the species, with the consequent formation of whole series of hybrids, which are to a high degree fertile, sometimes renders it wellnigh impossible to sort out the welter of forms occurring in a given spot.

To put all this in a different way, the marsh orchids are still in an active state of evolution, in which one of the important factors is clearly hybridisation. There is reason to think that although in some directions this evolutionary activity has, as it were, become stabilised in the production of well-marked species (e.g. the early marsh orchid, *Orchis latifolia*), in others the process is only half completed ; here we probably see before us all stages in the development of stable species from an unstable and highly variable population-complex.

As a result of the situation just described, it is extremely difficult to say how many species of marsh orchids there are in these islands, and still more to classify with any degree of certainty the forms and populations which do exist. There is still a wide diversity of opinion between various authorities, both as to the actual species occurring, and as to their relationship to the allied orchids which occur on the continent of Europe. For the purposes of this book I am adopting the comparatively simple viewpoint that there are five distinct marsh orchid species in this country, namely, the early marsh orchid (*Orchis latifolia*)*, the common marsh orchid (*O. praetermissa*), the dwarf purple orchid (*O. purpurella*), the Irish marsh orchid (*O. occidentalis*) and the flecked marsh orchid (*O. cruenta*). The other species which have been described will be mentioned and shortly discussed at what seem to be the most suitable places in relation to the five species recognised.

Unlike the species composing many of the other groups dealt with earlier, four of the five species of marsh orchids occur plentifully within the general regions in which they are found. The early marsh orchid is much the most widespread, occurring practically throughout the British Isles. The other three species are more or less complementary to one another geographically, the common marsh orchid occurring generally in England and Wales except the north of England, the dwarf purple orchid in Wales, northern England, Scotland and northern and eastern Ireland, while the Irish marsh orchid is found in western Ireland and north-western Scotland. *Orchis cruenta* is known only from western Ireland.

It is not easy to state accurately in a few words the salient features of these five species owing to their great variability, so the reader is advised to consult the comments under the individual species for details. The following short descriptions give, however, an approximate idea of the general appearance of each of them, though individual plants may depart in one or more features.

The early marsh orchid (*O. latifolia*, Pl. 42, p. 275 ; Pl. XVIIIa, p. 255) has more or less upright, yellow-green unspotted leaves hooded at the tips, and spikes of variously coloured flowers, from pale sulphur-yellow through pale flesh-coloured, rose-pink, deep indian red to deep purple-magenta ; the sides of the small diamond-shaped lip are folded back, while the lip bears a pair of very clear-cut loop markings at the base.

The common marsh orchid (*O. praetermissa*, Pl. 44a, p. 283 ; Pl. XIX, p. 270) is a larger, more robust plant on the whole, with broader, darker green, unspotted not hooded leaves, and spikes of large rose-

---

* H. W. Pugsley showed in 1925 that the name *Orchis latifolia* should be used for the plant appearing in many British Floras as *O. incarnata*. The name had formerly been used by British botanists to denote what was really a mixture of forms. This mixture has gradually been shown to include the two distinct species *O. praetermissa* and *O. purpurella*, the more controversial *O. pardalina*, and numerous hybrids between various marsh and spotted orchids.

magenta or pale magenta flowers ; the lip is broad and flat with small dots or spots in the centre.

The dwarf purple orchid (*O. purpurella*, Pl. 43b, p. 282), as the name implies, is usually a smaller plant than either of the two already mentioned. It has broad, dark green, hooded leaves, which are either unspotted or furnished with very small spots especially in the upper part, and a spike of rather small very bright reddish-purple or deep magenta flowers. The lip is somewhat like that in *O. latifolia*, but broader and flat (i.e. not folded back), bearing a number of heavy loop or broken line markings.

The Irish marsh orchid (*O. occidentalis*, Pl. XX, p. 271) has a number of dark green spreading leaves, which may rarely be unspotted but are usually more or less heavily spotted, and a spike of rather large usually deep purple flowers. The lip is large, broad, more or less distinctly 3-lobed with heavy loop or dash markings, though rarely the markings are in the form of dots.

Finally, the flecked marsh orchid (*O. cruenta*) is a moderate-sized plant with rather narrow erect dark green leaves which are spotted on *both* surfaces, the spots being variable in numbers and size. It has a rather dense spike of small pinkish purple or rose-magenta flowers. The lip is broader than long, either not lobed or obscurely so at the tip, and is marked with irregular loops or broken lines, rather as in the common spotted orchid (*O. fuchsii*) ; the sides are only slightly reflexed.

In course of time the student will learn to grasp the general ensemble or " facies " produced by the combinations of essential characters in each species, and to disregard, or at least make allowances for, the variability occurring in the different parts of the plant.

As their general name denotes, the marsh orchids are, on the whole, inhabitants of wet places, marshes, or even of very wet bogs and swamps, occurring in distinctly wetter places than the spotted orchids. They are, however, quite frequently found in wet meadows, among rushes or near streams. Rarely they occur in drier situations, but this is exceptional and there is no evidence of their persisting in such places. They are often extremely abundant where they occur, so much so as to colour the sward when they are in flower.

EARLY MARSH ORCHID (*Orchis latifolia*)

Not only is this species the most widespread of our marsh orchids, but it exhibits a range of colour in its flowers which not only exceeds that of any other British orchid, *Orchis morio* included, but rivals that of many garden flowers (Pl. 42, p. 275 ; 43a, p. 282). At one extreme we have very pale sulphur-yellow or almost white flowers (var. *ochroleuca*)—true albinos also occur occasionally—whereas at the other extreme are bright magenta shades (var. *pulchella*) which equal the flowers of *O. purpurella* in their brilliancy. The species will be found in many botanical works under the name *Orchis incarnata* (see footnote, p. 279), this name describing a very common and characteristic colour-form in which the flowers are a delicate flesh-colour, a tint found in no other British orchid.

The tubers in the early marsh orchid are divided into several (2–4) tapering parts, and are accompanied by a number of rather long spreading roots. Development from the seed is in the early stages rather rapid, the first leaf appearing in the second year, and the first tuber during the fourth year. More and larger leaves are produced each subsequent year, but it takes several years to store up sufficient resources for the production of flowers. This long development before flowering is compensated for by the relatively long life of the individual plants, which may persist in a flowering state for a period of many years. The aerial flowering stem may reach a height of a foot or eighteen inches in favourable localities, though 6–12 inches is more usual. Especially dwarf varieties are found among the sand dunes in coastal districts. The stem itself is rather thick and soft with a large hollow in the centre so that it is easily squashed, this being a characteristic feature of the species. There are from three to ten leaves (usually 4–7), which are rather stiff and erect, relatively narrow, usually of a distinct yellow-green colour and narrowly hooded at the tip. The lowest leaf is often quite short, but the middle ones normally reach or overlap the flower-spike. The dense cylindrical flower-spike is from one to four inches in length, and contains a large number of relatively small flowers (Pl. XVIIIa, p. 255), the rather long often coloured bracts projecting beyond the flowers especially in the early stages. The lateral sepals and lip have deeper coloured markings, those of the lip consisting of a pair of looped lines with enclosed spots or dashes. The ground colour, as already stated, varies to an amazing degree.

The characteristic tint is a delicate flesh-colour, paler or darker in different individuals, but usually constant for all the flowers on a given spike, though the flowers which have just opened are brighter than those which are well out. Many southern populations consist almost entirely of these " incarnate " forms, but not infrequently they are mixed with other colours. Deeper pinks, intensifying to deep rose, rose-madder, and rose-red, are also found especially as one goes farther north ; for instance, they are particularly abundant in Anglesey. These colours pass over into a kind of deep indian-red or almost pinkish brick-red, these shades being especially characteristic of the sand-dune variety which is known as var. *coccinea* (Pl. 43a, p. 282). Among plants with these pink or reddish tints are often found some in which the flowers are various shades of mauve or pale magenta. Finally one finds individuals, or sometimes whole populations, in which the flowers are a bright reddish-purple or magenta with deep magenta markings, a very beautiful form which has been named var. *pulchella*, and is probably more than merely a colour form. This type is very similar in colour to *Orchis purpurella*, with which it not infrequently occurs, but from which it can be distinguished by the yellow-green erect leaves, the reflexed sides of the entire lip, and the distinct loop markings. At the other end of the colour scale we get the variety *ochroleuca*, which has pale sulphur-coloured flowers with darker yellow markings and a more or less 3-lobed lip. This occurs in a number of localities in East Anglia and is also generally considered to be a distinct variety, not just a colour form.

The lip in the early marsh orchid is usually more or less diamond-shaped but not very pointed in front. The sides are turned down at quite an early stage in development, this giving the spike a very different appearance from that in *O. purpurella* and *O. praetermissa*, where the lip is almost flat or even concave. Occasionally the lip is broader and slightly 3-lobed in front, this being especially noticeable in the pale variety *ochroleuca*, but on the whole the flower structure in *O. latifolia* is remarkably constant. The spur is very stout relative to the size of the flower and more or less conical, that is to say, it tapers perceptibly from the mouth towards the point.

Orchis latifolia belongs to the Central Eurasian element of our orchid flora, occurring widely in Europe and in Siberia as far east as Lake Baikal, as well as in Persia and Turkestan. In northern Europe it extends almost to the Arctic Circle, but is not very abundant in high

PLATE 43

Robert Atkinson

b. Dwarf Purple Orchid (*Orchis purpurella*). Isle of Lewis; July

Robert Atkinson

a. Sand-dune form of Early Marsh Orchid (*Orchis latifolia* var. *coccinea*). Isle of Lewis; July

PLATE 44

Robert Atkinson

a. Common Marsh Orchid (*Orchis praetermissa*). Hampshire; June

Robert Atkinson

b. Leopard Marsh Orchid (*Orchis pardalina*). Kent; July

latitudes ; on the other hand, it occurs only in the northern parts of the Mediterranean region, being absent from most of southern Spain, southern Italy and Greece.

The distribution of the early marsh orchid in these islands is in conformity with that in Europe, the species being found almost throughout the country, extending northwards to the Orkney and Shetland Islands and including the whole of Ireland. There is, however, a large area in south-western Scotland, including most of the Clyde Basin, from which the species is absent.

In common with all the other members of this group, *O. latifolia* is almost always found in wet places, water-meadows, bogs, marshes and fens. It usually occurs, however, where the water draining into or through the bog or marsh contains a certain amount of lime so that the soil is faintly acid, neutral or alkaline. A favourite habitat consists of water-meadows near rivers, or damp low-lying hay-fields in similar situations, but, as it is usually neither a tall-growing nor brightly coloured species, it may easily be overlooked in such places. The species is not infrequently found growing on deep peat, but the ground-water in these places is calcareous, as in the Norfolk fens, the Somerset levels, and many Irish bogs. For this reason it does not occur in the drier parts, since the peat there may be more acid, but is only found where the limy water can keep down the natural acidity of the peat. It is consequently characteristically a fen plant, but the varieties behave rather differently from one another in this respect. The variety *ochroleuca* is apparently limited to true fens, where the water is markedly calcareous, while at the other end of the series is the variety *pulchella*, which appears to be the commonest form in the most acid situations in which the species occurs. Another lime-loving variety is the variety *coccinea* (Pl. 43a, p. 282), which occurs in many places in the wet hollows (slacks) among sand dunes. As mentioned on several previous occasions, dunes often form rather limy soils owing to the presence of numerous shells in the sand, and the slacks support a flora usually associated with calcareous places. Two other orchids occurring with the early marsh orchid in such localities are the marsh helleborine (*Epipactis palustris*) and the rare fen orchid (*Liparis loeselii*). Rarely the early marsh orchid is found in drier situations ; for instance, it has been recorded occasionally from chalk downs.

As the name indicates, the early marsh orchid flowers earlier than either the common marsh orchid or the dwarf purple orchid, coming into flower during the latter part of May or beginning of June, and lasting until the end of the latter month or the beginning of July. In the north it may still be found in flower in the latter part of July. In Ireland, however, the various forms of the Irish marsh orchid (*O. occidentalis*) come into flower before *O. latifolia*. Pollination is effected in the same way as in other species of *Orchis*, humble-bees of various sorts having been recorded as frequent visitors. It is clear that pollination and fertilisation is efficiently performed, as fruiting spikes usually show the majority of the flowers to have produced seeds. Not only are pollinia carried to other individuals of *O. latifolia*, but obviously to those of other species, as hybrids between this species and the various marsh and spotted orchids have been recorded on many occasions. These hybrids show all intermediate combinations between the features of the supposed parents, with the result that hybrid individuals in one locality may differ markedly from those in other places, or from others in the same spot. Inspection of the " pure " species growing in the vicinity make it often comparatively easy to decide on the identity of the hybrid, but where several marsh or spotted orchid species are present together there may be considerable difficulty. Characters of the early marsh orchid which may be recognised in a possible hybrid are the very hollow stem, the erect narrow yellow-green hooded leaves, the more distinctive colour-tints, the reflexed sides of the lip, and the double loop-markings on it. The early marsh orchid does not hybridise with the common spotted orchid (*O. fuchsii*) so frequently as does the common marsh orchid (*O. praetermissa*), owing to the small overlap in the flowering periods, *O. latifolia* being usually over before *O. fuchsii* is properly in flower. The early flowering of our species also reduces the chance of hybrids between it and *O. purpurella*, though such hybrids have been recorded at various localities. The heath spotted orchid (*O. ericetorum*) and common marsh orchid both come into flower while *O. latifolia* is still in full bloom, but curiously enough hybrids of these with the latter are quite uncommon.

COMMON MARSH ORCHID (*Orchis praetermissa*)

This species, which was overlooked (or rather confused with *O. latifolia*) by English botanists for many years until described by Dr. G. C. Druce in 1914, is certainly the most abundant marsh orchid in that part of England south and east of a line from the Humber to the

Bristol Channel. In this region it not only occurs in many localities, but often in immense numbers, though improved drainage is tending to reduce its numbers in many places. When full grown it is undoubtedly the finest of our marsh orchids, and indeed would challenge comparison with any other British orchid (Pl. 44a, p. 283). The sight of hundreds of the purplish-pink or rose-purple flower-spikes studding a damp meadow or marshy spot is one not easily forgotten.

The underground tubers and roots are very similar to those in the early marsh orchid, although usually a little more heavily built. So far as investigations show, development from the seed follows much the same lines. The aerial shoot usually reaches a height of from 6 to 18 inches, though in favourable spots or among tall vegetation plants of two feet or more may be found. The stem itself is usually more or less hollow, though not so much as in *O. latifolia* ; rarely plants with solid stems may be found. There are from 5 to 9 leaves, the larger 4–8 inches in length, which are always quite unspotted, either green or greyish green in colour (easily distinguishable in tint from the early marsh orchid), more or less spreading, and only very rarely hooded at the tip. Indeed hooding of the leaves is usually an indication of hybridisation. The many-flowered cylindrical spikes are from 2 to 6 inches in length and over an inch in diameter, with the lower bracts often projecting beyond the flowers. There is considerable variation in the colour of the flowers, though this is nothing like so great as in *O. latifolia*. The commonest colour is a kind of lilac-pink or pale magenta-pink, but some plants have pale pink flowers, whereas at the other extreme are bright magenta flowers approaching the colours in *O. purpurella* or *O. latifolia* var. *pulchella*. These brightly coloured forms are more abundant in the west, populations in the south-east being on the whole paler in colour.

The individual flowers are considerably larger than in *O. latifolia*, this being especially noticeable in the lip (Pl. XIX, p. 270). This petal is usually very broad and flat (or even concave in the early stages), the sides not turning down until the flower is going over ; it is either almost circular and unlobed or shortly 3-lobed with the central lobe a little longer than the others. Rarely the middle lobe projects some way beyond the laterals. The lip is paler in the centre, usually with numerous small spots, but sometimes with dashes or broken lines of a darker colour. These never form the distinct paired loops so characteristic of the early marsh orchid (compare Pl. XVIIIa,

p. 255). Individuals with no spots on the lip occur sometimes and frequently the spots are very obscure. The spur is very thick, very similar to the finger of a glove, but not tapering so much as in *O. latifolia*.

The common marsh orchid is a member of the Western European element of the British orchid flora. Outside of Britain it has been recorded from northern France, Belgium, Holland and the Rhineland, but the exact continental distribution is not known, as it is still confused with other species of marsh orchids. Quite recently populations have been described from Sweden, some plants of which closely resemble *O. praetermissa*, but which are considered to be hybrids between *O. latifolia* and *O. maculata*, the European spotted orchid (see p. 114). Although the evidence is scarcely adequate for expressing any definite opinion, it does seem possible that *O. praetermissa* may have arisen as a hybrid between the widely spread *O. latifolia* and the more narrowly distributed western European *O. fuchsii*, which on this view has in England taken the place of the much more variable *O. maculata*.

All this receives a certain amount of support from the distribution within the British Isles of *O. praetermissa*. It is decidedly a south-eastern species, occurring with certainty only in England and Wales, very doubtfully present in Scotland, and almost certainly absent from Ireland. Even in England it is only frequent in the southern half of the country, extending northwards in the east to a few localities in Yorkshire and several doubtful ones in Durham, and in the west to the neighbourhood of Southport. The species has been recorded from most Welsh counties, but it is evidently rare there except in the south. It has also been stated to occur in quite a number of localities in Scotland, especially along the eastern seaboard, but it is clear that most of these records refer to the so-called variety *pulchella*, which is now considered by all authorities to be an unspotted form of the dwarf purple orchid (*O. purpurella*). There is still some doubt about some of these populations, however, and the author would always be glad to see fresh specimens of Scottish plants thought to belong to *O. praetermissa*. It will be seen that the distribution of *O. praetermissa* coincides more or less with the area in which *O. fuchsii* is most abundant though, of course, the spotted orchid extends into Scotland and Ireland. On the whole the distribution of the common marsh orchid is complementary to that of the dwarf purple orchid (*O. purpurella*), although there is a slight overlapping, particularly in Wales. *O. praetermissa* is quite

PLATE 45

Robert Atkinson

a. Fly Orchid (*Ophrys muscifera*).
Oxfordshire; June

Robert Atkinson

b. Bee Orchid (*Ophrys apifera.*) Kent;
July

PLATE 46

Robert Atkinson

Early Spider Orchid (*Ophrys sphegodes*). Dorset; May

clearly a lowland species, though it occurs in bogs on the Cotswold Hills at altitudes of over 700 feet.

Like the early marsh orchid, the common marsh orchid is found growing in a great variety of wet places, damp meadows, water-meadows, lowland peat-bogs, fens, and marshes among sand dunes. Indeed the two species not infrequently occur together, although as they are in flower at slightly different periods this joint occurrence is not always very obvious. It is not easy to say how their ecological preferences differ, but it appears that *O. praetermissa* can grow in less peaty and more exclusively mineral soils or, to put it differently, in soils in which there is not so much humus. The common marsh orchid does not grow in very acid soils, but is characteristic of limestone or chalky areas in which the ground or drainage water is distinctly calcareous, producing fens or similar vegetation where peat accumulates. Here it is often associated with the marsh helleborine (*Epipactis palustris*) and the fragrant orchid (*Gymnadenia conopsea*, particularly var. *densiflora*), growing in quite wet places where there is standing water in spring and early summer. It also occurs frequently in marshy meadows or water-meadows among rushes, tussock sedge (*Carex paniculata*), ragged robin (*Lychnis flos-cuculi*), meadowsweet (*Filipendula ulmaria*), wild angelica (*Angelica sylvestris*), yellow iris (*Iris pseudacorus*), bog bean (*Menyanthes trifoliata*), marsh cinquefoil (*Comarum palustre*), marsh marigold (*Caltha palustris*) and other marsh plants. The species may frequently be found in the margins of reed-swamps among common reed (*Phragmites communis*), reed meadow-grass (*Glyceria maxima*), marsh horsetail (*Equisetum palustre*) several feet in height, with which are also found many of the plants already mentioned above.

On sandy soils *O. praetermissa* is found in bogs in which purple moor-grass (*Molinia caerulea*) and cotton grasses (*Eriophorum latifolium* and *E. angustifolium*) form the chief vegetation, but not usually where bog-mosses (*Sphagnum*) are developed to any great extent. In many such marshes or bogs the common marsh orchid occurs in zones of intermediate wetness, between the semi-aquatic plants occupying the central parts and the vegetation of the dry areas around. The common marsh orchid also grows in marshes among sand-dunes, as at Braunton Burrows in Devonshire and on the coasts of Glamorgan and Lancashire. Here it occurs with *Epipactis palustris*, and sometimes *Orchis latifolia* var. *coccinea*, among the creeping willow (*Salix repens*) and other marsh plants which form the vegetation of these " slacks ".

W.O.B.

U

Plants of *O. praetermissa* are sometimes found growing in quite dry places such as chalk downs, limestone grassland or old chalk pits. The plants are invariably much stunted and there is no evidence that the species can maintain itself continuously in such places ; these occurrences probably represent the occasional establishment of seedlings due to exceptional circumstances.

The common marsh orchid is later flowering than the early marsh orchid (*O. latifolia*), not usually coming into flower until the beginning of June, and lasting until the middle of July. In favourable situations or early years the flowers may open in May, while plants have been recorded still in flower in early August. Little has been recorded about insect visitors to the flowers, but judging by the frequent hybrids with *O. fuchsii*, the same kinds of insects must visit both species (see under *O. fuchsii*). *O. praetermissa* hybridises freely with the common spotted orchid (*O. fuchsii*), less commonly with the heath spotted orchid (*O. ericetorum*), and occasionally with other marsh orchids, as well as with species in other genera such as the frog orchid (*Coeloglossum viride*) and fragrant orchid (*Gymnadenia conopsea*). Hybrids with either *O. fuchsii* or *O. ericetorum* are to be found among almost every population of *O. praetermissa*, usually in small numbers, but sometimes very abundantly. These normally combine in various ways characteristics of the two parent species, such, for instance, as the spotted leaves of *O. fuchsii* and the deep colour and thick spur of *O. praetermissa*. Some individuals, however, possess ringed spots on the leaves, a feature which does not occur in either parent. The hybrid plants are often to be recognised by their exceptional stature and other indications of hybrid vigour. Similar hybrids may also not infrequently be found in rather drier spots among spotted orchids, where they stand out prominently on account of the deeper and richer coloration of the flowers.

Certain populations of marsh orchids, particularly in southern England, contain large numbers of individuals which, though resembling in many respects some of the hybrids mentioned above, show a relatively greater degree of homogeneity than might be expected from a mere collection of hybrid individuals. These have been considered to belong to a distinct species, which has been called the leopard marsh orchid (*Orchis pardalina*, Pl. 44b, p. 283 ; Pl. XXIa, p. 306). The plants resemble those of the common marsh orchid in general growth and stature, the shape and number of the leaves, and the size of the flower-spike and flowers. The leaves, however, are usually very heavily spotted with a mixture of ringed and solid spots, or ringed spots only. The flowers too are much darker in colour than in *O. praetermissa*, varying in ground colour from magenta-pink to pale magenta, with very vivid and heavy magenta or dark magenta broken line or loop markings on the lip, which is usually much more distinctly three-lobed than in the common marsh orchid. In some localities, for instance near Axmouth in Devon, plants referable to *O. pardalina* easily outnumber the other marsh orchids present, mostly *O. praetermissa*. Some authorities point out that either *O. praetermissa* or *O. fuchsii* (sometimes both species) is invariably present with *O. pardalina*, and that the latter just consists of a series of well-developed hybrid swarms between the two species. It should be mentioned, however, that the leopard marsh orchid has been reported recently from a number of places in Cornwall, a county in which *O. fuchsii* is extremely rare. It may be that we are here witnessing the early stages in the production of yet another marsh orchid by much the same means as it is suggested that *O. praetermissa* itself may have originated (see p. 114). A third view is that *O. pardalina* is already a good species, but that hybrids between it and other species are so common as to obscure its distinctive features. Populations said to contain this species in varying proportions have been recorded in southern England from Kent to Cornwall, and are particularly common in the south-west. It is interesting to note that the common marsh orchid itself tends to have brighter coloured flowers in this part of the country than farther east; this would result in more brilliantly coloured hybrids, but, of course, would not account for the high proportion of hybrids in the populations. At the moment there is insufficient evidence to prove which of these views is the correct one.

DWARF PURPLE ORCHID (*Orchis purpurella*)

This species, so far as distribution is concerned, is complementary to the common marsh orchid, occurring in northern England, Wales, the Isle of Man, Scotland and Ireland. As its name indicates, it is a relatively dwarf species (Pl. 43b, p. 282), distinguished by its broad dark green leaves, either unspotted or with relatively few small solid spots, and a short dense spike of usually brilliant magenta or red-purple flowers. It is in some respects the marsh counterpart of the heath spotted orchid (*O. ericetorum*), occurring in the same regions and general types of vegetation.

There is nothing remarkable about the underground parts of the plant, the tubers being divided into two to four divergent lobes. The aerial stem is relatively stout and often hollow (though never so much as in *O. latifolia*), or less frequently solid. It is usually from four to eight inches in height, although fine specimens may be as much as 15 or 16 inches, while some populations are consistently over the average given above. There are between four and nine leaves scattered along the lower part of the stem, the lower ones sometimes almost forming a kind of rosette. These leaves are more or less spreading (nothing like so erect as in *O. latifolia*), dark or grey-green, with a broadly hooded tip ; they are either unspotted or more usually have rather few very small almost pinpoint solid spots, which are more abundant near the tip. Forms with more heavily spotted leaves are known from eastern and northern Scotland, but these are rather local and may be of hybrid origin, from either *O. fuchsii* or *O. occidentalis*. The unspotted forms, which sometimes form almost pure populations, were formerly thought to constitute a northern variety of the common marsh orchid, but unspotted individuals are nearly always to be found among those with spotted leaves. The rather dense flower-spike is usually from 1–3 inches in length, but may reach four inches or even more in large plants. The flowers are about as large as in the early marsh orchid (*O. latifolia*) or perhaps rather larger ; they vary in ground colour from rose (an uncommon tint) through pinkish magenta to very brilliant red-purple or magenta, this latter colour being very similar to that in the variety *pulchella* of *O. latifolia*. The lip is broadly diamond-shaped or shortly 3-lobed, almost flat with the sides scarcely turned down, and bears very dark purple or crimson irregular loop or broken-line markings (Fig. 6G, p. 31). These are much heavier than the dot markings in *O. praetermissa*, but not so neat and clear-cut as the double loops in *O. latifolia*. Indeed, both in lip shape and markings, the dwarf purple orchid exhibits considerable variation, but there is rarely much difficulty in distinguishing fresh specimens from the similarly coloured forms of the early marsh orchid. The spur is thick, somewhat similar to that in *O. praetermissa*, and not so markedly conical as in *O. latifolia*.

The dwarf purple orchid belongs to the Western European element of our orchid flora, having been found in Norway, and perhaps in other parts of Scandinavia. There is no doubt that *O. purpurella* is closely allied to the widely spread European *O. majalis,* which has a somewhat similar appearance, not quite such deeply coloured flowers, and well spotted leaves.

As already indicated, *Orchis purpurella* has a distinctly northern and western distribution within the British Isles. It is found very generally in Scotland, and also occurs in northern and western England as far south as southern Yorkshire, Staffordshire and Shropshire, where, however, it is decidedly local and restricted to a few stations. In Wales it is common in the north but becomes less frequent as one goes southwards ; it is particularly abundant and variable in Anglesey. The distribution of the species in Ireland is still imperfectly known, owing to confusion in the past with both the early marsh orchid and the Irish marsh orchid (*O. occidentalis*). It has been found, however, in a number of places in the northern parts of the country, as in Counties Down, Antrim, Fermanagh and Donegal, and in the east in Co. Dublin. It has also been recorded from such diverse localities as Counties Wexford, Tipperary, Cork and Galway, but the general impression is that it is much less common in the west and south. Clearly a good deal more botanical exploration is needed before we can state at all accurately where the dwarf purple orchid occurs in Ireland. The author would always be glad to see fresh specimens from any part of that country. *O. purpurella* flowers much later in the season than *O. occidentalis* (July instead of May and June), and is therefore not likely to be confused with the latter species.

The dwarf purple orchid occurs in a wide variety of bogs, marshes and other wet places, often at quite considerable altitudes. Like most British orchids, it avoids extremely acid localities, but prefers spots where calcareous drainage water maintains neutral or slightly acid soil conditions. In most neutral mineral soils the species is found in small bogs around springs, or in hollows among rushes (*Juncus effusus* or *J. acutiflorus*), bog asphodel (*Narthecium ossifragum*), ragged robin (*Lychnis flos-cuculi*), various sedges (*Carex* spp.), marsh cinquefoil (*Comarum palustre*), marsh marigold (*Caltha palustris*) and other similar plants. It may also be found growing in deep quite quaking peat in Staffordshire, but presumably also with calcareous ground water. In the Yorkshire dales the species is abundant in marshes of this or the earlier type, and here it may be associated with *O. latifolia,* especially the deep red-purple variety *pulchella.* In the Hebrides *O.*

purpurella occurs with both *O. latifolia* and *O. fuchsii* sub-sp. *hebridensis* in marshes or damp meadows in which the soils are either neutral or slightly acid, while in Wales *O. purpurella* is found in damp meadows and marshes, sometimes with *O. praetermissa*. Many of the records suggest that rich soils are often preferred, the plants in such habitats being frequently larger than usual. Often the heath spotted orchid (*O. ericetorum*) is to be found on the drier more acid soils around the marshes, and in such cases hybrids are usually present. *Orchis fuchsii* is not infrequently associated with the dwarf purple orchid in the marshes themselves. An interesting habitat is in the Isle of Man, where the species is commonly found on rather steep sea-cliffs, especially where water is constantly trickling down.

O. purpurella is the latest flowering of the marsh orchids, coming into flower in the second half of June and continuing until late in July. There are very few records of insect visitors to the flowers, but the frequency of hybrids with other marsh and spotted orchids indicates various sorts of bees and flies which are known to visit these species. In addition to hybrids between *O. purpurella* and *O. latifolia*, *O. praetermissa*, *O. fuchsii* and *O. ericetorum*, most of which have been recorded from several localities, hybrids with the fragrant orchid (*Gymnadenia conopsea*) and with the frog orchid (*Coeloglossum viride*) have been found in Durham and in Scotland. The hybrids with the two spotted orchids are easily distinguishable from one another owing to the different lip shape, colour and markings. I saw some very vigorous examples of *O. purpurella* crossed with *O. ericetorum* in Stafford-shire, the plants producing as many as ten or more flowering stems, each with identically coloured and marked flowers, intermediate in most features between the two parents. In parts of Wales I have noticed that hybrids occur almost whenever the two species are found together. The flowers in most such plants are of a beautiful purplish-rose colour, with lip markings intermediate between the two parents. The plants are nearly always considerably taller than either *O. pur-purella* or *O. ericetorum* and stand up above the accompanying rushy and grassy vegetation. Similar very attractive hybrids occur in many parts of Scotland.

IRISH MARSH ORCHID (*Orchis occidentalis*)

It is only comparatively recently that the true nature of this plant has been recognised, the species having previously been confused with other orchids. It is the earliest flowering of our marsh orchids, being at its best during May, about a fortnight earlier than *O. latifolia*. As the name indicates, the species is a native of Ireland (Pl. XX, p. 271), where it is widespread in the west, but it has also been found in several parts of north-west Scotland, particularly in the Hebrides and the mainland near by. It is very variable, especially as regards the spotting of the leaves, as well as the markings and shape of the lip. The Irish marsh orchid is no doubt closely allied to the dwarf purple orchid, but may be distinguished by the paler, not quite so brilliantly coloured flowers and broader more distinctly 3-lobed lip. In addition, the leaves are often more heavily spotted, though plants with un-spotted leaves may be found, as in *O. purpurella*, especially in certain populations.

The stem in the Irish marsh orchid reaches a height of 4 to 8 inches with large specimens a foot or more high, and bears about 6 to 8 leaves. The lower ones are quite small, but the central ones are 2 to 4 inches long and usually much curved away from the stem. The leaves show a much greater variation in spotting than in any other marsh orchid, from leaves which are quite unspotted to those which are very heavily spotted ; the spots may be very small and numerous, larger and fewer, ringed or solid or coalescing to form large irregular blotches or transverse bars. Indeed there seems scarcely any type of spotting which is not represented in this species.

The flower-spike is short, only rarely reaching four inches in length in well-grown plants, and contains many closely placed rather large flowers. These are dark purple or red-purple in colour, much as in the dwarf purple orchid. The very broad lip, however, is usually clearly 3-lobed, often with the middle lobe very prominent and pointed, but sometimes the lobes are less distinct, or the lip may be nearly entire. The lip thus shows a wide range of variation, but practically all intermediate shapes can be found linking up the extreme forms. Usually the darker markings on the lip are in the form of heavy irregular lines or spots, but some plants have small dot-like markings somewhat recalling those in the common marsh orchid (*O. praeter-missa*), but more numerous.

Certain populations of marsh orchids in Co. Kerry consist pre-dominantly of rather large plants with unspotted leaves, and flowers in which the broad lip has *praetermissa*-like spotting. These have been described as a distinct species (*Orchis kerryensis*), and are clearly allied to *O. occidentalis*. Some botanists consider all the western Irish forms to be only varieties of one species, but more information seems desirable before any decision can be taken on this problem.

Orchis occidentalis is not found outside the British Isles and is therefore one of our endemic species of orchid. It also is a close relative of the European *O. majalis*, of which it is considered by many authorities to be only a geographical sub-species. In Ireland it is known at present only from the west, extending northwards from western Cork and Kerry through Limerick, Clare and Galway to Mayo. In many parts of this region it is to be found in almost all suitable localities, often in very large numbers. The species has also been recorded from western Sutherland on the Scottish mainland, and also from the islands of North and South Uist in the Hebrides. It is highly probable that it occurs elsewhere both on the mainland and in the islands. It is only recently that the marsh and spotted orchids of this region have been properly studied, and there are still large areas which await careful botanical exploration. The rather remarkable distribution shows certain resemblances to those of the Irish ladies' tresses (*Spiranthes romanzoffiana*) which, it will be remembered, also occurs in Ireland and in certain Hebridean islands (Coll and Colonsay), and of the Irish form of the common spotted orchid (*Orchis fuchsii* sub-sp. *o'kellyi*) which is found also in Sutherland.

The Irish marsh orchid generally grows in damp or quite wet pastures and meadows, which may at times be even boggy. Often the species occurs among coarse vegetation such as rushes or yellow iris (*Iris pseudacorus*), and sometimes among the tussocks of the purple moor grass (*Molinia caerulea*). Many of the localities seem to have somewhat acid soils, as the heath spotted orchid (*O. ericetorum*) is often associated with the marsh orchids, but, on the other hand, our species is abundant in the limestone area of the Burren in Co. Clare. Although exact data have yet to be obtained, it would seem that *O. occidentalis* prefers habitats similar to those favoured by other marsh orchids, that is, neutral or slightly acid soils with a certain amount of calcareous ground water draining through. In the Hebrides the species occurs in marshy hollows among dunes.

Orchis occidentalis is usually in flower during the months of May and June, being apparently at its best in the latter part of the former month. Little has been recorded of the insects which visit the flowers, but on analogy with other species it is probable that they are bees and humble-bees.

In addition to the western Irish localities mentioned already, there are also several places in Co. Wicklow where a closely allied marsh orchid is found. This has been classified by different botanists as a variety of *O. occidentalis*, as a sub-species of the continental *O. majalis*, or even as a distinct species, *O. traunsteinerioides* (Pl. 38b, p. 259). The distinguishing features of this orchid, the Wicklow marsh orchid, are the slender habit, narrow more or less upright leaves, and small red-purple flowers with a kind of wedge-shaped lip in which the middle lobe is often longer than the side lobes (Pl. XXIb, p. 306). The spotting of the leaves is very variable, as in *O. occidentalis*, consisting often of transverse bar-like or ringed spots, or the leaves may be quite unspotted. I have also seen specimens collected by Mr. R. D. Meikle in 1948 in Co. Fermanagh and in 1949 in Co. Antrim which seem to agree with the Wicklow plants.

Populations of very similar plants occur in several places in England, such as Berkshire, Yorkshire and Durham, and have also been reported from other places. There is a good deal of variation from one locality to another, but it seems probable that many of these plants belong to the same species or sub-species, whatever it may be. All possess narrow leaves, of which the lowest is narrower than those above it, comparatively few-flowered spikes, and the lip distinctly 3-lobed with the central lobe more or less prominent. These populations occur in a rather wide range of habitats, from quite wet bogs with cotton-grass, sedges and the like, to damp rushy meadows or upland pastures. All the localities appear to have calcareous ground or drainage water. It is clear that *O. traunsteinerioides*, if it be a species, is closely allied to *O. occidentalis* on the one hand, and to the European *O. traunsteineri* on the other. Indeed, it is possible that it will prove to be a British sub-species of this narrow-leaved marsh orchid, which is widely spread in northern and central Europe.

It is perhaps a significant fact that in all the localities in which the Wicklow marsh orchid has been found two other species are either actually present or occur nearby, namely, the early marsh orchid (*O. latifolia*) and the common spotted orchid (*O. fuchsii*) or one of its sub-species. May we possibly have here a series of hybrids between these two species, similar to those already suggested in connection with the leopard marsh orchid ? Nearly all the characters of *O.*

traunsteinerioides could be derived from hybridisation between *O. fuchsii* and the variety *pulchella* of *O. latifolia*, which is the form present in many of the localities concerned. However, much more information and detailed observations are needed before a definite decision can be made on these interesting plants. Anyone discovering any populations which appear to agree with the above, especially in the north or west, is asked to communicate with the author.

Flecked Marsh Orchid (*Orchis cruenta*)

The discovery of this interesting species in 1949 by Dr. J. Heslop Harrison in western Ireland is one of the major events in the recent history of the marsh orchids in this country. *O. cruenta* has been recorded from the British Isles on several previous occasions, but the plants concerned are now all considered to be forms of the dwarf purple orchid (*O. purpurella*). The species may be distinguished from all other British marsh orchids on account of the leaves being spotted on *both* sides, instead of only on the upper surface. The irregular reddish brown or reddish purple spots bear a strong resemblance to bloodstains, from which resemblance the scientific name has apparently been given. The Irish plants agree in general features with continental plants from the Alps and Scandinavia, but there are minor differences which may indicate that they constitute a special British sub-species of the European species. Further investigation is necessary before a definite decision can be reached on this point. It is generally accepted that *O. cruenta* is closely related to *O. latifolia* ; indeed some European botanists consider the two to be sub-species of one collective species.

In general appearance the species is similar to the early marsh orchid (*O. latifolia*). The flowering stem is usually from six inches to a foot in height, bearing from four to six rather spaced-out foliage leaves, of which the lowest is almost like the basal sheaths, while the uppermost resembles the bracts of the flower-spike. The intermediate leaves are from two to four inches in length and up to half an inch broad ; in continental plants, however, they are usually relatively broader, often as much as three-quarters to one inch in width. The leaves are marked on both sides with numerous irregular deep reddish or reddish-purple spots or blotches, but there is considerable variation from one plant to another in the size and number of the spots. In a small percentage of the plants the leaves are unspotted. The stem is also striped or flecked with red in the upper part, and this colour continues into the bracts. The flower-spike is rather dense, usually about 1 to 2½ inches in length, but reaching 4 inches in robust plants. The bracts are stained deep red-purple ; often the tips curve in towards the flowers, though this is more obvious in European plants. The flowers are small for a marsh orchid and red-purple in colour, much the same shade as in the common marsh orchid (*O. praetermissa*). The rather broad scarcely lobed lip has darker purple spots and dots, usually surrounded by more or less heavy double loops which are not so delicate as in *O. latifolia*. The sides of the lip are only slightly reflexed, not markedly so as in the early marsh orchid.

The flecked marsh orchid belongs to the Northern Eurasian Element of the British orchid flora. It occurs in northern and central Europe, though not in the extreme west, extending eastwards across central and northern Russia and Siberia to beyond Lake Baikal. In the Swiss and French Alps it occurs at altitudes of as much as 8,000 feet, but farther north it is found at much lower altitudes and even in the lowlands in Russia. In the British Isles it is so far known only from the extreme west of Ireland in counties Mayo, Galway and Clare, but it is possible that it occurs elsewhere in that country. It should also be looked for in Scotland, especially in limestone districts.

In Ireland the species is always found around the highly calcareous lakes of the Burren country, where it is often associated with the black bog-rush (*Schoenus nigricans*). It occurs in similar habitats in Europe, but there usually with the allied *Schoenus ferrugineus* and small sedges. It is clearly a fen plant, always occurring where the soil or soil-water is rich in lime.

Orchis cruenta flowers rather later than its ally the early marsh orchid (*O. latifolia*) or the Irish marsh orchid (*O. occidentalis*), coming into flower in the middle or latter part of June and lasting until the latter part of July. Presumably the flowers are visited and pollinated by the same insects as visit other marsh orchids, but so far there are no actual records from this country.

CHAPTER 16

THE BEE ORCHID AND ITS ALLIES

THE MEMBERS of this group probably exert a greater fascination on plant-lovers than any other British orchids. This is partly because they are all rather uncommon and uncertain in their appearance, features which encourage the exploratory and hunting instincts in human beings, and give a greater zest to expeditions in search of these species. But it is even more due to the quaint and, indeed, sometimes quite convincing resemblances of the flowers to various sorts of insects, from which they obtain their common names (bee, fly, and spider orchids). The genus *Ophrys*, to which all the species belong, is distinguished by the lip being devoid of any spur (Fig. 6A, p. 31) and by the two viscidia being covered by separate bursicles instead of the single one found in *Orchis* and its allies.

In general appearance the four species fall easily into two groups, in two species (fly and early spider orchids) the large and prominent sepals being green in colour, whereas in the other two (late spider and bee orchids) these sepals are more or less pink with a green central line. The bee and fly orchids (*O. apifera* and *O. muscifera* respectively, Pl. 45, p. 286) are widely spread in the British Isles, while, on the other hand, the early and late spider orchids (*O. sphegodes* and *O. fuciflora*, Pl. 46, p. 287 ; Pl. 47, p. 302) are restricted to the southern and south-eastern parts of England. Indeed *O. fuciflora* is now known only from several localities in Kent.

FLY ORCHID (*Ophrys muscifera*)*

This charming species is, in spite of its moderate size, one of the

* I do not agree with the recent adoption of the name *O. insectifera* for this species.

most elusive of British plants. The coloration of the flowers produces a sort of natural camouflage, which, taken in conjunction with the normal habitat of the species (among mixed vegetation in open woods, or between bushes), makes the flower-spike almost invisible to a person even when nearly treading on the plant. It may be recognised from the other species of *Ophrys* by the relatively long narrow lip which, with the narrow antennae-like petals, produces a remarkable resemblance to a fly-like insect (Pl. 45a, p. 286), the shining slate-blue band across the centre giving the impression of reflection from the folded wings of the insect.

The tubers in the fly orchid, as in other species of *Ophrys*, e or less egg-shaped (Fig. 2 C, p. 12), resembling those of of *Orchis*. There are also a number of rather fleshy which are infected by the mycorhizal fungus, : rs themselves are free from infection. Develop g is rapid in the early stages, the first foliage lea ter following germination of the seed, while the second year. The aerial shoot grad cessive years until large enough to pro suc- shoot is usually from six to fifteen inche as much as two feet in large well-gro developed late in the autumn each year winter, dying away at or just after flow are about three or four leaves, the lo broad and spreading, while the upper rather as in the early purple orchid ; bluish green, very smooth and shining contains from two to eight rather widel fourteen flowers have been found. The s pals, which are broad and blunt, are green or yellowish green in colour. Between them lie the two very narrow brown petals, which form the antennae of the " fly ". The lip, which is much larger than any other part of the flower, is reddish brown when fresh, becoming duller with age, and has a broad metallic blue band across the centre. It has a small lobe on each side near the base, and is usually cleft at the tip. The column is relatively short, and quite blunt at the tip, contrasting in this respect with the bee orchid. Partial albino flowers are sometimes found, in which the brown and blue colours are lacking, the lip being green and white or yellowish.

othes. wait eight hou cold, damp cave party. On new exp ments must be mad d in however narrow the suc- explorer. A violen This suddenly flood all be at best—trap th ay be neither M. Che ves are suffered this f ring the of it was alw ier. There What n are rather drive s the stem agair asps of e dark green or s ver-spike usually flowers, but up to

The fly orchid belongs to the European Element of the British orchid flora. It is generally distributed throughout Europe, extending northwards to Scandinavia and Finland, but southwards only to the northern parts of the Mediterranean region, such as northern Spain, central Italy, and the northern parts of the Balkan Peninsula. This is a more extensive distribution than that of the other members of this group.

In the British Isles the fly orchid is also widely distributed (Map 40, p. 356), though it is more abundant in the southern part of our islands. It occurs generally throughout southern England, but is less frequent and rather patchy in the northern half of the country, though it extends as far north as Durham and Westmorland. In Wales it is found only locally in the south and extreme north, but further botanical exploration may reveal it in additional localities. From Scotland the species has been definitely recorded only from near Killiecrankie in East Perth. Here again more careful search may lead to its discovery in other localities in the east of the country. In Ireland *O. muscifera* has been recorded from a number of counties, mostly in the west and in the central plain. It is more frequent in the western half of this latter region. The species, like the others of the group, is decidedly local in its occurrence, but may be quite abundant in favourable places or seasons.

Unlike the other three species of *Ophrys*, *O. muscifera* is primarily a woodland or shade-loving plant, though it may sometimes be found growing right out in the open. It is most characteristic of wood borders or of openings within woods, but it may be found in quite shady places, even where there is no other vegetation present. It is also frequently found in thickets or scrubby places, where, moreover, it is often difficult to detect. Sometimes the species occurs on open banks, chalk downs, old pastures, or irregular rocky grasslands. The fly orchid occurs almost invariably on calcareous soils, both on the chalk of southern England and on the older limestones of the north and in Ireland. One of its most characteristic habitats is in openings in the beechwoods, particularly the " hangers " which form the chief woodland vegetation on the North and South Downs and the Chiltern Hills. In Yorkshire, Durham and Westmorland it is found in the mixed oak and ashwoods on the Mountain and Magnesian Limestones.

In Ireland it is a characteristic member of the vegetation growing in the crevices of the extensive limestone pavements in the Burren region of County Clare, and in the adjacent counties of Galway and Mayo. In the central plain it is found in the scrub of hazel and other species on the calcareous " eskers " or glacial terraces, but also occurs in rather marshy places, where it is associated with such species as the marsh helleborine (*Epipactis palustris*) and fragrant orchid (*Gymnadenia conopsea*), as well as other marsh plants.

O. muscifera first comes into flower early in May, but it may be found in bloom throughout that month and in June. Extra late plants linger on until the beginning of July, but this is exceptional. On the whole the species is at its best in the latter half of May and the first two weeks of June. Although it seems to be fertilised frequently, it was not until 1929 that Godfery observed and identified the insect which visits it. This is a small burrowing wasp (*Gorytes mystaceus*), of which only males have been seen visiting the flowers. It is clear from observations that the insect mistakes the lip for a female of the same species, and in the course of attempted copulation the pollinia are removed and transferred to another flower. Godfery records that later on the wasps cease to visit the orchid, probably because by then the female wasps are emerging. This phenomenon, known as pseudo-copulation, has been observed in other European species of *Ophrys*, and in orchids in other parts of the world (see Chapter 3, p. 54). If the plant is entirely dependent on a single species of insect for pollination in the way described, it is clear that the production of fruit and seeds is related to the degree of activity of the male insects during a comparatively short period, between the time of emergence of the males and that of the females. Bad weather or other unfavourable conditions will severely limit this activity, and this uncertainty is evidently reflected in the irregular seed production noticeable from year to year and from place to place. Counts made by one investigator in 1903 and 1904 showed that of over 1,000 plants examined in each year, seed was set in only 2·1 and 7·5 per cent respectively, which very low figures are in agreement with observations elsewhere.

EARLY SPIDER ORCHID (*Ophrys sphegodes*)

The early spider orchid (called in many standard works *O. aranifera*) resembles the fly orchid in the green colour of the three spreading sepals (Pl. 46, p. 287). It is easily distinguished by the almost circular brown lip, which bears a strong resemblance to the body of the large fat spiders which are such a prominent feature in gardens and wild places in the early autumn. *O. sphegodes* is, in this country at least, usually a shorter and more compact plant than *O. muscifera*, with fewer flowers in the spike. It is also much more local in occurrence, though it may be very abundant in some places.

The underground parts are similar to those in the fly orchid, while in development the plant shows general agreement with that species. The stem reaches a total height of about three to nine inches in this country, though larger plants may be found in favourable spots. In Europe plants up to two feet high have been recorded, but the species is much more variable there. The leaves, of which there are usually three or four, are rather short and broad, green or greyish-green, the upper more or less clasping the stem. The flower-spike contains a few (often only two or three, but up to seven in large specimens) widely spaced, rather inconspicuous flowers, the whole being easily overlooked even from a short distance. The large oblong sepals are yellow-green or brownish-green in colour, while the rather shorter strap-shaped petals are a bright yellow-green, often with brownish margins. The very convex rounded lip is a warm brown when freshly expanded, but fades rather quickly to a dull pale yellow- or greyish-brown. In the centre of the lip are rather irregular bluish-grey or lead-coloured smooth markings often in the form of an H (Pl. IV, p. 27). These contrast strikingly with the velvety felt-like surface of the surrounding brown-coloured region. In the lower part of the lip there are often two slight swellings or hunches, but these are developed to varying extents in different individual plants, or are entirely absent. The top of the rather slender column is somewhat like the head of a bird, the two pouches (thecae) containing the pollinia resembling the two eyes, but the " beak " is rather stouter than in the allied bee orchid.

The early spider orchid is a member of the European Element of our orchid flora, being widespread throughout the western parts of central and southern Europe, and extending north to Belgium, central Germany and Czechoslovakia. It is generally distributed in the western Mediterranean region, but farther east is replaced by closely allied species (*Ophrys atrata* and *O. mammosa*). It is characteristic of the more Atlantic parts of the Continent, not extending beyond the Carpathians, nor into the North German plain, where the climate is more continental.

In Britain the species is restricted to England (Map 41, p. 356)

PLATE 47

Late Spider Orchids (*Ophrys fuciflora*). Kent; July

PLATE 48

Robert Atkinson

b. Bog Orchid (*Hammarbya paludosa*). Hampshire; July

Robert Atkinson

a. Fen Orchid (*Liparis loeselii*). Norfolk; June

except for a solitary record from Denbigh in N. Wales towards the latter part of the last century. Like so many others of our orchids, it is gradually becoming rarer and more restricted in distribution. At one time it must have occurred in suitable localities generally throughout the south-eastern half of England, as far to the west and north as Dorset, Wiltshire, Oxfordshire, Northamptonshire, Cambridge and Suffolk. Although still common in certain parts of Dorset, it is decidedly rare or perhaps even extinct in most of the other counties mentioned. Indeed the species is now to be found at all regularly only in Dorset, Sussex and Kent, though odd specimens or small colonies are occasionally recorded from other counties within the region mentioned.

O. sphegodes, like its relatives, is almost restricted to calcareous soils. Most of its recorded stations are on the chalk, but in Dorset the species occurs on the Purbeck limestones (Pl. 2, p. 47), while the Northamptonshire localities were on Oolitic and Liassic limestones. The spider orchid always occurs in open grasslands (downs or old pastures), usually where the turf is comparatively short, this no doubt being related to its low stature. A characteristic habitat is afforded by old quarries or other places where the ground has been disturbed ; many of the records of the species are from such spots. Often the species is extremely local, occurring in small patches, whereas it is not to be found anywhere around although much of the ground seems quite suitable. The early spider orchid is especially found near the sea, which feature possibly links up with its western distribution on the European mainland. So far little is known of the factors responsible for these preferences.

As the name indicates, the early spider orchid is one of our earliest species, coming into flower in the latter part of April and blooming throughout the greater part of May. Very late flowers may still be discovered exceptionally during the first week of June. The individual flowers remain open for a long time, but in few-flowered plants often only one flower can be found open at any one time. Unfortunately the original bright colours fade soon after the flower opens. Sugar is present in two shining eye-like patches at the base of the column, and the flowers may sometimes be visited by insects for this sugar. As hybrids with the fly orchid (*O. muscifera*) have been recorded on several occasions, the same insects must at least occasionally visit both species. So far no direct evidence of " pseudo-copulation " in this species has been observed. Seed production is usually rather poor, figures between six and eighteen per cent of flowers setting seed having been recorded. Rarely the early and late spider orchids are in flower together (beginning of June), and in such circumstances hybrids between the two species may arise. These have been observed rarely in Kent ; they combine the green sepals of *O. sphegodes* with the lip markings and trilobed lip-appendage of *O. fuciflora*.

LATE SPIDER ORCHID (*Ophrys fuciflora*)

This beautiful species (often called *O. arachnites* in Floras or other books) is even rarer than the early spider orchid, being known now with certainty only from Kent. It resembles the bee orchid (*O. apifera*) in having pink sepals (Pl. 47, p. 302), differing in this respect from the two species already described (*O. muscifera* and *O. sphegodes*), in which the sepals are green. Although very similar in colouring to the bee orchid, it may be distinguished most readily by the tip of the lip being turned up in front to form a thick three-lobed appendage, instead of being tucked up behind the main part of the lip. Other differences are the short triangular petals, the broader lip whose markings often form several small circles, and the shorter blunter tip to the column (see Pl. VI, p. 79).

Vegetatively the late spider orchid is very similar to the early spider orchid, and in its early development also agrees with that species. The stems reach a height of from four inches to a foot, though extra robust plants may grow fifteen inches or more. Most of the leaves form a spreading rosette at the base, but there are one or two erect sheathing ones on the stem ; they are very similar to those in *O. sphegodes*. The flower-spike consists of from two to six rather widely spaced flowers (Pl. XXIIa, p. 307), which have large pale or darker pink sepals with a central green vein. The petals are very much shorter than the sepals, either triangular or more or less dagger-shaped, and with a densely velvety surface. The lip, which is thought to resemble the body of a large garden spider, is four-angled rather than circular in shape, and often widens somewhat towards the front. At the very tip it is furnished with an upturned fleshy three-lobed appendage. The ground colour of the lip is a warm brown or reddish-brown, velvety hairy, with a number of yellowish or paler brown smooth lines forming a rather irregular pattern which may sometimes enclose three small circles across the middle of the lip. Behind this is a kind of pale " collar " enclosing a smooth area just in front of the column. There are sometimes two slight hunches towards the base of the lip, similar to those in the early spider orchid, but these are better developed in continental plants, particularly in southern Europe. The column has a rather blunt tip, hardly so pointed as in *O. sphegodes*, and contrasting markedly in this respect with the bird-like column in the bee orchid.

Apart from the markings on the lip, which show very considerable variation from plant to plant, numerous colour and other varieties have been recorded, depending upon the colour of the sepals, which may sometimes be white, the shape and colour of the petals, and the degree of development of the hunches. These are probably mostly just cases of individual variation, similar variations being found in our other species of *Ophrys*, though perhaps not to such a great extent. Plants with abnormally developed flowers, for example with two lips or several extra stamens, are sometimes encountered.

The late spider orchid is a member of the Southern Eurasian Group within our British orchids, being generally distributed throughout central and southern Europe, including the Mediterranean basin, and extending eastwards into Asia Minor. It is, however, more frequent in the western part of its general area of distribution. Northwards it reaches only Holland, central Germany and Moravia, that is, about the same northern limit as *O. sphegodes*.

In Britain (Map 42, p. 356) the late spider orchid is a very rare plant, being known only from Kent, though there are rather doubtful old records from Surrey, Dorset and Suffolk. The most recent of these records outside Kent is that from near Bere Regis in Dorset in 1891. The other records are much older, and mostly based on rather slender evidence. Even in Kent the species is very local, occurring in a few quite restricted localities in the Wye and Folkestone districts, though a hundred years ago it seems to have been much commoner and more generally distributed in the county.

Like the other British species of *Ophrys*, *O. fuciflora* is commonest on calcareous soils, and, indeed, is restricted to such in the northern parts of its range. In England it is known only from the chalk, where it occurs on open downs, rough banks and similar places. It is normally a constituent of areas of short turf, not being found among the taller grasslands where the man orchid (*Aceras*), pyramidal orchid (*Ana-*

camptis) and fragrant orchid (*Gymnadenia*) occur. In this respect it resembles both the early spider and bee orchids, which also favour short grassland, and with which it is often associated.

O. fuciflora, as its English name implies, flowers later in the year than *O. sphegodes*, its flowering period lasting from the latter part of May or beginning of June to the end of the latter month. Rarely it may come into flower while *O. sphegodes* is still blooming, but normally it is contemporaneous with the bee orchid. On the European continent the late spider orchid is known to be visited by males of a small bee (*Eucera tuberculata*), which apparently mistake the lip for a female of the same species, and remove the pollinia in the course of their visits. The conditions are similar to those already mentioned in the account of the fly orchid, where the wasp *Gorytes mystaceus* is the visitor. In both cases the insects suddenly cease their visits, presumably when the females emerge from pupation. No actual records of insects visiting the flowers have been made in this country, but as hybrids between the species and *O. sphegodes* or *O. apifera* (Pl. VI, p. 79) have been described, it is clear that some insects, at least, must visit two or more of the species concerned. An interesting field for observation lies here ready to hand for any persons who reside in or are visiting Kent. The hybrids referred to above are dealt with respectively under the other two species mentioned ; each has been observed only on a few occasions.

There are a few records in *O. fuciflora* of the type of self-pollination which is so general in the bee orchid. Sometimes while the flowers are in bud the stalks of the pollinia curl so as to carry the pollinia into contact with the stigmas below. This is not at all frequent, however, so it has been suggested that there may be special races or populations within the species which are self-pollinating, though the bulk of the plants depend on insect visits for pollination and fertilisation.

BEE ORCHID (*Ophrys apifera*)

There is perhaps no greater thrill than that experienced by the nature-lover when he sees his first bee orchid. The delicate colouring, and the almost uncanny resemblance of the beautifully marked lip to the body of an insect, coupled with the uncertainty of finding the plant in any spot where it is said to grow, invests it with an attractive-

PLATE XXI

G. Atkinson

b. Part of flower spike of Wicklow Marsh Orchid,
Orchis traunsteinerioides, from Newcastle, Co. Wicklow ($\times 2\frac{1}{2}$)

E. J. Bedford

a. Leopard Marsh Orchids, *Orchis pardalina*, in Sussex ($\times \frac{2}{5}$)

PLATE XXII

B. J. Hammond

b. Flower of Bee Orchid, *Ophrys apifera*. Note the pollinia hanging down on their thin caudicles (×2)

E. J. Bedford

a. Flower spikes of Late Spider Orchid, *Ophrys fuciflora*, showing variation in lip-markings, and

ness which is not equalled by any other British orchid. This is enhanced by the fact that, unlike the two spider orchids, the bee orchid is distributed throughout England, Wales and Ireland, and there is therefore a reasonable chance of discovering it somewhere in your neighbourhood be it ever so rare there. The uncertainty of finding the plant at all is always accompanied by the entrancing possibility of discovering immense numbers of individuals where previously the number has never risen above half a dozen in a year. For in the bee orchid, the quality of fluctuating, known in many other orchids, seems to reach its maximum development.

Ophrys apifera is more closely related to *O. fuciflora* than to the other British species of *Ophrys* (Pl. 45b, p. 286). Like the late spider orchid, it has pink sepals and a round fat lip which is brown with rather variable grey and yellow markings. The lip is smaller and more compact, however, and the tip is tucked up behind so as not to be noticeable, instead of being turned up in front (Pl. VI, p. 79). Other differences are the long strap-shaped petals and the long beak at the tip of the column, which gives this structure a quaint resemblance to a duck's head.

The bee orchid agrees vegetatively with the two spider orchids in possessing two large egg-shaped or globose tubers, and in the rosette of rather broad greyish-green leaves, which expand in the autumn and remain green all through the winter. The plant is, in this country, larger than the early spider orchid, the stem usually reaching a height of six to fifteen inches and occasionally approaching two feet. Apart from the five or six spreading basal leaves, there are usually one or two on the stem and closely enveloping it. The flower-spike contains two to seven (rarely as many as eleven) rather widely spaced flowers. The large spreading sepals vary from pale pink to bright violet-rose in colour, with several distinct green veins; rarely the sepals are white. The much smaller and narrower green or brownish petals are often more or less rolled up lengthways, making them appear even narrower. The lip looks bag-shaped or almost globose from in front owing to the lobes, including the narrow pointed tip, being turned back underneath (Fig. 6A, p. 31). It is reddish or purplish brown with a soft velvety surface, marked with a series of irregular smooth paler lines and dashes, the inner ones forming a sort of collar around a bright cinnamon or red-brown smooth base. The side lobes are cone-like above, very hairy, projecting downwards on each side of and behind the lower part of the lip. The tip of the column is drawn out into a beak-like forward-directed point, the whole resembling a duck's or other bird's head.

Like those of the spider orchids, the flowers of the bee orchid show great diversity from one plant to another in general colour and in the markings on the lip. Plants with white sepals are not infrequently encountered, while forms with various parts of the normal colour scheme lacking are recorded occasionally. In one variant the red colour is absent, leaving a yellowish-green base with no distinct markings on the lip ; this is presumably merely a partial albino form. It is well known that the yellow pigments in flowers are rarely lost, and complete albinos of these are therefore extremely rare.

A more remarkable variant, which has been looked upon as a distinct variety, or even as a separate species, is the so-called wasp orchid (var. *trollii*, Pl. XXIII, p. 314). In this the tip of the lip is not curved back but is continued downwards, the whole lip being dagger-shaped without any very clear-cut markings, but with brown or yellow and green mottlings or marblings. The flowers on any one individual wasp orchid often differ markedly from one another, sometimes approaching in appearance the normal bee orchid, or in other cases being clearly imperfectly formed. On the other hand, bee orchid plants sometimes have most of the flowers quite normal, whereas others are intermediate between this and the wasp orchid.

Like the late spider orchid, the bee orchid belongs to the Southern Eurasian Element among British orchids. In Europe it has a southern distribution, extending northwards only as far as Holland and north-western Germany, but not in Poland or Czechoslovakia nor to the east of these countries. Southwards the species is common in the Mediterranean region, in North Africa, and eastwards to Asia Minor, Syria, Palestine, the Crimea and the Caucasus.

In the British Isles (Map 43, p. 356) the bee orchid is widely spread throughout the greater part of England and Wales, but does not reach Northumberland. There is one record from Lanarkshire in Scotland, but the species is evidently extremely rare north of the Border. Even in northern England it is much less frequent than in the south, being very uncommon in Durham, Cumberland and Westmorland. The species is found in most of Ireland, but is absent from nine of the botanical regions (vice-counties). It is most abundant in the central plain and in the limestone region of the west. In north-eastern

Ireland it seems to have increased in numbers during the last twenty-five years.

Although not entirely restricted to calcareous soils, like the two spider orchids, the bee orchid is much more abundant on such soils than elsewhere. Apart from the chalk downs of south-eastern England, and the limestone hills of Yorkshire, the Midlands and the south-west, the species often occurs on clayey soils or marls, and is a not uncommon plant of dry more or less stabilised sand dunes. Its favourite habitats are dry banks, old quarries, railway embankments or cuttings, old pastures, roadsides, or indeed anywhere where the turf is comparatively short. The species is rarely found among grass more than a few inches in height, unless the vegetation cover is not continuous so that there are numerous small bare patches. Occasionally *O. apifera* occurs in shady positions, among bushes or beneath trees, but it is normally a plant of open places. I have, however, seen the species growing in mixed woods of oak, sycamore, beech and other trees on the chalk of the Chiltern Hills. Here it may occur in quite shady places where there is little other vegetation. The plants are rather drawn-up and slender, the flowers are paler in colour than in plants growing outside, while they come into flower about a month or so later. In Ireland the species is a common constituent of the vegetation of the calcareous glacial ridges (eskers) in the central plain, while in the Burren limestone region of counties Clare and Galway it is found growing in the crevices and grassy patches of the extensive limestone pavements there.

One of the most striking features of the bee orchid is the uncertainty of its appearance in any given spot. Most people know at least some places where a few specimens may be found almost every year, but usually the numbers of plants fluctuate in an amazing manner. For instance, at Magheramoine in Co. Antrim about 12 plants were seen in 1923 (the first record for north-eastern Ireland !), in 1924 there were hundreds or thousands according to different observers, in 1925 only 9, in 1926 they were again plentiful, whereas in 1928 the number had shrunk to 2. This is typical of many other places. I well remember visiting a large field of about 50 acres on the Liassic limestone of the Polden Hills in central Somerset, in which it was difficult to step without treading on a bee orchid plant (at a modest estimate there must have been tens of thousands of plants !). Nevertheless in the following year careful search revealed only about a dozen specimens altogether.

Unfortunately the field was ploughed up shortly after this, so that it was not possible to follow up the fate of the millions of seeds which must have been produced.

June is the usual month for finding the bee orchid in flower in southern England, but in the north it is still flowering in July. Rarely plants come into flower in the latter part of May, in favourable localities or in early seasons. The Chiltern Hills woodland plants, however, are fully out in the latter part of July, when plants growing on the downs outside the woods have well-developed seed capsules. From the resemblance of the lip to a rather plump bee or similar insect, it seems probable that originally the species was normally pollinated by the males of some insect as described for the fly and late spider orchids. The pollinia can be removed by the normal mechanism and indeed not infrequently are. Since hybrids between the bee orchid, on the one hand, and the late spider orchid (Pl. VI, p. 79) (or more rarely the early spider orchid), on the other, have been occasionally recorded, it is clear that the bee orchid is sometimes visited by insects which pollinate those species. Indeed from certain comments made by G. E. Smith in his *Catalogue of the Plants of South Kent* published in 1829, it seems almost certain that a male insect has been seen mistaking the flowers of the bee orchid for the females of its species, though the observer was quite unaware of the significance of what he saw. Unfortunately these observations have never been confirmed since, but it is clear that an interesting field of study is here available for any person who has easy access to colonies of *O. apifera*.

Nevertheless the great majority of flowers of the bee orchid are self-pollinated by means of a very ingenious mechanism. In this species the stalks (caudicles) of the pollinia are longer and more slender than in other species of *Ophrys*. Soon after the flower opens they shrink in such a manner that the pollinia are drawn forwards out of the stamen and dangle in front of the stigma, held in position by the viscidia which are still in their enveloping pouches. A slight breath of wind is sufficient to carry the hanging pollinia against the sticky stigmas to which they adhere, pollination being thereby effected (Pl. XXIIb, p. 307). That this method is efficient is indicated by the fact that nearly all the flowers in a colony will be found to have produced seed. It seems as though in the bee orchid this certain method of pollination and fertilisation has taken the place of the highly fortuitous method associated with " pseudo-copulation ".

It should be noted, however, that self-pollination, though ensuring the production of seed by most of the flowers, has its own disadvantages. Any defect or abnormality which is due to the nature of the individual, and not merely the result of some outside influence, tends to be reproduced or even accentuated when self-pollination is a general feature of the life-history. This no doubt explains the frequency and persistence of such abnormalities in the bee orchid, particularly those which are responsible for the production of the wasp orchid (var. *trollii*). This is known to be very persistent in some localities, and this fact has been used as an argument for considering it a true variety, but it seems more probable that repeated self-pollination is responsible for the continued occurrence of this curious type of departure from the normal structure. This and other abnormal types (e.g. white- or yellow-flowered forms) are more abundant in the more northern parts of the range of the species, where self-pollination is almost invariable. In the Mediterranean region, on the other hand, hybrids with other species are comparatively common, so it is obvious that cross-pollination by insects is much more frequent there than farther north.

CHAPTER 17

BOG ORCHIDS

THE TWO species forming this group, namely, the fen orchid (*Liparis loeselii*, Pl. 48a, p. 303) and the bog orchid (*Hammarbya paludosa*, Pl. 48b, p. 303), are very inconspicuous, being small plants with yellowish green or whitish green flowers, *Hammarbya* possessing the distinction of being our smallest native orchid—it may sometimes be only an inch in height ! As the common names indicate, both are inhabitants of very wet places, but they have very different tastes in this respect and are never found growing together. Both species are more closely related to the immense group of tropical orchids than to any other British orchids. Although, like all our other species, they are terrestrial plants, many of their tropical relatives are epiphytes which grow perched up in trees. Two different genera are represented, which are very similar in general growth and floral structure. The group is distinguished from nearly all our other native orchids by two features, one vegetative and the other floral. In both species the base of the stem is swollen to form a fleshy portion, known as a pseudobulb (see Pl. XXIVb, p. 315), because it resembles a true bulb in outward appearance. Pseudobulbs are commonly found in tropical orchids, especially in the epiphytic or tree-inhabiting species. The second feature is the nature of the stamen, which here forms a kind of little cap or lid on the top of the column, the pollinia being contained within this lid. This lid-like (*operculate*) stamen is of wide occurrence among the various groups of tropical orchids ; it also occurs in the coral-root (*Corallorhiza trifida*), but that is a saprophytic leafless plant.

In *Liparis* this lid is attached by a very delicate hinge or stalk, and easily falls off. In *Hammarbya*, on the other hand, the attachment is very firm, and the pollinia are usually exposed by the shrivelling of the lid. Other differences between the British species are the long winged column of *Liparis* in contradistinction to the short fat column in *Hammarbya*, and the globose pollinia in *Liparis* as compared with the flat ones in its ally.

FEN ORCHID (*Liparis loeselii*)

This is one of the rarer of our orchids, being known only from a few localities in East Anglia and South Wales, where, however, it may still sometimes be found in considerable numbers. It is a rather drab plant with a somewhat loose spike of small spidery green flowers (Pl. 48a, p. 303).

The aerial stem may be from two to nine inches in height, but usually only reaches four to six inches in British specimens. At the base is the swollen bulb-like portion, while at its side is the old pseudo-bulb formed from last year's stem, and usually covered by the withered and chaffy bases of the previous year's leaves. The pseudobulbs are first produced in the second year after germination, while the first leaf appears two years later. Although infected by the mycorhizal fungus during the early stages of growth, normal absorptive roots are soon developed, and the plants are able to maintain themselves independently of the fungus. The stem bears two erect rather broad-pointed, shining and rather greasy-looking leaves two to four inches in length, together with several sheathing scales at the base. The plants growing in South Wales have broader and blunter leaves, and constitute the variety *ovata* (Pl. XXIVa, p. 315). The inflorescence stalk, which is round at the base, becomes three-angled farther up, while at the top the angles are extended to form several narrow wings. The spike bears usually four to eight flowers, but in more robust specimens there may be a dozen, while rarely as many as eighteen have been recorded. The flowers are dull yellowish green in colour, the narrow sepals and petals spreading in various directions, while the broad upright lip is pressed close to the column in the lower part.

The fen orchid belongs to the Northern Eurasian Element of our orchid flora, but it has not such a pronounced northern distribution as other members of this group, for example, its ally the bog orchid. It is found generally in northern Europe, but only extends as far north as southern Norway and Sweden, and does not occur in the more northern parts of Russia. In the south it occurs in southern France and northern Italy, and also in the northern parts of the Balkan Peninsula, but is absent from the Mediterranean region proper, and from south-eastern Europe. In fact it avoids regions in which there is a marked summer drought, and also those in which the winter temperature is too low. It may perhaps better be termed a northern Atlantic species, since it clearly shows the best development in cool rainy regions, and avoids extremes of temperature. It is almost invariably a lowland plant, but in the Northern mountain regions ascends to about 2,000 feet.

In Britain the fen orchid is restricted to two main regions (Map 19, p. 350). One of these includes East Anglia and the adjacent Fen Country, in which region it is now known from Cambridgeshire, Norfolk and Suffolk, while it formerly occurred in Huntingdon. It was at one time much more widespread and abundant in these counties, but extensive drainage has destroyed many of its old haunts. There is also an old record of the species having occurred near Sandwich in Kent, but nothing has been seen of the plant there for over a hundred years. In what might be termed the East Anglian region the species occurs in fens or at the edges of lakes or pools, where the soil is almost continuously wet, but usually on a light or sandy soil. In these habitats the drainage water is always alkaline, so that the soil itself is either neutral or alkaline. The fen orchid, unlike the bog orchid, avoids places where the soil or drainage water is at all acid. It is only rarely found associated with bog moss (*Sphagnum* spp.), but other characteristic members of the vegetation are common reed (*Phragmites vulgaris*), the large sedge-like *Cladium mariscus* and various sedges (*Carex* spp.).

The second area of distribution is South Wales, where the species has been recorded from Glamorgan and Carmarthenshire. Here it occupies quite a different habitat, occurring in the damp hollows of the coastal sand dunes (Pl. XXIVa, p. 315). Usually the soil is covered by a thin layer of *Sphagnum*, but sometimes the plants grow in bare sand. In such places it is accompanied by other orchids such as the marsh helleborine (*Epipactis palustris*), common marsh orchid (*Orchis praetermissa*) and early marsh orchid (*O. latifolia*), most of which also occur with it in East Anglia. Other plants associated with the fen orchid in Wales are the dwarf willow (*Salix repens*), skullcap (*Scutellaria galericulata*) and bog pimpernel (*Anagallis tenella*). The Welsh plants have broader and blunter leaves than usual, and are

PLATE XXIII

R. Atkinson

Plant of Wasp Orchid (an abnormal form of the Bee Orchid), *Ophrys apifera*, f. *trollii* (× 1)

PLATE XXIV

E. J. Bedford

C. Thomas

considered to form a distinct variety, var. *ovata*. Apparently this variety is able to stand a greater degree of drought than the ordinary fen-inhabiting form, since the dune depressions (slacks) are often comparatively dry during the summer.

Liparis is usually to be found flowering in June and early July, but the flowers persist in a fresh state for a long time after the pollinia and the column are dried up or withered. The flowers are apparently unscented, and there is no record of the secretion of nectar. No insects have been observed visiting the flowers, which are, however, organised for normal cross-fertilisation. There appears to be some difference of opinion between authorities as to whether self-pollination and fertilisation takes place. Godfery holds that all pollination is by small insects, pointing out that fruit is not always set, as should be the case if self-pollination is the rule. Continental workers, however, state that almost immediately after the flowers open the pollinia may be found on the stigma, the poorly developed rostellum forming no effective barrier. These workers suggest that self-pollination is the rule, but it may be that different races or populations behave differently in this respect. There is no doubt that fruits are set freely and seed production is good.

Apart from new plants arising from seed, multiplication may take place on a modest scale by the production of more than one pseudo-bulb at the base of the stem. Each of these develops into a distinct stem, which become separated from one another in the following year, and eventually several individuals are formed. Groups of flowering plants are produced by this method, as many as six to ten occurring together.

BOG ORCHID (*Hammarbya paludosa*)

This little species, which will be found in most text books and Floras under the name of *Malaxis paludosa*, is in some respects one of the most interesting of our native orchids (Pl. 48b, p. 303). In the first place, it is one of the few species which normally grow in acid soils, and secondly, its flowers exhibit a peculiarity not found in any other British species. As already explained (page 29), the lip in most orchids is at the front or bottom of the flower, the ovary having twisted through half a circle (180°) to bring the lip to the front from its natural position at the back. In the bog orchid the lip is at the back or top of the flower, so at first sight it would seem that the ovary has not twisted at all. Careful examination, however, shows that, on the contrary, it has twisted so far that the lip has been carried right round to the back again, thus passing through a complete circle (360°) ! We are still without any real clue as to the significance of this remarkable pheno- menon.

With its dwarf stature and tiny dingy yellowish-green flowers *Hammarbya* is very difficult to see against the background of bog-moss cushions in which it almost invariably grows. Taken in conjunction with its very sporadic and local occurrence, this makes it one of the most tantalising of our native orchids, perhaps more difficult to find than any other species.

As in the fen orchid, there are two pseudobulbs (swellings of the stem), those of the current and previous years respectively, but these are always placed one above the other, with a narrow stem connecting them. The new pseudobulb is covered by the bases of the green foliage leaves (Pl. XXIVb, p. 315), whereas the old one, which is about the size of a pea, is enveloped in the dried-up remains of last year's leaves. Roots in the ordinary sense of the term are practically absent, those present being reduced to hairs, heavily infected with fungus and merely serving as a means of obtaining food for the plant through fungal activity. In fact the *Hammarbya* plant remains highly dependent on the fungus throughout its entire life, this no doubt being connected with the very special habitat in which it lives. There are from two to four small blunt rather fleshy spoon-shaped leaves, which usually bear at the tip several small bulb-like swellings. These can give rise to new plants on becoming detached, and serve to reproduce the species. The flowering stem is from one to five inches in height, bearing a many-flowered rather dense spike at its tip. The flowers are extremely small, smaller than those of any other British orchid, pale yellow or yellowish green in colour. The broad rather blunt lip, as already mentioned, is placed at the top of the flower owing to the excessive twisting of the ovary. There is a very short broad column with a lid- like anther just at the back of the top, the lid, however, shrivelling to expose the pollinia soon after the flower opens.

Like *Liparis*, *Hammarbya* is a member of the Northern Eurasian Element of our orchid flora, but it has a much more pronounced northerly distribution than its ally. In Europe it extends to, or almost to, the Arctic Circle in Scandinavia and Finland, and from thence eastwards across Russia and Siberia through the region of Lake Baikal to Japan. Southwards the species finds its limit in France, Switzerland, Austria and Hungary, but does not occur in the Mediterranean region nor in southern Russia and the Balkan Peninsula. Evidently the bog orchid prefers a cool moist climate.

The species occurs scattered throughout the British Isles (Map 20, p. 350), from Cornwall and Kent in the south to the Orkney Islands in the north, and in most parts of Ireland except the south-east. But in England it is very much less common in the south than farther north, and is even better distributed in Scotland. Indeed the bog orchid is a decidedly local plant in southern England, partly, no doubt, because the climate is not so favourable as farther north, but also because suitable habitats are only available in certain districts. There seems to be evidence that the species is becoming less common in the south, in this respect agreeing with the lesser twayblade (*Listera cordata*). Most of the records from the Ashdown Forest region of Sussex and Kent, for instance, are rather old, but the bog orchid is still to be found in a number of localities in the New Forest region of Hampshire, and the adjacent heathy district of eastern Dorset. Like most other orchids, *Hammarbya* is rather irregular in its appearance, there being often in any given year no trace of it where one or two years previously it had been fairly plentiful.

The bog orchid is always found in a very limited and specialised type of habitat ; this no doubt, in its turn, plays an important part in determining its detailed distribution geographically. As the name indicates, the species is an inhabitant of bogs, usually ones in which bog-mosses (*Sphagnum* spp.) are abundant, and in which the drainage water is acid in nature. These are to be found in moorland and heathy districts, and are often surrounded by areas covered with heather (*Calluna vulgaris*), heaths (*Erica cinerea* and *E. tetralix*), and other typical acid soil plants. The orchid plants grow with their roots in the large cushions formed by the bog-mosses, these cushions being usually more or less saturated with water and continually wet. On the whole, *Hammarbya* is not associated with those species of bog-moss which occur in the most acid places, but rather with those of intermediate acidity. Owing to the special conditions existing in these moss cushions, and the small size of its leaves, the plant is scarcely able to obtain enough nitrogenous or carbohydrate food by ordinary means. It therefore depends to a very great extent on the activities of its associated fungus, this being true throughout its life-history. No doubt these special conditions are also responsible for its decidedly sporadic flowering.

The bog orchid usually flowers in July and August, or even in September in northern localities or in late seasons. The flowers are very inconspicuous, but nevertheless they are well visited by insects, as the pollinia will usually be found to have been removed. There are no records of the insects concerned, but they are presumably small ones, flies or the like, which keep near the surface of the bog. Abundant seed is often set, but we know very little about its germination and the development of the young plants. The seeds float on water, and can therefore be carried considerable distances in wet bogs to new places suitable for germination.

The species is not, however, dependent on seed for its multiplication. At the tip of each leaf are small bud-like structures, which on becoming detached are each capable of developing into a new plant. Such vegetative buds develop much more quickly than the seeds, and are therefore a more certain method of reproduction. Their occurrence is associated with the constantly wet habitat in which the plant grows, these conditions favouring vegetative multiplication. Although free from the fungus when first formed, the young plants are rapidly infected at an early stage and soon resemble the adults.

CHAPTER 18

WHAT OF THE FUTURE?

I HOPE THAT by now all readers will have an increased appreciation of our native orchids, and will be helped in their efforts to study and understand these extremely interesting and beautiful plants. But this book will not have served its purpose fully if after reading it the reader does not ask himself " What can I do myself?"

Clearly the extent to which the nature-lover or more serious student can help in advancing the study of our orchids will depend upon many circumstances. For instance, the country dweller is always better situated than the inhabitant of a large city, while those living in the south-east, where so many of our orchids grow, have more chances of seeing and studying them than the northerner. Yet there are interesting problems in all districts, while even the occasional visitor to the countryside can play his or her part. Many will object that they have neither the time nor the scientific training to attempt the solution of any of the more subtle problems, and this is undoubtedly true. Nevertheless there are many things which even the least favourably placed person can do, provided he is genuinely interested.

A theme which the observant reader will notice repeated in many places in the accounts of the species is the gradual diminution in the number of individual plants and localities in which any species may be found. Much of this is bound up with the more intensive agricultural use of our countryside, particularly during the two recent wars. Enclosure, the felling of woods, ploughing and drainage must inevitably reduce the number and the areas of the habitats in which orchids can survive. In view of the present situation of world food-supplies this trend is likely to continue and even be accelerated. But it cannot have escaped the notice of the reader that in the past some species have suffered from the depredations of collectors and other enthusiasts. Here then is a way in which all can help. Most orchids depend to a great extent on the production of seed, either for reproducing themselves in their present habitats or for colonising new habitats which may become available. Therefore, please do not pick orchids unless you have some definite object in view. Admittedly they are very ornamental in the house, and when a species is extremely abundant perhaps little harm is done by picking a few spikes, particularly if you leave the basal leaves. Avoid, however, picking the odd specimen, for it may be the only one within miles. If you do not recognise it try to get a knowledgeable person to come and look at the plant *in situ*. The number of occasions on which the single recorded individual of a species within a district, or even vice-county, has been picked is quite impressive. There is little chance of our orchids extending their ranges or colonising new habitats if they are picked immediately they appear.

Much can also be done to preserve localities or habitats in which orchids are known to occur. Many local natural history societies are only too glad to use what influence they possess in support of any such attempt. Landowners and farmers can often be persuaded to preserve uncommon orchids on their land if properly approached. It is hoped that under the new Nature Conservancy it will be possible to schedule many areas of natural vegetation as nature reserves. Not a few of these either contain interesting orchids or provide suitable habitats for them ; certain areas proposed as nature reserves support some of our rarest orchid species. The success of such a policy, however, depends upon a strong public opinion, and here it is that all interested in orchids can co-operate in making sure that sufficient pressure is put on local authorities and other responsible persons so that they will play an active part in the setting-up and proper administration of such reserves.

It is hoped that biological research may be carried on in selected nature reserves, and no doubt some of this will deal with orchids. Here is an opportunity for the more serious student to work in conjunction with the universities and other research bodies. The co-operation of a local resident is often of great value in such studies, enabling observations to be carried on all the year round. Nevertheless, the student need not wait until the scientists descend on him, but can often initiate observations or even simple experiments on his own, or in conjunction with other local naturalists. Professional scientists are always glad to hear of such activities, and are usually willing to give guidance and advice as to the most profitable lines of investigation to follow and the best way of proceeding.

As regards subjects for investigation there is, of course, a wide range from which to choose. A simple line of work is the accurate recording of fluctuations in numbers of individuals of species over an extended period. Another is the marking of flowering plants of certain suspected monocarpic species to see what percentage of them flower a second time ; this can also be done with definitely monocarpic species, such as the bee orchid and fragrant orchid, as we have no exact idea of the proportions of plants which die or survive after flowering.

Most people interested in orchids can contribute in some way towards the completing of our records of the distributions of the individual species. These are well known in general terms for many species, but even here the exploration of little-known localities may result either in new discoveries or in filling up blanks in our knowledge. As regards the more difficult groups, the dactylorchids and helleborines, a great deal more investigation is needed to make our knowledge of distributions really satisfactory. Most of the older records are unreliable, being usually under the general names of " Orchis latifolia ", " O. maculata " or " Epipactis latifolia ". All these require refinding (if still existing in the old localities) and examining from the standpoint of modern concepts. The detailed distributions, especially the distributional limits, of species like the common marsh orchid and dwarf purple orchid are still very imperfectly known. This work can only be done by close co-operation between amateurs interested in orchids and professional botanists, since the small number of " experts " cannot hope to visit more than a tiny proportion of the total number of localities where orchids grow. They must therefore rely to a large extent on seeing specimens collected by others. Persons interested in this subject are advised to get into touch with local natural history societies or museums, with people who are known to be preparing local Floras, or with a large botanical institution such as the Royal Botanic Gardens, Kew.

An important subject for study, albeit somewhat protracted and needing plenty of patience, is the collecting and sowing of seeds, and the observation of the seedlings arising. Our information on these

matters is still very imperfect ; many of the times of first leaf and
flower production mentioned earlier on are based on inference from
the examination of many seedlings rather than from direct observation
after sowing. Following on these studies will be observations on the
lengths of individual existence of plants of the more perennial species
(marsh and spotted orchids, etc.), and, in certain cases, the rate of
multiplication, where such is a common feature of the species.

Much still remains to be discovered about the insect visitors to
plants. We know little about this in some species, as the reader has no
doubt realised. To get the best results active co-operation between
botanist and entomologist is necessary ; this could often be achieved
by natural history societies. Individual problems in this field are
mentioned in several places in this book. This work requires much
time and patience, but it is essentially a fine weather task, and therefore in many respects very pleasant. Darwin's classic researches on
this subject and, more recently, the observations by Col. Godfery,
show clearly what valuable results can be obtained by patient and
long-sustained observations.

It is hoped that these few remarks may spur orchid-lovers on
to contribute actively to our knowledge of these beautiful and wonderful plants. Far from detracting from our appreciation of their beauty
and charm, the study of them along one or more of the lines mentioned above only serves to deepen our attachment to them, and often
reveals new beauties and marvels.

ARTIFICIAL KEY
FOR THE DETERMINATION OF SPECIES
OF BRITISH ORCHIDS

THE FOLLOWING key is provided to enable the reader to identify the great majority of orchids which he or she may encounter. It should be noted, however, that orchids, like other plants, are extremely variable, and may sometimes produce individuals which are very different in flower colour or other features from a normal plant. No key can be devised to cover all the possible freaks which may be discovered. The commonest of these is the white-flowered form, or albino, which occurs occasionally in all orchids with pink, reddish or purplish flowers. It is hoped that such plants will usually fall into the correct species in using this key, since flower colour is nowhere employed as the only distinction between species.

The key is to be used in the following manner. Under each number at the left-hand margin the reader will find two alternative descriptions with which to compare the plant he is trying to identify. He starts with the first pair of alternatives. If the characters of his plant agree with the upper description of the pair, he will have *Cypripedium calceolus*, the lady's slipper, in front of him. If, however, his plant fits the lower alternative, he will pass on to the second pair of alternatives, as indicated by the No. 2 at the right-hand margin. He will then have a further choice, the upper alternative leading him to the third pair, whereas the lower alternative takes him to the pair under No. 5 at the left-hand margin. The reader then continues to compare his plant with the descriptions, passing on to the fresh alternatives as indicated by the right-hand numbers, until he comes to the name of the plant on the right-hand side.

Let us take, for example, a specimen of the common early purple orchid (*Orchis mascula*) and see how to use the key. Starting with the first pair of alternatives, we find that there are numerous small purple flowers, which takes us to No. 2. The plant has well-developed green leaves, taking us to No. 5. The plant possesses 3 to 7 leaves, usually in a rosette at the bottom of the stem, thus leading us to No. 11. There are no tubercles on the leaves, while the lip is at the front or bottom of the flower, taking us to No. 12. The lip is provided with a long tubular spur, while the stamen is firmly attached to the front of the column, which, indeed, is scarcely visible from the front. This leads us to No. 27. The long spur already mentioned takes us then on to No. 33. The spur is stout, and horizontally placed or ascending, the flowers are purple in not very dense spikes, and the leaves are often spotted, leading us to No. 35. The middle lobe of the lip is not ribbon-like nor spirally twisted, while the pollinia are attached to separate discs, so we go on to No. 36. The bracts are thin, membraneous, and much the same colour as the flowers. They equal the ovary, but the horizontal or ascending spur confirms that we pass on to No. 37. Our plant clearly does not agree with the description of *Neotinea* so we go on to No. 38. The bracts equalling the ovary, and the blunt spur horizontally placed or ascending, clearly leads us to No. 39. A comparison of our plant with the two descriptions under No. 39 shows plainly that it is, as we thought, *Orchis mascula*, the early purple orchid.

A few suggestions may be made as to the best way of using the key in the manner indicated above ; also a few warnings.

1. Read through the whole description in each alternative before coming to a decision. Several parts of the plant are usually mentioned, and if you are doubtful about one feature you may obtain a clear decision on another.

2. Where there are more than one plant available of a species, try to pick out an average specimen rather than an exceptionally large or small individual.

3. Some sort of magnifying glass, such as a botanical hand-lens, is necessary if you wish to name your orchids accurately. It is hoped, however, that many of the species can be run down even in the absence of a strongly magnifying glass. To be sure of the column differences mentioned in No. 12 of the key some magnification is needed.

4. The nature of the root is often mentioned as an additional confirmatory character. As the plant must be more or less dug up in

order to see this, you are asked not to check this feature unless there are numerous individuals available, or unless you have a suitable implement for removing some of the soil without disturbing the plant much.

5. Between the species at the end of the key, No. 45 onwards (the spotted and marsh orchids), hybrids are extremely common, and these will probably not run down exactly anywhere in the key. The whole population should be examined carefully, and only individuals which seem to agree with many others, tried in the key. These will probably belong to the pure species present.

6. All the technical terms used in the key are explained in the glossary, but the reader should consult the introductory chapters in order to obtain a clear idea of the arrangement and nature of the parts in an orchid flower.

The reader may notice that in the final sections of the key, dealing with the marsh orchids, in addition to the five primary species recognised in the general account, three other " species " are included. These are all still a matter of controversy among botanists, but are included in the key in order to simplify it, and to help any students who are particularly interested in this very complex group. It should be realised, however, that the species of this group are so variable, and still so imperfectly understood, that it is virtually impossible to construct a key to account for all known types.

The same caution should be borne in mind in dealing with the other difficult group, the helleborines. The key will enable the reader to distinguish all the main types, but occasionally individuals may be found which depart from the key characters in some minor respects.

1. Flowering stem bearing one (rarely 2) large flowers ; flowers 2 inches or more in diameter, red-brown and yellow ; lower petal (lip) bag-like with a narrow mouth . . . . . *Cypripedium calceolus* (p. 118)
Flowering stem bearing many small flowers, or if only 1 or 2, the flowers less than 1 inch in diameter and differently coloured . . 2

2. Plants pale brown or tinged pink, without any leaves 3
Plants with well-developed green leaves, or rarely with the leaves just developing at the time of flowering (*Spiranthes spiralis*) . . . 5

3. Flowers few (usually 2–4, but rarely as many as 7), nearly an inch in diameter, rather spaced out; stem tinged pink, swollen at the base;

lip uppermost, pink, with a thick blunt spur, 3-lobed with lines of
red spots on the middle lobe . . . . *Epipogium aphyllum* (p. 198)
Flowers numerous, or if fewer, close together, less than ½ inch in diameter, pale brown or yellowish white ; lip lowermost . . . 4

4. Whole plant pale brown ; stem up to 18 inches high, rather stout ;
flowers numerous, mostly in a rather dense spike but the lower ones
spaced out ; lip deeply 2-lobed . . . *Neottia nidus-avis* (p. 193)
Stem and ovaries tinged greenish ; stem with brown sheaths below,
up to 9 inches high, rather slender ; flowers 1–10, or as many as 18,
less than ¼ inch long, yellow-green ; lip tongue-shaped, white
. . . *Corallorhiza trifida* (p. 202)

5. Leaves 2, in a pair at or below the middle of the stem (rarely with a
third one), or near the base and then associated with a bulb-like
swelling of the stem 6
Leaves usually more than 2, or if only 2 then these not in a pair above
the base of the stem (the leaves are often spaced out along the stem,
or form a sort of rosette right at the base) 11

6. Flowers small, green, yellow-green or reddish brown, not or scarcely
scented ; root not tuberous 7
Flowers ½–1 inch in diameter, creamy white or greenish white, sweetly
scented ; lip with a long slender spur ; root composed of radish-
shaped tubers 10

7. Pair of leaves some distance above base of stem ; leaves broad and
blunt ; lip deeply 2-lobed ; ovaries globular 8
Pair of leaves near base of stem, which is swollen to form a bulb-like
structure ; lip not lobed; ovaries not globular 9

8. Plant up to 2 feet high, stout ; leaves elliptical or egg-shaped, 1–5
inches long ; flower-spike long, many-flowered ; flowers green with
yellow-green lip . . . . *Listera ovata* (p. 167)
Plant 2–8 inches high, slender ; leaves more or less heart-shaped, less
than 1 inch long ; flower-spike with 6–12 flowers ; flowers usually
tinged reddish . . . . *Listera cordata* (p. 171)

9. Leaves with small tubercles (buds) at the tips ; flowers minute ; lip
uppermost (back of flower); in acid bogs *Hammarbya paludosa* (p. 315)
Leaves without tubercles at the tips ; flowers about ¼ inch long ; lip
below column ; in fens and sandhills . . *Liparis loeselii* (p. 313)

10. Flowers about 1 inch in diameter ; spike about 2 inches across ; column broad, the two halves of the stamen much diverging downwards
. . . *Platanthera chlorantha* (p. 217)
Flowers about ½–¾ inch in diameter ; spike about 1–1½ inches across; column narrow, the two halves of the stamen parallel, not diverging downwards . . . . *Platanthera bifolia* (p. 214)

11. Leaves with small tubercles (buds) at the tips ; stem swollen to form a bulb at the base ; flowers very small, yellow-green ; lip uppermost (at back of flower) ; plant very small ; usually in acid bogs
. . . *Hammarbya paludosa* (p. 315)
Leaves without tubercles at the tips ; lip at front of flower ; stems not bulbous at base 12

12. Stamen attached low down on the back of the column, easily coming away ; sticky disc of pollinia (viscidium) uppermost ; lip without a true spur 13
Stamen attached very firmly to the front of the column so that it cannot be detached ; viscidium or viscidia lowermost ; lip with or without a spur ; roots always tuberous 27

13. Flowers arranged in one or more distinct spiral rows, with very short or no stalks, so that they appear close to the stem, white or pale creamy yellow, ¼–½ inch long ; leaves mostly arising from the lowest part of the stem, or in a tuft at ground level 14
Flowers not arranged in distinct spiral rows, usually with distinct stalks and some distance from the stem, variously coloured ; leaves usually scattered along the stem below the lowest flower, with the basal part of the stem leafless 17

14. Flowers in three distinct spiral rows, white or creamy yellow ; spike short and thick, about ¾ inch in diameter ; leaves 4–5, narrow, erect ; root tubers 2–6, cylindrical
. . . *Spiranthes romanzoffiana* (p. 183)
Flowers in one spiral row, white ; spike relatively long and narrow, ¼–½ inch in diameter 15

15. Lower part of stem creeping, often producing long slender runners ; roots slender ; leaves broad and pointed with distinct stalks, often marbled with paler green ; flowers short and blunt, hairy
. . . *Goodyera repens* (p. 188)
Stem entirely erect ; roots consisting of fleshy tubers ; leaves without

distinct stalks, broad or narrow ; flowers more or less tubular, narrow 16

16. Leaves very short and broad, more or less spread out on the ground, often not properly developed at the time of flowering ; root tubers egg-shaped, short ; plant usually less than 6 inches high ; flowers not hairy . . . . *Spiranthes spiralis* (p. 177)
Leaves long and narrow, more or less erect ; root tubers long and tapering ; plant usually over 6 inches high ; flowers hairy
. . . *Spiranthes aestivalis* (p. 180)

17. Flowers large, erect, white or bright rose ; column long ; lip parallel to the column at the base, curved outwards above, with yellow crests inside 18
Flowers rather small, usually greenish, or if whitish much tinged with brown and green, spreading or pendulous ; column short, thick ; lip often at right angles to the base of the column with two distinct parts, the inner part (hypochile) cup-shaped, the outer part (epichile) flat or curved underneath at the tip 20

18. Flowers bright rose, an inch in diameter, 3–10 in number ; leaves narrowly spear-shaped or oblong spear-shaped, spreading ; ovary shortly hairy . . . . *Cephalanthera rubra* (p. 132)
Flowers white, about ½–¾ inch long ; ovary not hairy 19

19. Sepals and petals pure white, often opening widely ; bracts very small ; leaves in two rows, narrow and more or less sword-shaped
. . . *Cephalanthera longifolia* (p. 128)
Sepals and petals creamy white, not opening out much, so that the flowers appear egg-shaped ; bracts longer than the flowers ; leaves broadly spear-shaped or elliptical, rather short
. . . *Cephalanthera damasonium* (p. 125)

20. Inner part of lip (hypochile) with an ear-like projection on each side, the epichile attached to it by an elastic joint ; underground part of plant consisting of a long creeping branched rhizome about 1 inch below the ground surface ; flowers rather large, brownish outside, white inside ; lip white with an upright keel in the centre ; in marshes . . . . *Epipactis palustris* (p. 136)
Lip hypochile without ear-like projections, the epichile attached rigidly to it ; underground parts consisting of a rather woody erect

rootstock with numerous rather fleshy roots ; in woods and dry
open places 21

21. Axis of flower-spike (rhachis) more or less densely covered with very
short spreading hairs ; flowers spreading in early stages, but fruits
sometimes becoming more or less pendulous 22
Rhachis quite devoid of hairs ; flowers more or less pendulous almost
from the beginning, fruits always pendulous ; flowers green, lip
epichile whitish ; leaves in 2 rows 26

22. Leaves rather stiff, in two opposite rows ; flowers brick-red, blackish
red or deep madder-red, with blunt sepals and petals ; ovary covered
with short hairs ; usually on limestone cliffs or screes
. . . *Epipactis atrorubens* (p. 148)
Leaves in 3 or more rows, or if apparently in 2 rows then the flowers
greenish 23

23. Leaves relatively small, long and narrow, spaced out along the stem ;
stems, and often the leaves, greyish purple or greyish purple-green ;
stems solitary, paired or frequently clustered, 3–15 together ; sepals
and petals pale olive-green inside, spreading ; lip epichile pink or
white with pink ridges, hypochile pale inside
. . . *Epipactis purpurata* (p. 152)
Leaves usually rather broad, sometimes tinged with purple (not greyish), often clustered in lower part of stem ; stems solitary or in clus-
ters of 2–5 ; sepals and petals green or purplish inside ; lip hypochile reddish inside cup 24

24. Sepals and petals very acute, pale green ; lip epichile white, narrow
and pointed, the tip not turned underneath ; leaves apparently in
two rows, rather thin ; stamen with a distinct stalk ; usually in
shady woods . . . . *Epipactis leptochila* (p. 157)
Sepals and petals obtuse or rather acute, green or purplish ; lip epichile often pinkish or reddish, broad and rather blunt, tip often
turned underneath ; stamen not stalked 25

25. Leaves in 3 rows, often appearing to be all round the stem, broad, the
lower part clasping the stem ; flowers usually tinged with pink or
red, $\frac{1}{3}$–$\frac{1}{2}$ inch in length ; lower sheaths on stem not loose
. . . *Epipactis helleborine* (p. 141)
Leaves in 2 rows, rather stiff, yellowish or medium green ; flowers
usually yellowish green, sometimes tinged with pink, about $\frac{1}{4}$ inch
in length ; lower leaf-sheaths loose ; on sand dunes
. . . *Epipactis dunensis* (p. 145)

26. Cup of lip hypochile very distinct from epichile ; flowers opening widely ; stamen not stalked . . . . *Epipactis pendula* (p. 161)

Cup of lip hypochile not very well developed, not sharply defined from epichile ; flowers usually only opening slightly or not at all ; stamen with a distinct stalk ; sepals and petals long and pointed

. . . *Epipactis vectensis* (p. 164)

27. Lip without any spur 28

Lip with a spur, which may be very short or bag-like . . . 33

28. Sticky discs of pollinia (viscidia) not covered by a small flap or flaps (bursicles) ; flowers yellow-green in a dense spike ; lip 3-lobed, rather like a dagger, the side lobes shorter than the middle one ; most of the root tubers at the ends of long slender stalks

. . . *Herminium monorchis* (p. 207)

Viscidia covered by one or two bursicles ; lip not dagger-shaped ; root tubers not or very shortly stalked 29

29. Both viscidia covered by a single bursicle ; lip deeply 4-lobed, lobes long and narrow, not hairy ; sepals and petals forming a rounded hood or helmet ; flowers numerous in a rather close spike

. . . *Aceras anthropophorum* (p. 240)

Each viscidium covered by its own bursicle ; lip not lobed, or if so the lobes broad and blunt, most of surface closely hairy ; sepals and petals not forming a helmet but spreading separately, the petals much smaller ; flowers few (up to 12) in a loose spike 30

30. Sepals green ; petals not hairy 31

Sepals pink with a central green line ; petals more or less covered on front with white hairs ; lip brown with lighter markings ; side lobes of the lip tucked underneath ; tip of the column forming a beak 32

31. Lip much longer than broad, 3-lobed with short blunt side lobes, reddish brown with a slate-blue bar across the middle ; petals almost thread-like, reddish or purplish ; tip of column scarcely pointed . . . . *Ophrys muscifera* (p. 298)

Lip almost circular, oval or squarish, about as long as broad, hardly lobed, reddish brown with irregular lead-coloured marks often resembling an H ; petals strap-shaped, green or brownish ; tip of column with a beak-like point . . . *Ophrys sphegodes* (p. 301)

32. Tip of lip turned up in front to form a 3-toothed appendage ; petals triangular, very hairy ; beak of the column rather blunt ; lip squarish or sometimes broader in front . . . . *Ophrys fuciflora* (p. 304)
Tip of lip pointed, turned up at the back and not very obvious ; petals strap-shaped ; beak of the column slender and curved, so that the column resembles a duck's head ; lip round with square collar-like markings at the base . . . . *Ophrys apifera* (p. 306)

33. Spur thread-like, equalling or longer than the ovary ; flowers small, pink or lilac-pink, in rather dense spikes ; leaves usually narrow, unspotted 34
Spur stouter, shorter than or rarely equalling the ovary, in latter case usually placed horizontally ; flowers variously coloured . . 35

34. Spikes more or less pyramidal when young, lengthening later ; lip with two erect converging keels in front of the spur opening ; the two pollinia attached to a single viscidium
. . . *Anacamptis pyramidalis* (p. 233)
Spikes never obviously pyramidal ; lip without erect keels ; the two pollinia attached to separate viscidia ; flowers strongly scented
. . . *Gymnadenia conopsea* (p. 223)

35. Middle lobe of the 3-lobed lip very long (1–2 inches), ribbon-like and spirally twisted, side lobes much shorter ; pollinia both attached to a single viscidium ; flowers dull greyish green or purple-green, base of lip white with purplish spots ; plant 9–18 inches tall ; leaves broad, often withering at the time of flowering
. . . *Himantoglossum hircinum* (p. 236)
Middle lobe of lip not ribbon-like nor spirally twisted, not more than ½ inch in length ; pollinia attached to separate viscidia . . 36

36. Bracts (small leaves at the base of the flowers) thin and membraneous, often tinged the colour of the flowers, usually shorter than the ovary, or if the bracts equal or exceed the ovary the spur is horizontal or ascending in position ; viscidium always covered by a bursicle . 37
Bracts firm, of the same texture as the leaves, but often tinged with red or purple, longer than the ovary and often longer than the flowers ; spur descending 43

37. Flowers small, white or pale pink, in a dense spike ; spur very short, bag-like ; leaves in pink-flowered plants usually with reddish spots ; lip 3-lobed, lobes narrow ; western Ireland only
. . . *Neotinea intacta* (p. 230)

Flowers usually large, but sometimes small with very dark red or almost black sepals ; lip 3- or 4-lobed, the middle lobe in the former case broad and somewhat 2-lobed or indented at the tip . . 38

38. Bracts equalling or slightly longer than the ovary ; spur horizontal or ascending, nearly equalling the ovary, blunt or even enlarged at the tip 39
Bracts much shorter than the ovary ; spur short, descending, not enlarged at the tip ; sepals and petals more or less adherent to form a pointed helmet or hood 40

39. Lip usually longer than broad, with the front lobe considerably longer than the side lobes ; side sepals erect, almost back to back, without green parallel veins ; leaves green, often with irregular purple-black blotches ; spike 10–45 flowered . . *Orchis mascula* (p. 260)
Lip usually broader than long, with the front lobe not much longer than the side lobes ; all sepals forming a short almost globular helmet, side ones with green or bronze-purple parallel veins ; leaves always unspotted, greyish green ; spike up to 12-flowered
. . . *Orchis morio* (p. 256)

40. Flowers opening from the top of the spike downwards ; lip with a long strap-shaped central part and 4 very narrow lobes, two at the base and two at the tip with a tail-like small lobe between the latter two ; sepals and centre of lip white or pale pink, ends of lobes red or purplish . . . . *Orchis simia* (p. 245)
Flowers opening from the bottom of the spike upwards . . . 41

41. Helmet formed by the sepals and petals pinkish or whitish, paler than the lip ; basal lobes of lip narrow, but broader towards their tips, middle lobe longer than broad with 2 broad rounded lobes at the tip and a small point between them ; centre of lip white with red spots, lobes red or mauvish red ; plant 9–16 inches high
. . . *Orchis militaris* (p. 248)
Helmet dark purplish or blackish red, darker than the lip ; lip white or pale mauvish white with dark mauve spots ; middle lobe usually as broad as, or broader than, long 42

42. Tall plant, 1–3 feet high ; leaves 4–9 inches long, 1–2 inches broad ; flowers about $\frac{1}{2}$ inch across ; helmet deep dull purple or red-purple ; lip usually suffused with pink or pale purple, front lobe very broad, more or less bilobed at the tip . . . . *Orchis purpurea* (p. 251)

Dwarf plant, 3–8 inches high ; leaves 1–2 inches long, $\frac{1}{2}$ inch broad ;
flowers small ; helmet dark or almost blackish red ; lip white, side
lobes rather broad and blunt . . . . . *Orchis ustulata* (p. 254)

43. Spur short, less than half the length of the ovary ; flowers small, white,
    pale yellow, green or reddish green ; plants usually less than 1 foot
    in height ; leaves short and broad, in a basal tuft, unspotted ; vis-
    cidia not enclosed in a bursicle 44
    Spur longer, more than half the length of the ovary, rather like the
    finger of a glove ; flowers various shades of pink, red, lilac or purple ;
    plant often over 1 foot in height ; leaves arranged all along the lower
    part of the stem, sometimes with purplish or blackish spots ; viscidia
    enclosed in a bursicle 45

44. Flowers about $\frac{1}{8}$ inch long, white or pale yellow, in a rather dense spike ;
    lip short and broad, equally 3-lobed . *Gymnadenia albida* (p. 221)
    Flowers $\frac{1}{8}$–$\frac{1}{4}$ inch long, green or reddish, in a loose spike ; lip strap-
    shaped, much longer than broad, shortly 3-lobed at the tip ; spur
    very short, bladder-like . . . . . *Coeloglossum viride* (p. 210)

45. Lateral sepals spreading widely or drooping ; flowers white, pale or
    medium pink, or lilac, with darker pink lines, loops or dots on the
    lip and petals ; stem solid ; leaves usually spotted ; spur rather
    slender, about $\frac{1}{16}$ inch or less in diameter ; lip broad, 3-lobed in the
    lower half 46
    Lateral sepals more or less upright, with the backs often touching ;
    flowers flesh-pink, madder-red, pale magenta or magenta-purple,
    with darker markings on the lip and petals ; stem often with a
    central hollow ; leaves spotted or unspotted ; spur rather stout,
    over $\frac{1}{16}$ inch in diameter, often more or less conical 47

46. Middle lobe of lip longer than the side lobes, or all three equal in
    length ; lowest leaves broader and very blunt or rounded at the
    tip, upper progressively narrower and more acute, total number
    7–16, usually with numerous round or elliptical purplish black
    spots which are often wider at right angles to the length of the leaf ;
    spur about $\frac{1}{16}$ inch in diameter . . . . . *Orchis fuchsii* (p. 267)
    Middle lobe of lip much smaller and usually shorter than the side
    lobes ; all leaves rather narrow and acute, total number 5–8 ;
    spots on leaves often rather faint or obscure, not broader at right
    angles to the length of the leaf ; spur only about $\frac{1}{25}$ inch in diameter
    . . . *Orchis ericetorum* (p. 273)

47. Leaves unspotted 48
   Leaves variously spotted 52

48. Leaves erect, yellow-green, narrowly hooded at the tip ; stem very
   hollow ; flowers flesh-coloured, madder-pink, indian-red or bright
   magenta ; lip not usually lobed (if distinctly 3-lobed, then flowers
   pale straw-coloured), with the sides turned down, and with two
   clear but delicate loop-markings ; spur stout, tapering towards the
   tip . . . . *Orchis latifolia* (p. 281)
   Leaves more or less spreading, deep or greyish green, not or broadly
   hooded at the tip ; stem slightly hollow or solid ; lip scarcely lobed,
   or more or less distinctly 3-lobed, sides not much turned down . 49

49. Lip large, with small dots or indistinct loops ; flowers lilac-pink,
   magenta-pink or pale magenta ; tall plants 9 inches to 2 feet high,
   with large spear-shaped leaves 50
   Lip small, with heavy loop or broken line markings ; flowers dull
   purple to bright magenta (rarely pink) 51

50. English plant ; leaves fresh or deep green, more or less erect ; lip not
   much lobed ; spots on lip nearly all in centre, sometimes forming
   indistinct central loops . . . . . *Orchis praetermissa* (p. 284)
   Irish plant ; leaves bluish green, rather spreading ; lip distinctly 3-
   lobed ; spots on lip distributed all over, forming an indistinct line
   about the middle of each side . . . . *Orchis kerryensis* (p. 294)

51. Lip generally not or slightly lobed, broadly diamond-shaped, dull or
   bright magenta with rather heavy broken loop, dash or hieroglyphic
   markings ; leaves broadly hooded at tip ; plants often up to 18
   inches high . . . . *Orchis purpurella* (p. 289)
   Lip usually distinctly 3-lobed, with middle lobe long and pointed, but
   sometimes side-lobes indistinct, dull purple with broken loop or
   line markings ; leaves not hooded at tip ; plants rarely more
   than 9 inches high . . . . . . *Orchis occidentalis* (p. 292)

52. Spots on both sides of leaves, rather variable in size and numbers ;
   upper part of stem with red streaks ; flowers small, pinkish purple ;
   lip broader than long, not much lobed, sides not much reflexed,
   with irregular loop-markings ; western Ireland
                                          . . . *Orchis cruenta* (p. 296)
   Spots on upper surface of leaves only 53

53. Spots on leaves always ringed or leopard-like, often very numerous ; plant tall, up to 2 feet 6 inches high, with broad leaves ; flowers pink or magenta-pink with very heavy broken loop or line markings on the lip and petals ; southern England only

         . . . *Orchis pardalina* (p. 288)

Spots on leaves not usually ring-like, or, if so, leaves narrow and plant small 54

54. Spots on leaves very small, dot-like, usually near the tip ; flowers bright magenta, with heavy broken line markings on lip ; lip broadly diamond-shaped ; leaves broad, hooded at tip ; plant usually rather dwarf and stocky . . . . *Orchis purpurella* (p. 289)

Spots on leaves variable in shape and size ; flowers dull purple or magenta with variable markings ; leaves broad or narrow, not hooded at tip 55

55. Lip broader than long, either 3-lobed with middle lobe long and pointed, or almost entire, pointed in front ; leaves broad ; spotting on leaves sometimes very heavy and close ; western Ireland

         . . . *Orchis occidentalis* (p. 292)

Lip longer than broad, wedge- or kite-shaped, broadest in front, more or less 3-lobed with middle lobe sometimes projecting ; leaves narrow ; spotting on leaves usually rather sparse, of either solid or ringed spots ; eastern Ireland and England

         . . . *Orchis traunsteinerioides* (p. 295)

GLOSSARY

Acid. Applied to soils or soil water in which free acids occur, thus making the soils sour. Such soils are usually associated with the absence of lime or other so-called basic substances.

Albino. A plant in which the flowers are devoid of the usual colour pigments, normally red or blue or combinations of these. Green pigments may, however, still be present. Less frequently yellow pigments may be lacking to produce albinos.

Alkaline. Applied to soils or soil water which are rich in soluble bases, e.g. lime or potash.

Anther. The pollen-containing part of a stamen. It is usually divided longitudinally into two parts, the thecae.

Anthocyanin. Reddish or bluish pigments occurring in flowers and also in the stems or leaves of plants, giving them a reddish or purplish tinge.

Apomixis. The development of ovules into seeds without the intervention of the male reproductive body.

Bases. Substances such as lime, potash, etc., which neutralise acids.

Basic. Adjective from base (see above).

Bigeneric hybrid. A hybrid between two species belonging to different genera.

Bracts. The small leaves occurring at the bottom of the stalk of each flower.

Bursicle. A sort of small flap or pouch covering the sticky disc (viscidium) and preventing it from drying up. This is pushed back by the insect when it visits the flower.

Calcareous. Containing lime ; applied to soils or drainage water.

Capsule. A fruit, usually not fleshy when ripe, which opens by several splits or holes, thus enabling the seeds to escape.

Caudicle. The lower stalk-like part of a pollinium, attaching the pollen-masses to the sticky disc or viscidium.

Chlorophyll. The green colouring matter present in the stems and leaves of most plants.

Column. A special structure right in the centre of the orchid flower. It is composed of a continuation of the flower-stalk, together with the upper part of the female reproductive organ (pistil) and the lower part of the male reproductive organ (stamen). It is very variable in shape in different orchids.

Cotyledons. The first leaves produced by the embryo plant, present in the seed and often opening out on its germination.

Dominant. Any species in a vegetation type which by virtue of its size or abundance imposes its own character on the plant community as a whole, e.g. pines in a pinewood, heather in a heather moor.

Ecological. Pertaining to Ecology.

Ecology. The study of plants and animals in relation to their environment.

Element, Floral. A portion of the total flora of a country sharing some features in common, usually with respect to geographical distribution.

Endemic. A plant is said to be endemic to a continent, country or smaller region when it is restricted to the region in question.

Epichile. The outer part of the lip when there are two distinct parts to this organ, as in *Epipactis.*

Epiphyte. A plant which lives perched on other plants, usually on shrubs or trees. Many tropical orchids come into this category.

Exclusive species. A species of plant which can grow only in a special habitat or environment.

Fertilisation. The fusion of the male and female reproductive units within the embryonic seed (ovule).

Fertilisation, Cross-. When the male and female reproductive units come from different flowers.

Fertilisation, Self-. When the male and female reproductive units come from the same flower.

Filament. The stalk of a stamen, bearing the anther.

Fungus (plural *Fungi*). A member of a large group of plants which are devoid of chlorophyll and cannot manufacture their own food. The fungi include moulds, mildews, mushrooms and toadstools.

Genus (plural *Genera*). A group of allied species, e.g. *Orchis.*

Glaciation. The covering of a country or region by land-ice during an Ice Age.

Habitat. The totality of the conditions of the environment in which a plant is situated, e.g. climate, nature of soil, supply of water, associated plants. The effects of all these taken together produce the habitat.

Humus. The partially decayed portions of plants present in the soil, either as large pieces or as minute particles.

Hybrid-swarm. A large number of hybrids occurring together, and showing all intermediates between the two parent species from which they arose.

Hymenopterous. Insects belonging to the large group of the *Hymenoptera,* including bees, wasps, ants, saw-flies, ichneumon flies, etc.

Hypochile. The inner or basal part of the lip when there are two sharply defined regions, as in *Epipactis.*

Inflorescence. A group of flowers, more or less sharply defined from the purely vegetative parts of the plant.

Labellum. See Lip.

Lip. One of the petals which is usually quite different from the others in shape and size, and is often of very complicated construction. It is usually at the bottom or " front " of the flower.

Loculus (plural *Loculi*). The cavity within each half of the anther, containing the pollinia.

Monandrous. Applied to a flower containing only one stamen.

Monocarpic. Applied to plants which only flower once, after which they die. The life period prior to flowering may extend from a few months to 50 or 100 years.

Mycorhiza. The association of a fungus with the roots or other parts of a plant.

Mycorhiza, Ectotrophic. Mycorhiza in which the fungus occurs mainly outside its host, enveloping the roots with a dense covering.

Mycorhiza, Endotrophic. Mycorhiza in which the fungus occurs inside the body of its host.

Mycorhizome. The initial plant-body produced following the germination of an orchid seed. It is usually underground and not at all like an ordinary plant seedling. It is always heavily infected with the appropriate fungus.

Nectar. A sweet syrupy and rather sticky liquid produced in the flower, usually by special glands (nectaries). These are often on the lip, especially in or near the hollow spur. Nectar contains sugars and other substances and is used as food by insects.

Operculate. Describing an anther forming a kind of little cap at the top of the column, attached only at the back.

Ovary. The lower part of the female reproductive organ (pistil) containing the embryonic seeds (ovules). The ovary is always situated below the rest of the flower in orchids, and is often not easily distinguishable from the flower-stalk.

Ovules. The as-yet unfertilised seeds, containing the female reproductive bodies. They occur within the ovary.

Parasite. A plant which obtains its energy-producing food directly from another living being, often living inside its host.

Perennation. The maintenance of life through the unfavourable climatic conditions offered by winter (in temperate regions) or a lengthy dry season (in the Tropics).

Perennial. Applied to a plant which exists through more than one winter season (or dry season in the Tropics).

Perianth. The outer, non-reproductive, parts of the flower, often distinguished into an outer series (sepals) and an inner series (petals).

Petals. The three inner parts of the perianth in an orchid flower, one on each side usually towards the back, and a single one in front (the lip).

Pollen Grains. The male reproductive bodies, produced in large numbers within the stamens. In most plants the pollen grains, when ripe, separate readily, but in the orchids they are joined together in large masses, the pollinia.

Pollen-apparatus. The entire structure carried off by an insect, including one or more pollinia, their stalks and the viscidium.

Pollinarium. See Pollen-apparatus.

Pollination. The transference of pollen from the stamen of a flower to the stigma of the same or another flower.

Pollination, Cross-. When the pollen is transferred to the stigma of another flower, either on the same or another plant.

Pollination, Self-. When the pollen is transferred to the stigma of the same flower.

Pollinium (plural *Pollinia*). A more or less compact mass consisting of immense numbers of pollen grains held together by threads or adhesive material. There are quite large differences in the compactness and individual structure of the pollinia in different orchids.

Polymorphic. Of many forms. Applied to a species or other natural group which shows great variation from one individual or population to another.

Population. A group of orchids occurring together in a well-defined area or habitat.

Protocorm. See Mycorhizome.

Pseudobulb. A swelling of the aerial stem, resembling a bulb, but not really of the same nature. It usually serves as a storage for water.

Raw-humus. A decaying layer of dead leaves, twigs, etc., covering the soil, which is acid in nature. It is usually formed on non-calcareous soils.

Rhizome. An underground stem, usually horizontal in position. It may be slender, as in mint or lily of the valley, or thick and fleshy as in iris.

Root-bud. A bud developing underground from a root, usually growing to the soil surface to form an aerial shoot.

Rootstock. A short and more or less vertically placed underground stem, as in primrose.

Rostellum. The sterilised third stigma of an orchid flower, which lies between the functional stigmas and the stamen. It is often lengthened to form a beak-like structure, hence the name, but it may be differently shaped in different species. The sticky discs of the pollinia (viscidia) are a part of the rostellum.

Runner. A slender creeping stem usually just at or above the level of the ground, as for example, in the strawberry. They may, however, also occur below the level of the ground.

Saprophyte. A plant which obtains its energy-producing food from the dead remains of plants or animals.

Scree. A more or less unstable slope of broken stones or rock fragments, usually below a cliff from which the stones have fallen.

Sepals. The three outer parts of the perianth in an orchid flower, consisting usually of one at the back of the flower (dorsal or intermediate sepal), and one on each side towards the front (lateral sepals).

Sheaths. The bases of the leaves which form sheaths of varying length enveloping the stem. The lower leaves on the stem usually consist entirely of sheath, the flat green part (lamina or blade) not being developed.

Shoot. A stem together with the leaves borne on it.

Slacks. The low valleys, often quite extensive, which lie between the sand ridges in a sand-dune system.

Spur. A hollowed-out bag-like or tubular outgrowth from the lip, or sometimes from other members of the perianth. The spur often contains nectar, or within its fleshy walls there may be a syrupy liquid.

Stamen. The male reproductive organs of the flower, usually surrounded by the non-reproductive perianth. There are one or two stamens in the orchid flower, always attached to a special central structure termed the column.

Staminode. A stamen which has lost its capacity for reproduction, and has usually become much altered in shape and size.

Stigma. The uppermost part or parts of the female reproductive organ, taking an active part in the fertilisation of the flower. On it are deposited the male reproductive bodies (pollen grains) in the process of pollination.

Stolon. See Runner.

Sub-species. A sub-division of a species distinguished by several correlated characters, and usually possessing a distinct geographical distribution within that of the species as a whole.

Theca (plural *Thecae*). The two halves of the fertile part of the stamen (anther), each containing one or more pollinia. When ripe the thecae split so that the pollinia can be removed.

Tolerant Species. A species of plant which can grow in a great variety of situations or habitats.

Tuber. A fleshy swollen underground stem or root, a potato being an example of the former, and the dahlia of the latter.

Variety. A sub-division of a species, differing from the typical plants of the species in a few comparatively unimportant characters. A variety usually has no special geographical distribution.

Vegetation type. A grouping of plants of a particular nature or type of growth, producing a readily recognisable appearance, e.g. woodland, grassland, heath.

Viscidium (plural *Viscidia*). A sticky disc or plate joined to the pollinium, enabling it to adhere to an insect's body and to be carried away to another flower.

Wintergreen plants. Plants in which the leaves are developed late in the growing season, and remain green and expanded during the winter, dying away the next summer.

Zygomorphic. Describes a flower in which the two sides are mirror-images of one another, but the front is quite different from the back. All orchid flowers are zygomorphic.

BIBLIOGRAPHY

REFERENCES to many of the earlier papers will be found in God-fery's " Monograph ", but a few of the more important ones are given here. Nearly all the papers on British Orchids published since 1933 are included in this list. There are also very extensive bibliographies in Vermeulen and Ziegenspeck.

AMES, O. (1937). Pollination of Orchids through Pseudo-copulation. *Bot. Mus. Leafl. Harvard Univ. 5* : 1–26.

BROOKE, B. J. (1938). Notes on the Occurrence of *Orchis simia* Lamarck in Kent. *J. Bot. London, 76* : 337–41.

— (1950). The Wild Orchids of Britain. London, The Bodley Head.

BROOKE, B. J., AND ROSE, F. (1940). A New British Species of *Epipactis*. *J. Bot. London, 78* : 81–89.

BURGEFF, H. (1936). Samenkeimung der Orchideen. Jena.

CAMUS, E. G. & A. (1921, 1929). Iconographie des Orchidées d'Europe et du Bassin Méditerranéen. Paris.

COLEMAN, E. (1927–28). Pollination of the Orchid *Cryptostylis leptochila* F. Muell. *Victorian Nat. 44* : 20–22 ; 333–40.

CORREVON, H., & POUYANNE, —. (1923). Nouvelles Observations sur le Mimétisme et la Fécondation des *Ophrys speculum* et *lutea*. *J. Soc. Nat. Hortic. France,* sér. 4, *24* : 372–77. (See references there to earlier papers.)

DARWIN, C. (1877). The Various Contrivances by which Orchids are Fertilised by Insects. London, 2nd ed.

DOWNIE, D. G. (1940). On the Germination and Growth of *Goodyera repens*. *Trans. Bot. Soc. Edinb. 33* : 36–51.

— (1941). Notes on the Germination of some British Orchids. *Trans. Bot. Soc. Edinb. 33* : 94–103.

— (1943). Notes on the Germination of *Corallorhiza innata*. *Trans. Bot. Soc. Edinb. 33* : 380–82.

DRUCE, G. C. (1930). The Comital Flora of the British Isles. Arbroath, T. Buncle.

GILSON, H. C. (1930). The British Palmate Orchids. Winchester.

GODFERY, M. J. (1933). Monograph and Iconograph of Native British Orchidaceae. Cambridge, University Press.

HAGERUP, O. (1947). The Spontaneous Formation of Haploid, Polyploid and Aneuploid Embryos in Some Orchids. *K. Danske Vidensk. Selsk. Biol. Medd. 20* : no. 9.

HARLEY, J. L. (1950). Recent Progress in the Study of Endotrophic Mycorhiza. *New Phytol. 49* : 213–47.

HESLOP HARRISON, J. (1948). Field Studies in *Orchis* : I. The Structure of Dactylorchid Populations in Certain Islands in the Inner and Outer Hebrides. *Trans. Bot. Soc. Edinb. 35* : 26–66.

(1949). Notes on the Dactylorchids of North-western Donegal. *Irish Nat. J. 9* : 291–98.

(1949). *Orchis cruenta* Müll. ; a new Irish Marsh Orchid. *Irish Nat. J. 9* : 329–30.

JESSEN, K. (1949). Studies in Late Quaternary Deposits and Flora-History of Ireland. *Proc. Roy. Irish Acad. 52*, sect. B : 85–290. (Contains an extensive bibliography.)

KNUDSON, L. (1930). Flower Production by Orchids grown Non-symbiotically. *Bot. Gazette, 89* : 192–99. (See here for references to earlier papers.)

KUSANO, S. (1911). *Gastrodia elata* and its Symbiotic Association with *Armillaria mellea*. *J. Agric. Coll. Tokyo, 4* : 1–68.

LLOYD, L. C. (1940). The Orchids of Shropshire. *North Western Nat.* Dec. *1940* : 1–8.

MATTHEWS, J. R. (1926). The Distribution of Certain Members of the British Flora, III : Irish and Anglo-Irish Plants. *Ann. Bot. 40* : 773–97.

(1937). Geographical Relationships of the British Flora. *J. Ecol. 25* : 1–90.

MOLLISON, J. E. (1943). *Goodyera repens* and its Endophyte. *Trans. Bot. Soc. Edinb. 33* : 391–403.

PETTERSSON, B. (1947). On some hybrid Populations of *Orchis incarnata* × *maculata* in Gotland. *Svensk Bot. Tidskr. 41* : 115–41.

PUGSLEY, H. W. (1925). On some Marsh Orchids. *J. Linn. Soc. London Bot. 49* : 553–92.

(1934). The Irish Forms of *Neotinea intacta* Rchb. f. *J. Bot. London, 72* : 54–55.

(1936). New British Marsh Orchids. *Proc. Linn. Soc. London, 148* : 121–25.

(1939). Recent Work on Dactylorchids. *J. Bot. London, 77* : 50–56.

(1946). *Orchis traunsteinerioides* Pugsl. in Britain. *Naturalist, 1946* : 47.

RAMSBOTTOM, J. (1922). Orchid Mycorhiza. *Trans. Brit. Mycol. Soc. 8* : 28–61.

(1929). Orchid Mycorhiza. *Proc. Int. Congr. Plant Sci. Ithaca, 1926, 2* : 1676–87.

ROSE, F. (1949). *Orchis purpurea* Huds. *in* Biolog. Flora Brit. Isles, *J. Ecol.* *36* : 366–77.

SALISBURY, E. J. (1942). The Reproductive Capacity of Plants. London.

SCHLECHTER, R., & KELLER, G. (1928–1940). Monographie und Iconographie der Orchideen Europas und der Mittelmeergebietes. Berlin— Dahlem.

STAPF, O. (1917). A Cartographic Study of the Southern Element in the British Flora. *Proc. Linn. Soc. London, 129* : 81–92.

STEPHENSON, T. & T. A. (1921). The Forms of *Orchis maculata*. *J. Bot. London, 59* : 121–28.

(1923). The British Forms of *Orchis incarnata*. *J. Bot. London, 61* : 273–78.

TAHOURDIN, C. B. (1925). Native Orchids of Britain. Croydon.

TANSLEY, A. G. (1939). The British Islands and their Vegetation. Cambridge, University Press.

THOMAS, C. (1942). An Addition to the Native British Orchidaceae. *J. Bot. London, 79* : 200–05.

VERMEULEN, P. (1947). Studies on Dactylorchids. Utrecht.

WILMOTT, A. J. (1927). The Irish *Spiranthes Romanzoffiana*. *J. Bot. London, 65* : 145–49.

(1936). British Marsh Orchids. *Proc. Linn. Soc. London, 148* : 126–30.

(1937). The Endemic Flowering Plants of the British Isles. *Trans. South-Eastern Union Sci. Soc. 1936* : 33–51.

WOLLEY-DOD, A. H. (1937). Flora of Sussex. Hastings, K. Saville.

YOUNG, D. P. (1949). Studies in the British *Epipactis*, I and II. *Watsonia, 1* : 102–13.

ZIEGENSPECK, H. (1936). *Orchidaceae* in Kirchner, Loew & Schroeter, Lebensgeschichte der Blutenpflanzen Mittel-Europas. *1,* part 4. Stuttgart.

MAPS SHOWING
THE DISTRIBUTION OF MOST OF OUR
NATIVE SPECIES OF ORCHIDS

THE BRITISH distributions of all the species of British orchids, with the exception of the dactylorchids (7 species), are shown in the following maps. The maps are arranged in groups consisting of allied species, so as to enable the reader to compare the distributions easily. In two of the groups (maps 17–20 and 28–31), there are two pairs of allied species, but the different pairs are not related to one another.

In all the maps the distribution is shown by shading the whole of each vice-county in which the species occurs, not by charting individual localities ; as a consequence the ranges are only approximately accurate. Every effort has been made to obtain the correct distribution of each species at the time of construction of the maps (1949), but there will no doubt be many minor errors. This is inevitable owing to the marked yearly fluctuations in numbers and flowering exhibited by most orchids, and the inequality of observation and recording in different parts of the country.

In the difficult group of the helleborines (*Epipactis*) older records are often unreliable, while fresh records for the more critical species are constantly being published. The distributions of the dactylorchids (marsh and spotted orchids) are so imperfectly known that it was found impracticable to prepare reasonably accurate maps even on a vice-comital basis.

A complete list and map-key of the British vice-counties, with definitions of their boundaries, is shortly to be published by the Ray Society. A list and map is published in J. E. Lousley's *Wild Flowers of Chalk and Limestone* in this series (pp. 224–25).

1. Lady's Slipper, *Cypripedium calceolus*   2. Red Helleborine, *Cephalanthera rubra*

3. Sword-leaved Helleborine, *Cephalanthera*   4. Large White Helleborine, *Cephalanthera*
                    longifolia   *damasonium*

5. Marsh Helleborine, *Epipactis palustris*

6. Violet Helleborine, *Epipactis purpurata*

7. Dark Red Helleborine, *Epipactis atrorubens*

8. Broad-leaved Helleborine, *Epipactis helleborine*

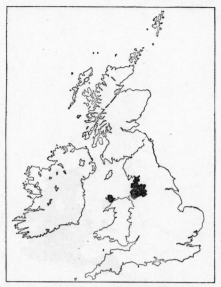

9. Dune Helleborine, *Epipactis dunensis*

10. Green-leaved Helleborine,
Epipactis leptochila

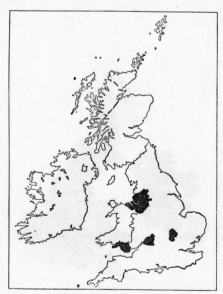

11. Pendulous-flowered Helleborine,
Epipactis pendula

12. Isle of Wight Helleborine,
Epipactis vectensis

13. Autumn Ladies' Tresses, *Spiranthes spiralis*

14. Summer Ladies' Tresses, *Spiranthes aestivalis*

15. Irish Ladies' Tresses, *Spiranthes Romanzoffiana*

16. Creeping Ladies' Tresses, *Goodyera repens*

17. Common Twayblade, *Listera ovata*   18. Lesser Twayblade, *Listera cordata*

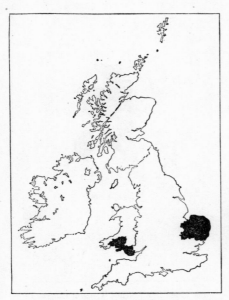

19. Fen Orchid, *Liparis loeselii*   20. Bog Orchid, *Hammarbya paludosa*

21. Bird's Nest Orchid, *Neottia nidus-avis*

22. Common Coral Root, *Corallorhiza trifida*

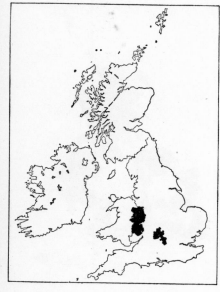

23. Spurred Coral Root, *Epipogium aphyllum*

24. Frog Orchid, *Coeloglossum viride*

25. Musk Orchid, *Herminium monorchis*

26. Fragrant Orchid, *Gymnadenia conopsea*

27. Small White Orchid, *Gymnadenia albida*

28. Greater Butterfly Orchid, *Platanthera chlorantha*

29. Lesser Butterfly Orchid, *Platanthera bifolia*

30. Green-veined Orchid, *Orchis morio*

31. Early Purple Orchid, *Orchis mascula*

32. Dense-flowered Orchid, *Neotinea intacta*   33. Pyramidal Orchid, *Anacamptis pyramidalis*

34. Lizard Orchid, *Himantoglossum hircinum*   35. Man Orchid, *Aceras anthropophorum*

36. Soldier Orchid, *Orchis militaris*

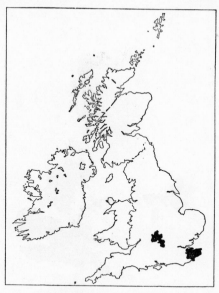

37. Monkey Orchid, *Orchis simia*

38. Lady Orchid, *Orchis purpurea*

39. Burnt Orchid, *Orchis ustulata*

40. Fly Orchid, *Ophrys muscifera*

41. Early Spider Orchid, *Ophrys sphegodes*

42. Late Spider Orchid, *Ophrys fuciflora*

43. Bee Orchid, *Ophrys apifera*

INDEX

Figures in heavy type refer to pages opposite which illustrations wlll appear. Figures in italics indicate the detailed accounts of the species concerned. Figures followed by an asterisk refer to pages on which Distribution Maps appear.

Aberdeenshire, 83, 212

Abnormalities, **26**, 37–39, 169, 234, 305

Aceras anthropophorum, 31 (fig. 6), 36, 62, 66, 72, 77, 88, 108, 229, **234**, **238**, *240–243*, 253, 354*

Achillea ptarmica, 186

Acid soils, 73, 95

Acrotonae, 105, 106, 107

Agrostis, 92, 100

Albinos, 34–35, 132, 246, 255, 268, 281

Albinos, partial, 35, 299, 308

Alder, 84, 86

Alder-willow woods, 86, 204

Alnus rotundifolius, 86

Alopecurus pratensis, 92

American Element, 62, 68

Ammophila arenaria, 100, 101, 147, 204

Anacamptis pyramidalis, **26**, 49, 50 (fig. 11), 53, 62, 63, 76, 78, 88, 89, 100, 102, 108, **223**, 224, 225, **226**, 229, 232, *233–236*, 354*

Anacamptis pyramidalis × *Gymnadenia conopsea*, 236

Anacamptis pyramidalis × *Orchis fuchsii*, 236

Anagallis tenella, 186, 314

Andrena, 122

Angelica sylvestris, 287

Anglesey, 67, 101, 146, 282, 291

Angraecum sesquipedale, 53

Anther, 104

Anther loculus, 33 (fig. 7), 47

Anther thecae, 47

Anthocyanin, 35–36, 37, 109

Antrim, 138, 291, 295, 309

Ants, 53, 243

Apomixis, 57

Arbutus unedo, 82, 231

Armagh, 68

Armillaria mellea, 6, 18

Arrhenatherum elatius, 87, 225, 235

Arum maculatum, 196

Aseptic cultivation of orchids, 7

Ash, 74, 78, 80, 119, 120, 170, 263

Ash-oakwoods, 80, 130, 300

Ashdown Forest, 95, 222, 317

Ashwoods, 78–79, 262, 270

Asperula odorata, 196

Atlantic Period, 232

Autumn ladies' tresses, 3, 10, 63, 89, 91, 92, 100, 107, **159**, 175, *177–180*, 185, 232, 349*

Bagshot Sand, 275

Banff, 150

Basitonae, 104, 105, 106, 108

Bedfordshire, 75, 77, 162, 208, 241

Bee orchid, 3, 10, 14, **26**, 31 (fig. 6), 33, 35, 54, 55, 58, 63, 76, **79**, 83, 84, 89, 91, 100, 108, 180, 225, 232, **286**, 298, *306–311*, **307, 314**, 321, 356*

Bee orchid, self-pollination of, 55–56

Beech, 74, 78, 125, 162, 190, 309

Beechwoods, 74–78, 130, 133, 144, 152, 154, 159, 165, 193, 196, 201, 215, 235, 253, 262, 270, 300

Beechwoods on chalk, 75, 127

Beechwoods on sands, gravels and loams, 78

Bees, 42, 47, 49, 56, 122, 128, 131, 135, 145, 176, 187, 226, 250, 254, 292, 306

Bees, hive, 140, 170, 236, 239, 248, 259, 272

Bees, solitary, 223, 259, 272

Beetles, 44, 122, 170, 209, 212, 226

Bell-heather, 173

Bent grass, 92, 100

Berkshire, 85, 165, 247, 295

Bilberry, 82, 83, 94, 173

Birch, 74, 82, 84, 86, 145, 165, 170

Birchwoods, 81, 85, 109, 190, 196, 204, 275

Bird's foot trefoil, 100

Bird's nest, 155, 196

Bird's nest orchid, 3, 16, 17, 18, 22, 46, 53, 64, 75, 77, 78, 79, 81, 82, 107, 121, 127, 154, 155, 160, **171**, **191**, 192, *193–198*, 201, 202, 351*

Blackberries, 133

Black bog-rush, 98, 297

Blackthorn, 77, 235

Blaeberry, 83

Bluebell, 80, 263

Blue-eyed grass, 184

Blunt-flowered rush, 96

Bog asphodel, 97, 291

Bog bean, 287

Bog-moss, 24, 93, 97, 183, 275, 287, 314, 317

Bog orchid, 11, 24, 29, 61, 65, 73, 84, 97, 104, 105, 108, 173, 177, 187, 207, **303**, 312, **315**, *315–318*, 350*

Bog pimpernel, 186, 314

Bog rush, 183

Bogs, 84, 94, 95, 97, 173, 182, 183, 186, 225, 283, 287, 291, 317

Brachypodium pinnatum, 87, 242, 262

Bracken, 81, 83, 145, 155, 169, 173

Brambles, 76, 130, 154, 159, 196, 250

Braunton Burrows, 287

Breconshire, 222

Briza media, 242

Broad-leaved fen orchid, **315**

Broad-leaved helleborine, 28 (fig. 4), 31 (fig. 6), 35, 46, 56, 63, 67, 73, 75, 76, **78**, 81, 82, 84, 85, 86, 91, **95**, 107, 109, 123, **130**, 136, *141–145*, 148, 149, 152, 157, 160, 196, 215, 347*

Broad-leaved marsh orchid, 70

Bromus erectus, 87, 225, 235, 242, 262

Bromus hordeaceus, 92

Brown ophrys, 55

Brown-winged orchid, *251–254*

Buckinghamshire, 64, 76, 247, 248, 249

Burnt orchid, 3, 9, 66, 108, **239**, 244, **250**, *254–256*, 355*

Burren Hills or Mountains, 90, 91, 151, 230, 232, 262, 272, 294, 297, 300, 309

Bursicle, 31 (fig. 6), 33 (fig. 7), 47

Butterflies, 49, 52, 214, 223, 226, 235, 256

Butterfly orchids, 3, 30, 34, 38, 52, 53, 63, 70, 73, 76, 92, 104, 167, 170, 214

Butterworts, 97

Caithness, 204

Calluna vulgaris, 5, 93, 97, 215, 317

Caltha palustris, 96, 287, 291

Cambridgeshire, 303, 314

Capsule, 59

Carboniferous limestone, 78, 79, 89, 90, 119, 120

Cardamine pratensis, 98

Carex, 97, 183, 216, 226, 291, 314

Carex panicea, 97

Carex paniculata, 96, 287

Carex pulicaris, 97

Carmarthenshire, 222, 314

Carpinus betulus, 82

Catalogue of the Plants of South Kent, 310

Cattleya, 105

Caudicle, 40 (fig. 5), **47**, 104, 105

Celandine, 80

Central Eurasian Element, 62, 64, 69, 133, 138, 150, 195, 211, 225, 249, 282

Central Irish plain, 95, 96, 99

Cephalanthera, 8, 77, 105, 123, 124–135, 136, 163

Cephalanthera damasonium, 3, 22, 62, 63, 72, 75, 79, 107, **110**, 124, *125–128*, 165, 196, 220, 253, 346*

Cephalanthera longifolia, 62, 63, 75, 76, 79, 107, **111**, 121, 124, *128–131*, 346*

Cephalanthera rubra, 15, 23 (fig. 3), 62, 64, 76, **94**, 107, **110**, 123, 124, **126**, 128, *132–135*, 346*

Cephalantherinae, 107

Chalk, 72, 208, 239, 256

Chalk downs, 71, 88, 109, 139, 155, 169, 179, 209, 215, 225, 235, 239, 242, 256, 259, 262, 271, 283, 288, 300, 303, 305, 309

Chalk pits, 89, 288

Chalk scrub, 77

Channel Islands, 182

Cheshire, 172, 222

Chiltern Hills, 75, 76, 110, 127, 208, 246, 249, 300, 309, 310

Chlorophyll, 16, 192, 194, 198, 202

Cirsium acaule, 256

Cladium mariscus, 96, 314

Clare, 67, 90, 98, 151, 179, 225, 231, 232, 262, 272, 294, 297, 301, 309

Classification, 102–117

Clay-with-flints, 80, 155

Cleveland Hills, 119

Clustered helleborine, *152–157*

Clyde Basin, 283

Cocksfoot, 92

Coeloglossum bracteatum, 211

Coeloglossum viride, 36, 38, 62, 64, 88, 90, 100, 108, 115, 117, **202**, 206, *210–214*, 225, 352*

Coeloglossum viride × *Gymnadenia conopsea*, 213

Coeloglossum viride × *Orchis fuchsii*, 213

Coeloglossum viride × *Orchis praetermissa*, 288

Coeloglossum viride × *Orchis purpurella*, 292

Coll, 68, 185, 271

Colonsay, 68, 185, 186

Colour forms, 34–36, 119, 143, 154, **223**, **251**, 257, 261

Column, 29, 33 (fig. 7)

Comarum palustre, 186, 287, 291

Common coral-root, 16, 17, 64, 65, 83, 86, 100, 108, **190**, 192, 193, *202–205*, 312, 351*

Common ladies' tresses, 175, *177–180*

Common marsh orchid, 28 (fig. 4), 66, 67, 86, 92, 94, 96, 98, 101, 108, 114, 115, 139, 216, 227, **270**, 279, **283**, *284–289*, 314, 321

Common meadow grass, 100

Common reed, 96, 139, 287, 314

Common spotted orchid, 12 (fig. 2), **18**, **19**, 26, 30 (fig. 5), 34, 36, 61, **62**, 66, 73, 75, 77, 78, 79, 81, 82, 84, 85, 86, 88, 91, 92, 101, 108, 109, 110, 114, 115, 139, 213, 220, 225, 230, 239, 253, **259**, 266, *267–273*, 295

Common twayblade, 3, 8, 13, 16, 20, 22, 26, 28 (fig. 4), 36, 58, 63, 70, 71, 73, 75, 76, 77, 78, 81, 82, 84, 85, 86, 92, 94, 99, 100, 101, 107, 109, 121, **158**, *167–171*, 194, 196, 215, 220, 253, 350*

Common twayblade, pollination of, 44–46

Coral-roots, 105

Corallian limestone, 79, 119

Corallorhiza, 105, 203

Corallorhiza trifida, 16, 17, 62, 64, 83, 100, **190**, 192, *202–205*, 312, 351*

Corallorhizinae, 108

Cork, 68, 185, 187, 232, 291, 294

Cornwall, 263, 289, 317

Cotswold Hills, 76, 89, 110, 133, 208, 209, 235, 287

Cotton grasses, 93, 94, 97, 226, 275, 287, 295
Cotyledon, 2
Coumarin, 240, 247, 251, 254
Cowberry, 83, 94
Cowslip, 92, 259
Crack willow, 86
Cranberry, 97, 173
Creeping ladies' tresses, 10, 21, **46**, 65, 73, 83, 85, 107, **171**, *188–191*, **190**, 204, 349*
Creeping ladies' tresses, dependence on fungus of, 15
Creeping willow, 101, 287
Crested dog's tail, 88
Cross-leaved heath, 94, 215, 275
Crowberry 94
Cryptostylis leptochila, 54
Cuckoo flower, 98, 260
Cumberland, 120, 190, 203, 256, 258, 308
Cycnoches chlorochilon, **58**
Cymbidium, 58, 105
Cynosurus cristatus, 88
Cypripedieae, 107
Cypripedium calceolus, 3, 31, (fig. 6), 33, (fig. 7), 41, 43 (fig. 8), 62, **63**, 64, 79, 103, 107, *118–122*, 346*
Cypripedium parviflorum, 121

Dactylis glomerata, 92
Dactylorchids, 70, 117, 244, 265, 266, 321, 345
Dactylorchis, 117
Daphne laureola, 253
Dark red helleborine, 22, 56, 64, 79, 91, 107, **138**, 145, *148–151*, 232, 347*
Darwin, Charles, 51, 53, 170, 236, 322
Dead-men's fingers, 260
Deer grass, 93, 94
Dehiscence of fruits, 59
Denbigh, 303
Dense - flowered fragrant orchid, 99
Dense-flowered orchid, 67, 69, 71, 91, 100, 108, 151, **219**, **223**, 229, *230–233*, 354*
Derbyshire, 89, 150, 172, 222
Derbyshire Dales, 89, 225, 260, 262

Devonshire, 67, 159, 165, 173, 238, 263, 287, 289
Diandrae, 103, 107, 122
Dispersal of seeds, 59
Distribution, 60–101
Distribution, Ecological, 71–101
Distribution, Geographical, 61–71
Dog violet, 76
Dog's mercury, 80, 154, 163, 253
Dogwood, 76, **77**
Donegal, 291
Dorset, 89, 126, 208, 303, 305, 317
Doubling of flowers, 37
Down, 138, 272, 291
Drosera, 97, 173
Druce, G. C., 200, 271, 284
Dryopteris filix-mas, 154
Dublin, county, 179, 259, 291
Dumfries, 234
Dune helleborine, 57, 66, 67, 101, 107, **131**, 135, 136, *145–148*, 161, 348*
Duration of life of orchids, 10–16
Durham, 67, 79, 89, 119, 120, 130, 159, 190, 228, 255, 286, 292, 295, 300, 308
Dwarf gorse, 225
Dwarf orchid, 225, **239**, 244, **250**, *254–256*
Dwarf purple orchid, 31 (fig. 6), 33 (fig. 7), 36, 66, 67, 92, 97, 98, 99, 101, 108, 227, 279, 280, **282**, 286, *289–292*, 296, 321
Dwarf thistle, 256
Dwarf willow, 147, 314

Early marsh orchid, 34, 64, 73, 92, 94, 96, 97, 98, 100, 101, 108, 114, 183, **255**, **275**, 278, 279, *281–284*, **282**, 295, 314
Early purple orchid, 7, 8, 33, 34, 36, 63, 72, 77, 78, 80, 81, 82, 84, 85, 91, 92, 94, 100, 106, 108, 112, 220, 225, 244, 253, 257, **258**, *260–264*, 353*
Early purple orchid, pollination of, 46–49
Early spider orchid, **27**, 35,

47, 55, 66, 88, 89, 90, 108, **287**, 298, *301–304*, 306, 356*
East Anglia, 96, 208, 282, 314
Elements, Geographical, 61–68
Empetrum nigrum, 94
Endemic Element, 62, **68**, 162
Endemic species, 61, 68, 294
Endemic species, origin of, 70
Epichile, 31 (fig. 6), 123, 136
Epidendreae, 108
Epilobium hirsutum, 98
Epipactinae, 107
Epipactis, 8, 53, 56, 68, 70, 77, 105, 110, 123, 135–166, 345
Epipactis, pollination of, 46, 56–57, 135
Epipactis atropurpurea, 150
Epipactis atrorubens, 22, 56, 62, 64, 79, 91, 107, 110, **138**, 145, *148–151*, 163, 232, 347*
Epipactis atrorubens × *E. helleborine*, 151
Epipactis cambrensis, 146
Epipactis cleistogama, 110
Epipactis dunensis, 57, 62, 66, 84, 101, 107, 110, **131**, 135, 136, *145–148*, 163, 348
Epipactis gigantea, 135
Epipactis helleborine, 28 (fig. 4), 31 (fig. 6), 46, 56, 62, 63, 67, 73, 75, 78, **78**, 86, 91, **95**, 107, 110, 123, **130**, 136, *141–145*, 148, 149, 155, 157, 158, 160, 163, 165, 196, 347*
Epipactis latifolia, 141
Epipactis leptochila, 56, 62, 66, 67, 75, **95**, 107, 110, 135, 141, **142**, 152, 154, *157–160*, 163, 196, 201, 348*
Epipactis media, 150
Epipactis ovalis, 150
Epipactis palustris, 62, 64, 73, 89, 96, 99, 107, **127**, 135, *136–141*, 226, 283, 287, 301, 314, 347*
Epipactis palustris, var. *ochroleuca*, 138

Epipactis pendula, **19**, 57, 62, 68, 75, 84, 107, 136, **142**, *161–164*, 348*

Epipactis purpurata, 46, 56, 61, 62, 66, 75, 81, 82, **95**, 107, 110, **139**, 142, *152–157*, 158, **162**, **163**, 163, 347*

Epipactis rubiginosa, 150

Epipactis vectensis, 18, 57, 62, 68, 75, 85, 107, 136, **143**, 161, *164–166*, 348*

Epipactis violacea, 153

Epiphytes, 11, 106

Epipogiinae, 107

Epipogium aphyllum, 16, 17, 21, 29, 62, 65, 75, 104, 105, 107, 160, 192, **194**, *198–202*, 351*

Epipogium roseum, 199

Equisetum, 96

Equisetum palustre, 287

Erect brome, 87, 88, 225, 235, 242, 262

Erica cinerea, 94, 173, 317

Erica tetralix, 94, 97, 215, 275, 317

Ericaceae, 93

Eriophorum, 93, 97, 226, 275

Eriophorum angustifolium, 97, 287

Eriophorum latifolium, 97, 287

Erodium cicutarium, 100

Eskers, 301, 309

Essex, 82

Eucera tuberculata, 306

Eurasian Element, 61, 62, 63, 129, 143, 169, 215, 218, 258, 262

European Element, 62, 66, 154, 241, 255, 268, 300, 302

Exclusive species, 71

False brome, 87, 242, 262

False oats, 87, 225, 235

Fen orchid, 11, 64, 65, 96, 101, 105, 108, 283, **303**, 312, *313–315*, 350*

Fens, 86, 94–97, 283, 287, 314

Fens and bogs, intermediates between, 97

Fermanagh, 272, 291, 295

Ferns, 154

Fertilisation, 58

Fertilisation, cross-, 40

Fescues, 92, 100

Festuca, 92, 100

Festuca ovina, 88

Festuca rubra, 88, 92

Fife, 234

Filament, 104

Filipendula ulmaria, 96, 186, 287

Flecked marsh orchid, 65, 98, 108, 279, 280, *296–297*

Flies, 44, 53, 122, 170, 174, 197, 209, 226, 239, 243, 254, 256, 272, 277, 292, 317

Flintshire, 162, 165

Flora of Sussex, 133

Flower stalk, twisting of, 103, 104

Flowers, incomplete separation of, **19**, 37

Flowers, structure of, 27–33

Fluctuation, 14

Fluctuation in autumn ladies' tresses, 180

Fluctuation in bee orchid, 309

Fluctuation in early purple orchid, 263

Fluctuation in fragrant orchid, 223

Fluctuation in green-veined orchid, 258

Fluctuation in red helleborine, 134

Fluctuation in summer ladies' tresses, 182

Fly orchid, 12 (fig. 2), 38, 55, 66, 72, 75, 77, 81, 83, 84, 88, 91, 108, 121, 127, 196, 220, 253, **286**, *298–301*, 306, 356*

Food storage, 13–15

Fragaria vesca, 196

Fragrant orchid, 11, 14, 20, 27, 28 (fig. 4), 31 (fig. 6), 38, 52, **62**, 64, 73, 84, 86, 88, 91, 92, 94, 97, 102, 108, 109, 115, 170, 182, 183, 207, **211**, 216, 220, 221, *223–227*, 233, 239, 287, 301, 321, 352*

Fragrant orchid, hybrid between frog orchid and, **78**

Fragrant orchid, pollination of, 51–52

Frog orchid, 36, 38, 64, 88, 92, 100, 108, 115, **202**, 206, *210–214*, 216, 225, 352*

Fruit valves, **59**

Fruits, 59

Furness, 120

Galway, 67, 90, 98, 151, 179, 225, 230, 231, 262, 272, 291, 294, 297, 301, 309

Gastrodia elata, 6, 18

Gastrodia septentrionalis, 6

Germination of seeds, 2–4

Gethsemane, 260

Glacial Period, 69, 71, 231, 232

Glamorgan, 287, 314

Gloucestershire, 64, 75, 76, 89, 133, 143, 159, 162, 208, 235, 239

Glyceria maxima, 96, 287

Goat sallow, 86

Godfery, M. J., 131, 156, 157, 160, 163, 164, 166, 170, 233, 236, 248, 256, 266, 271, 301, 315, 322

Gongora, 58

Good, R. D'O., 237

Goodyera, 105, 175, 176, 187–191

Goodyera repens, 15, 21, **46**, 62, 65, 73, 83, 84, 107, **171**, *188–191*, **190**, 204, 349*

Gorytes mystaceus, 301, 306

Grampian Mountains, 212

Grass-heath, 92

Grassland, 73, 86–93

Grassland, chalk, 87–89

Grassland, hill, 92

Grassland, limestone, 87–90, 169, 271, 288

Grassland, neutral, 92, 270

Grassland on peaty soils, 93

Grassland, short limestone, 88

Grassland, tall limestone, 87

Great hairy willow-herb, 98

Greater butterfly orchid, 75, 77, 78, 81, 82, 92, 94, 99, 106, 108, 109, 121, **203**, 206, 214, 216, *217–221*, **222**, 225, 253, 353*

Green-leaved helleborine, 56, 66, 75, 81, 107, 135, 141, **142**, 144, 152, 154, *157–160*, 161, 166, 196, 201, 348*

Green-veined orchid, 2, 9, 34, 35, 63, 72, 77, 88, 92, 108, 112, 244, **251**, *256–260*, 353*

Green-winged orchid, 244, *256–260*

Grey sallow, 86

Gymnadenia, 117, 221, 265

Gymnadenia albida, 62, 65, 90, 108, **202**, 207, *221–223*, 227, **255**, 352* .

Gymnadenia albida × G. conopsea, 227

Gymnadenia conopsea, 28 (fig. 4), 31 (fig. 6), 38, 51, 53, 62, **62**, 64, 73, 84, 86, 88, 89, 94, 102, 108, 109, 115, 170, 182, 207, **211**, 216, 220, 221, *223–227*, 233, 239, 287, 301, 352*

Gymnadenia conopsea, var. *densiflora*, 99, 109, **218**, 224, 225, 226, 287

Gymnadenia conopsea × Orchis ericetorum, 227

Gymnadenia conopsea × Orchis fuchsii, **62**, 227

Gymnadenia conopsea × Orchis praetermissa, 227, 288

Gymnadenia conopsea × Orchis purpurella, 227, 292

Gymnadenia odoratissima, 228

Gymnadeniinae, 108

× *Gymnaglossum jacksoni*, **78**

Habenaria, 102, 106, 206

Habenaria Group, 117, 206–228

Hagerup, O., 57

Halictus, 176

Hamlet, 260

Hammarbya paludosa, 11, 24, 29, 61, 62, 65, 73, 84, 97, 104, 105, 108, 173, 177, 187, 207, **303**, 312, **315**, *315–318*, 350*

Hampshire, 81, 95, 127, 165, 173, 182, 238, 241, 275, 317

Hampshire Basin, 80

Hangers, 75, 127, 300

Hard rush, 98

Harrison, J. Heslop, 185, 296

Hawthorn, 77, 235

Hazel, 78, 80, 82, 119, 120, 131, 263, 301

Hazel-coppice, 81, 155, 196, 253, 260

Heart-leaved twayblade, *171–174*

Heath (plant), 93, 94, 97, 317

Heath spotted orchid, 30 (fig. 5), 34, 35, 66, 73, 81, 82, 84, 85, 86, 92, 93, 94, 97, 100, 108, 226, **254**, 266, 267, 270, *273–277*, **274**, 292, 294

Heath spotted orchid, multiplication in, 20–21

Heath vegetation, 85, 92, 109

Heather, 5, 81, 82, 83, 92, 93, 94, 97, 169, 173, 179, 190, 215, 220, 222, 225, 317

Heather moors, 109, 275

Heaths, 81, 93–94, 215, 222, 225, 270, 275

Hebridean orchid, 100, 101, **250**, **266**, 271

Hebrides, 68, 100, 101, 110, 175, 185, 270, 271, 272, 275, 291, 294

Hedera helix, 154

Helictotrichon pratense, 87, 235, 242

Helictotrichon pubescens, 87, 235, 242

Helleborines, 8, 10, 14, 35, 53, 68, 70, 75, 77, 84, 105, 110, 111, 123–166, 167, 321, 345

Helleborines, pollination of, 56–57

Helleborus foetidus, 253

Hemlock stork's bill, 100

Herefordshire, 150, 200, 222

Herminium monorchis, 21, 62, 65, 88, 108, 109, **195**, 206, *207–210*, 225, 352*

Herminium monorchis, multiplication in, 21

Hertfordshire, 76, 82, 249

Hieracium pilosella, 256

Highlands of Scotland, 83, 188, 190

Himantoglossum hircinum, 31 (fig. 6), 62, 63, 77, 88, 100, 108, **227**, 229, *236–240*, 354*

Himantoglossum hircinum, subsp. *calcaratum*, 237

Hippocrepis comosa, 256

Holcus lanatus, 92

Holly, 82

Home Counties, 126, **127**, 144, 260

Honey fungus, 6, 18

Hornbeam, 82

Horseshoe vetch, 256

Horsetails, 96, 98

Hover-flies, 205, 243

Humble-bees, 47, 49, 128, 135, 140, 145, 151, 176, 180, 187, 191, 201, 250, 259, 264, 272, 284, 295

Huntingdon, 314

Hybrid-swarm, 112

Hybridisation, origin of species by, 114, 278

Hybrids, 111–117, 265, 284

Hybrids, artificial, 111, 115

Hybrids, bigeneric, 114–117

Hybrids, natural, 111

Hybrids, putative, 113

Hydrocotyle vulgaris, 186

Hymenoptera, 205

Hymenopterous insects, 131, 209, 223

Hypochile, 31 (fig. 6), 123, 136

Ice-age, 60, 69, 70, 71, 231, 272

Ichneumon flies, 44, 170, 174, 209, 212

Insect visitors to flowers, 41, 52–54, 322

Inverness, 63, 83, 130, 195, 227

Ireland, 63, 65, 66, 67, 68, 70, 71, 78, 79, 82, 85, 87, 90, 91, 92, 95, 96, 97, 98, 99, 100, 110, 130, 138, 139, 144, 145, 150, 172, 173, 174, 175, 178, 179, 183, 195, 196, 216, 219, 222, 225, 226, 231, 234, 257, 260, 262, 270, 274, 283, 286, 291, 294, 297, 300, 308, 309, 317

Iris foetidissima, 253

Iris pseudacorus, 96, 287, 294

Irish ladies' tresses, 12 (fig. 2), 61, 68, 69, 71, 96, 97, 107, **170**, **175**, 175, 176, *183–187*, 272, 349*

Irish marsh orchid, 36, 68, 70, 97, 98, 108, 109, 230, **271**, 272, 279, 280, *292–296*

Isle of Man, 289, 292

Isle of Wight, 75, 164

Isle of Wight helleborine, 18, 57, 68, 85, 107, 110, 136, **143**, 161, *164–166*, 348*

Ivy, 75, 154, 159, 163, 165, 196

Jessen, K., 231
Jointed rush, 276
Juncus, 101
Juncus acutiflorus, 276, 291
Juncus conglomeratus, 98
Juncus effusus, 96, 98, 276, 291
Juncus inflexus, 98
Juncus obtusiflorus, 96
Jurassic, 256

Kent, 67, 75, 76, 81, 89, 100, 133, 139, 159, 165, 168, 208, 222, 238, 241, 242, 243, 247, 250, 251, 252, 253, 275, 289, 303, 304, 305, 314, 317
Kerry, 82, 185, 232, 293, 294
Kettle-cases, 260
Kirkcudbright, 234
Koeleria cristata, 88

Labellum, 27
Ladies' tresses, 8, 11, 105, 175–191
Lady orchid, 63, 76, 77, 108, **239, 243**, 244, *251–254*, 355*
Lady's slipper, 3, 7, 8, 10, 15, 16, 19, 31 (fig. 6), 33 (fig. 7), 38, 41, **63**, 64, 65, 79, 103, 107, *118–122*, 124, 130, 346*
Lady's slipper, pollination of, 41–43
Lady's slipper, structure of flower in, 31
Lady's slippers, 32
Lake District, 82, 86, 89, 130, 145, 150
Lanarkshire, 308
Lancashire, 67, 84, 89, 95, 101, 111, 120, 146, 147, 149, 162, 166, 203, 287
Large white helleborine, 3, 22, 63, 70, 72, 75, 77, 79, 81, 107, **110**, 124, *125–128*, 144, 165, 196, 220, 253, 346*
Late spider orchid, 55, 63, **79**, 88, 89, 108, 298, **302**, *304–306*, **307**, 356*
Lateral sepals, 29
Lawns, orchids on, 179, 263
Leaf-buds, 24–25, 316, 318
Leaves, spotting of, 36
Leaves, venation of, 28 (fig. 4)

Leitrim, 272
Leopard marsh orchid, 36, 66, 67, 98, 114, **283**, 288, 289, **306**
Lesser butterfly orchid, 31 (fig. 6), 73, 81, 82, 84, 85, 88, 92, 94, 97, 108, 206, **210**, *214–217*, 218 (fig. 17), **222**, 353*
Lesser celandine, 19
Lesser spearwort, 98
Lesser twayblade, 22, 23 (fig. 3), 24, 31 (fig. 6), 46, 65, 73, 83, 84, 85, 94, 97, 107, 109, **159**, 167, *171–174*, 189, 190, 350*
Lias, 235
Liassic limestone, 89, 242, 303, 309
Lichens, 93
Lily family, 27, 29, 32, 103, 124
Limerick, 294
Limestone cliffs, 90–91, 148, 150
Limestone pavements, 90–91, 151, 179, 232, 273, 309
Limestone scrub, 77
Lincolnshire, 241, 242
Ling, 5
Lip, 27, 31 (fig. 6)
Liparidinae, 108
Liparis loeselii, 11, 62, 64, 96, 105, 108, 283, **303**, 312, *313–315*, 350*
Liparis loeselii, var. *ovata*, 101, 313, **315**, 315
Listera, 105
Listera cordata, 22, 23 (fig. 3), 31 (fig. 6), 46, 62, 65, 73, 83, 94, 97, 107, 109, **159**, 167, *171–174*, 189, 204, 350*
Listera ovata, 3, 8, 22, 23, 28 (fig. 4), 36, 44, 45 (fig. 8), 62, 63, 71, 75, 76, 78, 88, 89, 107, 109, 121, **158**, 167, 194, 204, 220, 253, 350*
Listerinae, 107
Lizard orchid, 31 (fig. 6), 53, 63, 77, 88, 100, 108, **227**, 229, *236–240*, 354*
London, 179
London Basin, 80
Londonderry, 68, 185
Long purples, 260
Lotus corniculatus, 100

Lough Neagh, 96, 185
Lousley, J. E., 248, 250
Louth, 258
Lychnis flos-cuculi, 98, 287, 291

Magnesian limestone, 78, 79, 89, 119, 120, 130, 228, 256, 300
Malaxis paludosa, 315
Man orchid, 13, 20, 27, 31 (fig. 6), 35, 36, 53, 66, 70, 72, 77, 108, 229, **234, 238**, *240–243*, 253, 354*
Maple, 263
Marram grass, 100, 147, 204
Marsh cinquefoil, 186, 287, 291
Marsh fragrant orchid 99, **218**, 224, 226
Marsh helleborine, 8, 20, 64, 70, 73, 89, 96, 99, 101, 107, **127**, 135, *136–141*, 183, 226, 283, 287, 301, 314, 347*
Marsh horsetail, 287
Marsh marigold, 96, 98, 287, 291
Marsh orchids, 2, 8, 11, 13, 14, 20, 27, 70, 89, 96, 98, 99, 112, 113, 117, 170, 226, 266, 278–297, 345
Marsh pennywort, 186
Marshes, 94, 95, 98–99, 101, 182, 186, 225, 283, 291, 292
Mat grass, 93, 215, 276
Maxillaria, 58
Mayo, 67, 82, 90, 98, 131, 179, 231, 232, 258, 294, 297, 301
Meadow foxtail, 92
Meadowsweet, 96, 97, 98, 186, 287
Meath, 258, 262
Mediterranean Element, 62
Mendip Hills, 78
Mentha aquatica, 98
Menyanthes trifoliata, 287
Mercurialis perennis, 80, 154, 253
Merioneth, 172
Middle Oolite, 119
Middlesex, 82, 179, 249
Midlands, 80, 87, 256, 309
Military orchid, 240, *248–251*
Mimicry, 54–55
Mirror ophrys, 54

Molinia caerulea, 93, 96, 97, 183, 226, 276, 287, 294
Monandrae, 103, 107
Monkey orchid, 8, 63, 72, 88, 108, **235**, **238**, 240, 244, *245-248*, 355*
Monocarpic plants, 14, 113, 254, 263
Monocotyledons, 26
Monotropa hypopitys, 155, 196
Montgomery, 172
Moorlands, 93-94, 173, 215, 275, 317
Moors, cotton grass, 94
Mosses, 93, 159, 173
Moths, 49, 52, 53, 183, 214, 216, 220, 226, 235, 256
Mountain limestone, 78, 130, 225, 300
Mouse-ear hawkweed, 256
Mull, 138, 235
Musk orchid, 21, 65, 88, 89, 108, 109, **195**, 206, *207-210*, 225, 352*
Mycorhiza, 4-7
Mycorhiza, ectotrophic, 5, 16
Mycorhiza, endotrophic, 5, 16
Mycorhizal fungus, 5, 72
Mycorhizome, 7-9
Myrica gale, 97, 183, 216

Names of Herbes . . , 169, 179
Nannfeldt, J. A., 68
Nardus stricta, 93, 215, 276
Narrow-leaved marsh orchid, 70, 295
Narrow-lipped helleborine, *157-160*
Narthecium ossifragum, 97, 291
Nature reserves, 320
Nectar, 41
Neotinea intacta, 62, 67, 91, 100, 108, 151, **219**, **223**, 229, *230-233*, 354*
Neottia, 193
Neottia nidus-avis, 3, 16, 17, 22, 46, 53, 62, 64, 75, 107, 121, 127, 154, 160, **171**, **191**, 192, *193-198*, 201, 351*
Neottieae, 107
New Forest, 95, 97, 182, 275, 317
Norfolk, 65. 84, 175, 190, 208, 283 314
Norfolk Broads, 86, 95

North Downs, 75, 127, 250, 253, 262, 300
Northamptonshire, 89, 242, 303
Northern Eurasian Element, 62, 64, 69, 199, 208, 297, 313, 316
Northern Montane Element, 62, 65, 69, 172, 189, 222
Northumberland, 204, 255, 258, 308
Nottinghamshire, 126
Nutrition, 5-6

Oak, 74, 78, 119, 120, 159, 170, 196, 309
Oak-hazel woods, 119
Oakwoods, 76, 79-83, 85, 130, 196, 235, 260, 270
Oakwoods, coppiced, 80, 219, 262
Oakwoods, heathy, 81
Oakwoods, pedunculate, on clays and marls, 80, 155
Oakwoods, pedunculate, on sands, 80, 81, 144, 155, 275
Oakwoods, sessile, 81-83, 201
Oat grasses, 87, 235, 242
Odontoglossum, 105
Ononis repens, 100
Oolitic limestone, 76, 89, 133, 208, 235, 242, 256, 303
Operculate stamen, 105, 312
Ophrydeae, 108
Ophrys, 11, 20, 54, 55, 72, 104, 112, 114, 298-311
Ophrys apifera, **26**, 31 (fig. 6), 62, 63, 76, 78, **79**, 88, 89, 90, 100, 108, 180, 225, 232, **286**, 298, *306-311*, **307**, 356*
Ophrys apifera, var. *trollii*, 308, 311, **314**
Ophrys apifera × *O. fuciflora*, **79**, 306, 310
Ophrys apifera × *O. sphegodes*, 310
Ophrys arachnites, 304
Ophrys aranifera, 301
Ophrys atrata, 302
Ophrys fuciflora, 62, 63, **79**, 88, 108, 298, **302**, *304-306*, **307**, 356*
Ophrys fuciflora × *O. sphegodes*, 304, 306
Ophrys fusca, 55

Ophrys insectifera, 298
Ophrys lutea, 55
Ophrys mammosa, 302
Ophrys muscifera, 12 (fig. 2), 62, 66, 72, 75, 76, 78, 88, 90, 108, 121, 127, 196, 220, 253, **286**, *298-301*, 356*
Ophrys muscifera × *O. sphegodes*, 303
Ophrys speculum, 54
Ophrys sphegodes, **27**, **47**, 62, 66, 88, 89, 108, **287**, 298, *301-304*, 356*
Orchids of fens, marshes and bogs, 94-99
Orchids of grasslands, 87-93
Orchids of heath and moorland, 93-94
Orchids of sand dunes, 99-101
Orchids of woodland and scrub, 74-86
Orchids, synopsis of British, 107-108
Orchids, tropical, 7, 11, 13, 35, 53, 58, 59, 103, 115, 206, 312
Orchis, 8, 11, 20, 54, 68, 72, 104, 111, 114, 117, 176, 244-297
Orchis, sub - genus *Dactylorchis*, 265
Orchis cruenta, 62, 65, 98, 108, 279, 280, *296-297*
Orchis elodes, 273
Orchis ericetorum, 30 (fig. 5), 35, 62, 66, 73, 81, 84, 86, 92, 93, 94, 99, 108, 216, 220, 226, **254**, 266, 271, *273-277*, **274**, 292, 294
Orchis ericetorum × *O. fuchsii*, 277
Orchis ericetorum × *O. praetermissa*, 288
Orchis ericetorum × *O. purpurella*, 292
Orchis fuchsii, 12 (fig. 2), **18**, **19**, 30 (fig. 5), 61, 62, **62**, 66, 73, 74, 75, 76, 78, 86, 88, 89, 99, 108, 109, 110, 114, 115, 216, 220, 225, 230, 239, 253, **259**, 266, *267-273*, 289, 295
Orchis fuchsii, subsp. *hebridensis*, 100, 110, **250**, **266**, 269 (fig. 18), 270, **271**, 292

Orchis fuchsii, subsp. *o'kellyi*, 91, 110, **267**, 269 (fig. 18), 270, 271

Orchis fuchsii, down or grassland form of, 78, 270

Orchis fuchsii, ecological forms of, 74, 270

Orchis fuchsii, woodland form of, 270

Orchis fuchsii × *O. praetermissa*, 288

Orchis fuchsii × *O. purpurella*, 292

Orchis incarnata, 279, 281

Orchis kerryensis, 294

Orchis latifolia, 62, 64, 73, 89, 96, 98, 108, 114, 226, **255**, **275**, 278, 279, *281–284*, 291, 292, 295, 314

Orchis latifolia, var. *coccinea*, 101, 282, **282**, 283, 287

Orchis latifolia, var. *ochroleuca*, 96, 281, 282, 283

Orchis latifolia, var. *pulchella*, 94, 97, 281, 282, 283, 291, 296

Orchis latifolia, hybrids with other dactylorchids, 284

Orchis latifolia × *O. maculata*, 286

Orchis latifolia × *O. purpurella*, 284, 292

Orchis maculata, 110, 114, 266, 268, 273

Orchis maculata, var. *meyeri*, 268

Orchis majalis, **67**, 70, 291, 294

Orchis majalis, subsp. *traunsteinerioides*, 295

Orchis mascula, 8, 36, 46, 48 (fig. 10), 62, 63, 72, 77, 78, 80, 88, 90, 106, 108, 112, 220, 244, 253, **258**, *260–264*, 353*

Orchis mascula, var. *obtusiflora*, 261

Orchis mascula × *O. morio*, 259

Orchis militaris, 62, 64, 76, 77, 108, 240, **242**, 244, *248–251*, 355*

Orchis militaris × *O. purpurea*, 251

Orchis morio, 9, 35, 62, 63, 72, 77, 88, 92, 108, 112, **244**, **251**, *256–260*, 353*

Orchis occidentalis, 36, 62, 68, 70, 97, 98, 108, 230, **271**, 272, 279, 280, *292–296*

Orchis occidentalis, var. *traunsteinerioides*, 295

Orchis pardalina, 36, 62, 66, 67, 99, 114, 279, **283**, 288, 289, **306**

Orchis praetermissa, 28 (fig. 4), 62, 66, 86, 89, 92, 94, 96, 98, 99, 101, 108, 114, 115, 216, 226, **270**, 279, **283**, *284–289*, 292, 314

Orchis praetermissa, var. *pulchella*, 286

Orchis praetermissa × *O. purpurella*, 292

Orchis purpurea, 62, 63, 76, 108, **239**, **243**, 243, 244, *251–254*, 355*

Orchis purpurella, 31 (fig. 6), 33 (fig. 7), 36, 62, 66, 67, 97, 98, 99, 108, 279, 280, **282**, 286, *289–292*, 296

Orchis simia, 62, 63, 88, 108, **235**, **238**, 240, 244, *245–248*, 355*

Orchis simia × *O. militaris*, 248

Orchis traunsteineri, 70, 295

Orchis traunsteinerioides, 62, 68, 70, 96, **259**, 295, **306**

Orchis ustulata, 3, 62, 66, 88, 90, 108, 225, **239**, 244, **250**, *254–256*, 355*

Orchis ustulata, development of seedling, 3 (fig. 1), 9

Orkney Islands, 169, 190, 215, 219, 262, 270, 274, 283, 317

Osier, 86

Osmunda regalis, 96

Ovary, 32, 102

Ovary, twisting of, 103, 315

Ovules, 32

Oxfordshire, 75, 200, 201, 208, 239, 241, 245, 247, 249, 303

Oxycoccus quadripetala, 97, 173

Palmate orchids, 114, 244, 265

Parasites, 192

Peat, 73, 86, 93, 94, 130, 186, 275, 283, 291

Peat-bog, 287

Pedunculate oak, 79

Pendulous-flowered helleborine, **19**, 57, 68, 107, 136, **142**, *161–164*, 165, 166, 348*

Pennine Hills, 78, 79, **81**, 85, 89, 90

Perennation, 6–10

Perianth, 27

Perthshire, 66, 83, 130, 138, 154, 300

Petals, 27, 29

Phalaris arundinacea, 96

Phleum arenarium, 100

Phragmites vulgaris, 96, 287, 314

Physurinae, 107

Pine-heath, 83

Pinewoods, 15, 83–85, 109, 173, 190, 204

Pinewoods, Scottish, 83, 190

Pinewoods, southern, 84, 275

Pinguicula, 97

Pinus sylvestris, 83

Plantations, coniferous, 84, 170

Plantations of broad-leaved trees, 170

Plantations, pine, 84, 144, 162, 170, 190

Platanthera, 52, 54, 117, 219

Platanthera bifolia, 31 (fig. 6), 62, 63, 73, 76, 78, 81, 84, 88, 90, 94, 108, 167, 170, 206, **210**, *214–217*, 218 (fig. 17), 220, **222**, 353*

Platanthera chlorantha, 62, 63, 75, 76, 78, 88, 89, 106, 108, 109, 121, 167, 170, **203**, 206, 216, *217–221*, **222**, 225, 253, 353*

Platanthera metabifolia, 219

Poa pratensis, 100

Polden Hills, 89, 235, 309

Pollen, 29

Pollen-conveying apparatus, 102

Pollen masses, 29

Pollinarium, 102

Pollination, 40–52

Pollination, cross-, 40

Pollination, self-, 55–57

Pollination, self-, in *Cephalanthera damasonium*, 128

Pollination, self-, in *Epipactis dunensis*, 147

Pollination, self-, in *Neottia*, 197

Pollination, self-, in *Ophrys apifera*, 310
Pollination mechanisms, 40, 41–52, 105
Pollinia (pollinium), 29, 30 (fig. 5), 103, 104, 105
Pollinia, movement of, 48, 50 (fig. 11), 51
Pollinia, structure of, 44, 47
Poplar, 86
Poterium sanguisorba, 256
Praeger, R. Ll., 130, 186
Primrose, 253
Primula vulgaris, 253
Privet, 76, 77
Protocorm, 7
Pseudobulb, 13, 312
Pseudo-copulation, 54–55, 301, 303, 310
Pugsley, H. W., 279
Purbeck Hills, 89
Purbeck limestone, 303
Purple moor-grass, 93, 96, 97, 183, 226, 276, 287, 294
Pyramidal orchid, **26**, 34, 52, 63, 76, 77, 78, 82, 88, 100, 102, 108, **223**, 224, 225, **226**, 229, 232, *233–236*, 239, 354*
Pyramidal orchid, pollination of, 49–51

Quaking grass, 242
Quarries, 303, 309
Quercus petraea, 79, 80, 81, 201
Quercus robur, 79, 80

Rabbits, 85, 247, 251, 254
Races, ecological, 109, 173, 270
Races, geographical, 109
Races, local, 110, 114
Ragged robin, 98, 287, 291
Rams-horns, 260
Ranunculus ficaria, 19, 80
Ranunculus flammula, 98
Red fescue, 88, 92
Red helleborine, 23 (fig. 3), 24, 64, 76, **94**, 107, **110**, 123, 124, **126**, *132–135*, 346*
Red helleborine, dependence on fungus of, 15
Reed canary grass, 96
Reed meadow-grass, 96, 287
Reed-swamp, 96, 287
Regals, 260

Rest harrow, 100
Rhizoctonia, 6
Rhizome, 8, 10
Rhyncospora, 97
Roast-beef plant, 253
Rock ledges, 212, 262
Root-buds, 22–24, 128, **134**, 151, 171, 174, 197
Root-tubers, 11, 12 (fig. 2)
Roots, independent growth of, 22, 24
Rootstock, 8, 10
Roscommon, 258
Rose, F., 252, 253, 254
Ross-shire, 63, 66, 130, 144
Rostellum, 32, 47, 102, 104
Rowan, 82
Royal fern, 96
Rubus, 154, 196
Runners, 15, 21, 189 (fig. 14), 191, 198, 202
Rushes, 92, 96, 98, 186, 226, 287, 291, 294
Rutland, 208

Salad burnet, 256
Salisbury, E. J., 259
Salix alba, 86
Salix atrocinerea, 86
Salix caprea, 86
Salix fragilis, 86
Salix repens, 101, 147, 287, 314
Salix viminalis, 86
Salt marshes, 71
Sand-dunes, 84, 99–101, 138, 145, 147, 151, 162, 163, 170, 179, 204, 211, 235, 239, 262, 281, 287, 294, 309, 314
Sand-dunes, slacks in, 99, 101, 138, 283, 287, 315
Sanicula europaea, 196
Saprophytes, 192
Saprophytic orchids, 6, 16–18, 83, 105, 106, 155, 192–205
Saxifrage, 231
Scars, 79, 119
Schoenus ferrugineus, 297
Schoenus nigricans, 98, 183, 297
Scilla non-scripta, 80, 263
Scirpus, 101
Scirpus caespitosus, 94, 97
Scotland, 63, 64, 65, 67, 82, 85, 86, 87, 90, 92, 98, 101, 138, 144, 150, 172, 173, 185, 190, 195, 204, 216,

219, 222, 225, 234, 258, 260, 270, 274, 275, 286, 291, 292, 294, 300, 308, 317
Scots pine, 74, 83, 84, 85, 147
Screes, 78, 91, 119, 145, 148
Scrub, 73, 76, 77–83, 127, 131, 144, 204, 220, 252, 253, 259, 275, 300
Scutellaria galericulata, 314
Sea-cliffs, 260, 262, 292
Sea timothy, 100
Sedges, 96, 97, 139, 183, 186, 216, 226, 275, 291, 295, 314
Seed production, 58
Seedling, development of, 7–9
Seeds, 59
Seeds, dispersal of, 59
Seeds, germination of, 2–4
Selenipedium chica, 103
Sepais, 29
Serapiadinae, 108
Sesleria coerulea, 88, 90
Sessile oak, 79, 81, 201
Sheep's fescue, 88
Shetland Islands, 169, 215, 219, 225, 262, 274, 283
Short-spurred fragrant orchid, 228
Shropshire, 159, 172, 200, 255, 291
Sieglingia decumbens, 92
Silver birch, 162
Sisyrinchium angustifolium, 184
Skullcap, 314
Skye, 150
Slender-lipped helleborine, 56, **95**, **142**
Sligo, 82
Small tongue orchid, 54
Small white orchid, 65, 90, 92, 108, **202**, 207, *221–223*, 227, **255**, 352*
Smith, G. E., 310
Sneezewort, 186
Soft brome, 92
Soft rush, 96, 98, 276
Soil, influence of, 72
Soldier Orchid, 64, 72, 76, 77, 108, **242**, 244, *248–251*, 355*
Somerset, 78, 79, 80, 89, 100, 126, 133, 172, 179, 208, 216, 235, 241, 242, 309

Somerset Levels, 95, 283
South Downs, 75, 127, 253, 262, 300
South Wales, 67, 78, 101, 110, 146, 159, 314
Southern Eurasian Element, 62, 63, 69, 178, 181, 234, 237, 246, 252, 305, 308
Sphagnum, 97, 183, 275, 287, 314, 317
Spider orchids, 54, 72
Spiranthes, 105, 175–187
Spiranthes aestivalis, 8, 11, 62, 63, 97, 107, 170, **174**, 176, *180–183*, 349*
Spiranthes gemmipara, 187
Spiranthes romanzoffiana, 12 (fig. 2), 61, 62, 68, 96, 107, **170**, **175**, 176, *183–187*, 272, 349*
Spiranthes spiralis, 3, 8, 62, 63, 88, 89, 90, 100, 107, **159**, 176, *177–180*, 185, 232, 349*
Spiranthinae, 107
Sports, 116
Spotted orchids, 2, 8, 11, 13, 20, 36, 66, 70, 99, 112, 113, 117, 170, 216, 220, 226, **227**, 260, 265–277, 345
Spur, 27, 31 (fig. 6)
Spurge laurel, 253
Spurred coral-root, 16, 17, 18, 21, 29, 65, 75, 104, 107, 160, 192, 193, **194**, *198–202*, 351*
Staffordshire, 21, 291, 292
Stamen, 29, 30, 103, 104, 105
Stamen, operculate, 105
Stamens, additional in flower, 38–39
Staminode, 31 (fig. 6), 33 (fig. 7), 38, 42
Stanhopea, 201
Stigma, 32, 33 (fig. 7), 102
Stinking hellebore, 253
Stolons, 21
Strawberry tree, 82, 231
Sub-specific groups, 109–111
Suffolk, 144, 165, 238, 303, 305, 314
Summer ladies' tresses, 8, 11, 63, 97, 107, **170**, **174**, 176, *180–183*, 349*
Sundews, 97, 173
Surrey, 81, 110, 157, 208, 241, 242, 247, 250, 253, 275, 305
Sussex, 75, 95, 133, 162, 208, 222, 247, 253, 263, 275, 303, 317
Sutherland, 144, 150, 272, 294
Swamps, 86, 109
Swan orchid, 58
Sweet-scented orchid, 223
Sweet gale, 97, 183, 216
Sweet woodruff, 196
Sword-leaved helleborine, 63, 70, 75, 81, 82, 107, **111**, 121, 124, 126, *128–131*, 346*
Sycamore, 309
Syrphid flies, 250, **272**

Thames, River, 70, 208, 245, 246, 249
Thames Valley, 275
Theatrum Botanicum, 120
Thomas, C., 147, 161
Thrips, 197
Tipperary, 179, 291
Tolerant species, 70, 73, 74
Turner's *New Herball*, 144
Tussock sedge, 96, 287
Twayblades, 10, 105, 167–174, 204

Underground flower-spikes, 18, 195, 197
Underground orchids, 18

Vaccinium myrtillus, 82, 83, 94
Vaccinium vitis-idaea, 83, 94
Vandeae, 108
Variation, 33–37
Vegetation types, 73
Vegetative multiplication, 19–25
Vermeulen, P., 117
Viola riviniana, 159, 196
Violet helleborine, 46, 56, 61, 66, 75, 81, 82, **95**, 107, **139**, 142, *152–157*, 160, **162**, **163**, 347*
Viscidium (viscidia), 29, **47**, 104, 105

Wales, 63, 64, 65, 67, 82, 85, 86, 90, 92, 98, 99, 100, 101, 138, 143, 145, 172, 177, 219, 222, 234, 258, 267, 275, 286, 291, 292, 300, 303, 308
Warwickshire, 126

Wasp orchid, 308, 311, **314**
Wasps, 46, 56, 145, 151, 157, 160, 301
Water-meadows, 283, 287
Water mint, 98
Wayfaring tree, **77**
Weald, 80, 222
Welsh Border, 82
West Lothian, 154
West Meath, 258
Western European Element, 62, 66, 146, 159, 274, 286, 290
Westmorland, 119, 120, 149, 178. 258, 300, 308
Wexford, 179, 291
White willow, 86
Wicklow, 82, 295
Wicklow marsh orchid, 68, 70, 96, **259**, 295, **306**
Wigtownshire, 262
Wild angelica, 287
Wild arum, 76, 163, 196
Wild hyacinth, 263
Wild rose, **77**
Wild strawberry, 196
Willows, 86
Wiltshire, 89, 139, 213, 236, 303
Wintergreen plants, 10, 177, 234, 237, 240, 299, 307
Wood sanicle, 196
Wood violet, 159, 196
Woodlands, 73, 74–86, 252, 253, 300, 309
Worcestershire, 126, 154, 182, 200
Wyre Forest, 182

Yellow flag, 96, 98
Yellow iris, 287, 294
Yellow ophrys, 55
Yew, 75
Yorkshire, 79, 82, 89, 90, 119, 130, 178, 190, 225, 227, 238, 256, 286, 291, 295, 300, 309
Yorkshire, North Riding, 119, 120
Yorkshire, West Riding, 119, 150, 155, 222
Yorkshire Dales, 262
Yorkshire fog, 92
Yorkshire Wolds, 26
Young, D. P., 147

Ziegenspeck, H., 13, 264
Zygomorphic flowers, 29